A History of
Genetic Psychology

A History of Genetic Psychology

THE FIRST SCIENCE OF HUMAN DEVELOPMENT

Robert E. Grinder

UNIVERSITY OF WISCONSIN

John Wiley and Sons, Inc.

NEW YORK · LONDON · SYDNEY

For Alison

Preface

A few years ago I attempted my first reading of G. Stanley Hall's *Adolescence*. I had encountered countless references to it in recent texts, and I anticipated that a thoughtful study of its content would yield perspectives on the problems of adolescents in the last decades of the nineteenth century. But the classic treatise baffled me! A perusal of articles in Hall's *American Journal of Psychology* and *Pedagogical Seminary* proved similarly bewildering. A reconsideration of recent comments on Hall's views revealed little more than chance resemblance to what he seemed to have been saying. Many others, it seemed, miscomprehended the assumptions and aims of genetic psychology as well. Therefore, with considerable palpitation owing largely to the inadequacy of my background in the vast domains of the history of science, I went to work to unshroud the issues.

In *A History of Genetic Psychology* I sketch the major principles that underlie genetic psychology and, by reprinting excerpts from original sources, I try to show how these principles emerged in historical discourse. The flowering period of genetic psychology appears to have terminated a complicated, long-building coalescence of metaphysical and naturalistic systems of thought, and a few comments about this rather unusual fusion may help the reader to understand the plan of the book.

The text concludes on the note that genetic psychologists were engulfed by the revelations of evolutionary theory regarding the future of man; they distinguished between (*a*) the growth and development of children as instinctively controlled and fragilely liable to arresting social pressures and (*b*) the growth and development of adolescents as malleable and susceptible to environmental thrusts that, in contrast to their effects on children, might advance evolution. In accepting the possibility of dynamic interaction between human experience and environmental flux, genetic psychologists hastened the onrush of the social sciences. Their basic assumptions, however, were derived from optimistic, impractical interpretations of heredity and growth and were based upon an untenable nature-is-right theory of human development. A discussion of these constitutes the major emphasis of the book.

Genetic psychology makes sparse linkage with contemporary issues; its enduring importance, however, does not inhere in its specific endowments to psychological theory. The genetic psychology movement dispatched the transition of the study of man's psychical development from biology to psychology and the social sciences, and its historical significance is revealed in the pattern by which assumptions drawn from the earlier natural sciences were focused upon man. Quick-minded G. Stanley Hall and his students at Clark University fashioned genetic psychology from the products of the nineteenth-century natural sciences of botany, biology, geology, paleontology, and embryology. The result was a rudimentary science of human development strongly influenced by Jean Lamarck, Charles Darwin, Ernst Haeckel, and Herbert Spencer. Genetic psychologists and their precursors encountered problems in creating the first science of human development unlike those that confront students of psychology today. The early theorists struggled against formidable ecclesiastical opposition to formulate developmental laws. The incomparable theory of evolution led them to heady, wistful generalizations that only partially emancipated them from metaphysical bondage.

Readers may be surprised to find unmentioned the names of Francis Galton, who made startling predictions about the inheritance of abilities, and biometricians Karl Pearson and R. A. Fisher, who invented statistical criteria for evaluating Mendelian rules for the transmission of hereditary traits. In the taxonomy of the history of science, as *A History of Genetic Psychology* implicitly explains, these men and other pioneers who figured importantly in the rise of modern conceptions of heredity and behavior belonged to a tradition alien to that of genetic psychology.

I am pleased to thank the publishers who granted permission to reprint various documents; credits have been extended to them at appropriate places in the text. I am also indebted to the patient and competent staff librarians of the magnificent libraries at the University of Wisconsin for their assistance, and to the generous heirs to the estate of the Reverend John Haynes Holmes, astute student of human nature, from whose personal library I obtained early editions of the books of Drummond, Haeckel, Huxley, Spencer, Wallace, and Weismann.

I owe special thanks to Dorothy U. Ratcliff and Mary G. Porter; the organization and the ideas of the book are solely my responsibility, but their consummate editorial skills have greatly enhanced whatever merit it may possess.

I undertook this project in an attempt to clarify my own ideas on the development of genetic psychology. It began as a short paper, grew to a monograph, and finally to a collection of readings. I have prepared the book largely for my own satisfaction and benefit, but I hope that my labors will prove useful to others.

ROBERT E. GRINDER

Madison, Wisconsin
April 1967

Contents

A History of
Genetic Psychology

Prospectus

THE men of science, in the closing decades of the nineteenth century, rallied unanimously to uphold the principle that different species of animals and plants have evolved continuously through simpler, less complex forms from a common primordial origin. Fragmentary vestiges of a hypothesis of mutability are clearly distinguishable in the earliest expressions of Greek philosophy. However, during the interim centuries, proclamations of mutual relations among forms of organic life became the luckless casualties of successive ideological controversies. Hoisted to new preeminence in the resurgence of science, evolutionary doctrine served as a beacon for the birth of genetic psychology and led to the founding of the developmental disciplines that are recognized today as child and adolescent psychology.

The term *genetic* appears to have been first used in reference to growth, variation, and heredity around 1831,[1] a moment that coincided with Karl Ernst Von Baer's discovery of the egg cell in the ovary of mammals. By tracing the development and differentiation of the egg cell and by demonstrating the embryological affinity of diverse animal forms, Von Baer launched embryology not only as a modern science but, more importantly, as a comparative science.[2] Von Baer appears to have been unmoved by the wider implications of his epochal research, but Charles Darwin, Ernst Haeckel, Herbert Spencer, John Fiske, and G. Stanley Hall kindled the basic concept of interrelatedness into a vigorous genetic psychology. Pirating voraciously from biology, paleontology, botany, zoology, and other allied natural sciences, these nineteenth-century titans of the first science of human development anchored an interest in *every* aspect of growth. G. Stanley Hall, first of the child development specialists and founder of the American Psychological Association, exulted that his "experiments with such common plants as celery and lettuce show a behavior in them that can hardly be entirely excluded."[3] Lewis

[1] G. Murphy, *Historical Introduction to Modern Psychology* (New York: Harcourt, Brace and Co., 1949).
[2] E. Nordenskiöld, *The History of Biology*, translated by L. B. Eyre (New York: Tudor, 1935), p. 364.
[3] G. S. Hall, A Glance at the Phyletic Background of Genetic Psychology, *The American Journal of Psychology*, 1908, 19, 150–212, p. 186.

M. Terman, Hall's impressionable student who later became the foremost innovator of intelligence tests in America, was similarly inspired: "Genetic psychology would begin with the first cell and make an exposition of every fact in the process of development of the organism in its rise to maturity, through the period of activity, in the decline again to the inanimate."[4]

The bent of pioneer genetic psychologists toward appending exotic speculations is understandable. For nearly three hundred years science had been shackled by the Mosaic belief that God designed and populated the world with species whose essence, however manifold their individual manifestations might be, was fixed permanently at creation. The literal interpretation of the account of creation as given in Genesis, and articulated in the articles of special-creation and species immutability, was first assimilated in theology late in the sixteenth century by the eminent Schoolman Francisco Suarez. It was subsequently enshrined in literature in the seventeenth century by John Milton in the Seventh Book of *Paradise Lost*, and reached an apogee in the eighteenth with the works of Swedish botanist Carl Linnaeus.

The belief in the fixity of species was bolstered immeasurably in science by the invention of the microscope. The early microscopists, with fallible instruments and fertile imaginations, thought that they saw a minute, preformed "homunculus" neatly encased within the sperm cell. Every thing having been created supernaturally, it followed that the visible homunculus represented only the present generation. It was the last of many homunculi to be unpeeled, one being inside the other, with countless succeeding generations waiting their turn. These fanciful speculations reached their culmination in the work of the distinguished natural philosopher of Geneva, Charles Bonnet (1720–1793), who denied all formation, development, or generation and, instead, declared that at the moment of creation all generations of individuals, destined to live until the consummation of time, were born.

Because all life-forms were held to be fixed categorically at creation, the preformationists believed that the embryonic features of a given species unfolded simultaneously; all limbs separated themselves at the same time and grew at exactly the same rate; none came before or after the other. Growth being nothing more than a swelling up of parts already present,[5] development in the sense that new structures and functions emerge through combinations and transformations of relatively simple

[4] L. M. Terman, A Study in Precocity and Prematuration, *The American Journal of Psychology*, 1905, 16, 147–183, p. 148.
[5] J. Needham, *A History of Embryology* (Cambridge, England: Cambridge University Press, 1959), p. 207.

structures, and evolution in the sense that different species are related, were both disreputable and heretical concepts. Interest in the comparative sciences—anatomy, paleontology, zoology, and embryology—was also viewed as irrelevant and blasphemous. The preformation era mainly countenanced calculations about the size of the encased homunculi; for example, what would have been the size of an eighteenth-century rabbit when it was created inside its first parent in the year 4004 B.C.? One obviously debatable answer, offered by an embryologist in tune with the times, suggested that its size at creation probably was one-ten-thousand-millionth of its present size!

The doctrine of preformationism inadvertently helped to lift the sciences of organic development out of the Dark Ages, when it was believed that in gestation the progeny of one species might pass into another. Given the finite population of species on earth, the hereditary outcome of every pregnancy was a matter of chance. Stories of amazing transformations, such as women giving birth to frogs with snakes' tails, seemed so credible in an era in which alchemists professed to transfigure quartz into glistening gold, that even Francis Bacon said: "It would be very difficult to generate new species, but less so to vary known species, and thus to produce many rare and unusual results."[6] Scientific progress involves challenging the contentions of others and producing counterexamples to support one's own position,[7] and in this instance, preformationists disputed their predecessors of the Dark Ages and reduced the extraordinary and the unpredictable to a semblance of order and comprehensibility.

In the inexorable advance of science, preformationism was displaced, too. Evolutionary theorists eventually subdued the crusty, preformation-minded special-creationists. After centuries of oppression, however, the organic sciences that the evolutionists inherited were substantively sterile. If preformationism and special-creationism were abandoned, how indeed would one explain the development of physical characteristics, instinctual behavior, and conscious awareness? The evolutionists were bereft; they sported newly formulated laws of species interrelatedness, which fit facts where facts existed, but precious few facts were available. Hence, lacking sound scientific precedent and being reluctant to discard metaphysical linkage entirely, the evolutionists and the genetic psychologists whom they spawned assimilated a variety of ancient, long-standing developmental viewpoints as basic corollaries of the theory of evolution, and these, in turn, were absorbed in their freewheeling speculation.

[6] F. Bacon, *Novum Organum* [1620], *The Physical and Metaphysical Works of Lord Bacon*, edited by J. Devey (London: George Bell and Sons, 1894), p. 496.
[7] G. S. Brett, *History of Psychology*, edited and abridged by R. S. Peters (New York: Macmillan, 1953), p. 33.

Genetic psychology emerges, in historical retrospect, as a transitory discipline. The contemporary sciences of organic development are as unlike genetic psychology as the latter is dissimilar to special-creationism. Genetic psychology advanced science when it embraced the theory of evolution as the basic principle of development; the developmental disciplines of the present century advanced science when they wriggled free of the traditions and fanciful appendages that had been inadvertently introduced by the genetic psychologists in their excitement and impatience to explore every aspect of growth and development.

TWENTIETH-CENTURY DEVELOPMENTAL SCIENCE AND GENETIC PSYCHOLOGY CONTRASTED

Esoteric vocabularies, complex technologies, and progressively diverging interests exacerbate the heterogeneity of modern viewpoints about development. At mid-twentieth century, nonetheless, consensus abounds on the propositions pertaining to fundamental aspects of development—origins of life, mechanisms of fertilization, determinants of hereditary features, and operations of scientific laws—which are the sustenance from which hypotheses and assumptions ensue. First, there is agreement that intricate life-forms have evolved from a simple form of ancestor. Biologists presume that life on earth arose at least once from a fortuitous combination of prebiotic organic elements. The evolutionary speculators of early Greece took it for granted that life could be generated spontaneously from matter. In the Middle Ages, the Renaissance, and the beginning of the nineteenth century, scientists such as Bacon, Harvey, and Newton felt that, although man might have a divine origin, rodents and insects could be generated directly from decaying substances. The venerable belief in spontaneous generation is today vastly more sophisticated. We treat with comic overtones the possibility that mature life-forms may generate themselves from matter, but the possibility that the basic inanimate elements of the cell—carbon, nitrogen, hydrogen, oxygen, phosphorus, and sulfur—eventually may be compoundable into life is taken very seriously. Molecular biology already has synthesized such major components of simple viruses as proteins and nucleic acids, and preliminary theories for synthesizing primitive host cells have been advanced.[8]

Second, with the exception of certain types of cytoplasmic particles that are supplied by the female, it appears that both male and female contribute equally to fertilization and to heredity. The life of each mammal is recognized as beginning when a sperm cell from the male fertilizes

[8] E. C. Pollard, The Fine Structure of the Bacterial Cell and the Possibility of its Artificial Synthesis, *American Scientist*, 1965, **53**, 437–463.

an ovum, or egg, from the female. Both parents are known to contribute an equal number of chromosomes or carriers of heredity, and development is continuous as the egg divides and subdivides into a large number of cells.

Third, general acceptance has been reached on the basic process by which hereditary factors influence individual variations from generation to generation. Heredity is usually viewed as particulate; the chromosomes of the germ or sex cell possess a finite quantity of minute particles called genes, which are the basic determinants of hereditary characteristics. These tiny molecules are said to faithfully reproduce themselves and serve as sites for the physiological activity of body cells, whose energy is invested in developing bones, nerves, muscles, and organs. On the assumption that each person's genes preserve their identity through the life cycle, less complex hereditary features such as probable distributions of blood type, eye color, baldness, and diabetes are relatively easily anticipated within families. More complicated hereditary features such as intelligence and special abilities, however, are still exceedingly difficult to predict.

Most genes when affected by external agents appear as mutant forms that are deleterious to the organism carrying them. The tiny minority of mutations that increase probability of survival are regarded as the innovators of evolutionary change. In general, mutations occur spontaneously; the rate of occurrence can be accelerated by X-rays and by mutagenic chemicals, but not at all by specific changes in the physical or psychological makeup of parents.[9] On the basis of this recognition, scientists agree that except under extraordinary conditions, genes are uninfluenced by parental propensities toward exercise, illness, injury, laziness, or ambition. Thus the genes possessed by an untutored lad of 15 will be essentially identical to those he possesses at 50, however propitiating or debilitating his life may become.

Fourth, many developmental specialists, as well as nearly all physical and natural scientists, concur in believing that every phenomenon should be conceived as the mechanical or necessary consequence of an antecedent *causa efficiens*. The conviction that the universe is bound together by an unbroken chain of mechanically dependent phenomena and is governed by a monistic or all-pervading natural law dominates present-day scientific cosmography. Senior scientists living today recall the concern echoed in Le Conte's lament that "this view and this method, when pushed to what seems to many their logical conclusion, end in identification of man with mere animals, of spirit with mere physical and chemical

[9] T. G. Dobzhansky, *The Biological Basis of Human Freedom* (New York: Columbia University Press, 1956), pp. 3–25.

forces, immortality with mere conservation of energy, and thus leads [*sic*] to blank and universal materialism. Thus, while it [*sic*] increases our knowledge, it [*sic*] destroys our hopes."[10] Le Conte's vivid pessimism, however, was unwarranted. One who utilizes a principle of invariance in analyzing natural events need not be an unbending materialist. Few contemporary scientists are adherents of rigid, all-inclusive scientific determinism. The indeterminacy of electrons, atoms, and molecules has introduced a new kind of incalculableness in nature. Without miring in unanswerable questions posed by the likes of Descartes and Berkeley regarding mind, matter, and the intrinsic nature of reality, one may assert that few empirical laws of science are indeed as empirical as they appear.[11] Scientists are now more cognizant of both the advantages and limitations of determinism. They are emboldened as well. Science is basically a process of abstraction, and determinism is at its best in logical analyses, involving inferences and derivations, and in statistical (probabilistic) tests of functional relations. Judiciously applied, the scientific method, and the observational, experimental, and logicomathematical procedures that it incorporates, have proved to be enormously effective in revealing reliable and insightful natural laws. No better method has yet been devised for achieving ordered knowledge of the natural world and for conducting rational studies of relations among concepts describing natural-world events.

To proponents of genetic psychology, on the other hand, the chromosome and gene were unknown entities until late in the nineteenth century; Mendel's particulate theory of heredity lay buried in an obscure journal until early in the twentieth; the thought that development might be explicable in terms of mechanical variation excited apprehension in an era still struggling to be liberated fully from metaphysical bondage. Genetic psychology, however, shared the basic denominator—the theory of evolution—with its twentieth-century successors. Also, it upheld their belief in spontaneous generation. Alternative explanations were entertained; a few intransigents believed, for example, that life had been inseminated on earth by germs of lower organisms floating through space, but most evolutionists accepted spontaneous generation as the dominant theory of the origin of life and as a complement to evolutionary theory in supplanting special-creationism. On the issues of fertilization, hereditary variation, and reliance on natural law, in contrast, evolutionary theory only partially emancipated Darwin, Spencer, Hall, and their cohorts from medieval thought forms.

---

[10] J. Le Conte, *Evolution: Its Nature, Its Evidences, and Its Relation to Religious Thought* (New York: Appleton, 1908), p. 306.
[11] H. Feigl, Philosophical Embarrassments of Psychology, *The American Psychologist*, 1959, **14**, 115–128.

Genetic psychology shares with the science of past centuries acceptance of the theories of (*a*) *pangenesis,* for an explanation of fertilization, (*b*) *acquired characters,* for an account of hereditary variation, and (*c*) *vitalism* or *teleology,* for an interpretation of the controlling force within nature. During the formative years of genetic psychology, the savants approved the theories as self-evident truths rather than as conditional hypotheses. The corollaries and deductions that issued from these theories, together with increased refinement in the theory of evolution, constitute the main dimensions of genetic psychology, and for this reason the salient aspects of each of the three are here briefly detailed.

Pangenesis

Charles Darwin, in 1868, dignified one of the major cornerstones of genetic psychology in a two-volume treatise aimed at proving "the provisional hypothesis of pangenesis."[12] Centuries earlier, Hippocrates observed that "the seed comes from all parts of the body" and, similarly, Democritus noted that semen "proceeds from all parts of the body, and chiefly from the principal parts, as the flesh and muscles."[13] Darwin primarily contributed elaboration and documentation to the antediluvian theory of hereditary transmission: every cell, tissue, and organ in the body secrets infinitesimally minute particles called gemmules. Scattered throughout the body, they are eventually congregated by blood currents in the semen, where they constitute the basis of fecundation.

Darwin accumulated an enormous quantity of testimonials from domestic breeders to illustrate that sex and resemblance of progeny to parents is determined by the nature of gemmules distributed during copulation. A given characteristic in a child would approximate that of either the mother or the father to the degree that a particular parent copiously furnished gemmules for its construction: "When individuals of the same family which differ somewhat, and when races or species are crossed, the one is often prepotent over the other in transmitting its character."[14] The basis for the viewpoint is the assumption that every part of the body distributes reproductive gemmules:

The child, strictly speaking, does not grow into the man, but includes germs which slowly and successively become developed and form the man. In the child, as well as in the adult, each part generates the same part. . . . An

---

[12] C. Darwin, *The Variation of Animals and Plants under Domestication* [1868], 2 vols. (New York: Appleton, 1896), Vol. II, pp. 349ff.
[13] C. Zirkle, The Inheritance of Acquired Characters and the Provisional Hypothesis of Pangenesis,' *The American Naturalist,* 1935, **69,** 417–445, pp. 431–432.
[14] Darwin, *op. cit.,* p. 59.

organic being is a microcosm—a little universe, formed of a host of self-propagating organisms.[15]

Acquired Characters

The theory of acquired characters augments pangenesis with a complemental explanation of hereditary variation. In its simplest form, the doctrine asserts that somatic modifications, acquired by individuals during their lifetime, are preserved in reproduction, hence are inherited by the succeeding generation. To Aristotle falls the honor of having made the earliest unambiguous exposition on acquired characters:

Children are born with a likeness to their parents, not only in congenital but also in acquired characteristics; for before now, when the parents have had scars, the children have been born with a mark in the form of the scar in the same place, and there was a case at Chalcedon where the father had a brand on his arm and the letter was marked on the child, only confused and not clearly articulated. That is pretty much the evidence on which some believe that the semen comes from all the body.[16]

Science achieved unprecedented unanimity on the theory of acquired characters. Zirkle estimates that between Aristotle and Darwin, only the renowned philosopher Immanuel Kant rejected the belief, and his stance reflects the adumbration of an intractable special-creationist: "In the entire organization of nature, in spite of all variations, individual creatures of the same species remain essentially unaltered."[17] A majority of the respected authorities in the Middle Ages consorted with Kant in holding species to be immutable, but in conjunction with pangenesis they differed from Kant to the extent of viewing the theory of acquired characters as a satisfactory explanation of intraspecies variation.

Acquired characters were first introduced to evolutionary theory by a French naturalist, Jean Lamarck, in the first decade of the nineteenth century. In sharp contrast to the dramatic effects to which Aristotle had alluded, Lamarck dismissed the idea that rapid and sudden variations might occur in adjacent generations. Species were transformed in imperceptible increments, he said, through individual adaptations to alterations in conditions of life brought about by changes in climate, food availability, and geological structure. Lamarck emphasized that a permanent alteration in a species would materialize only when environ-

---

[15] *Ibid.*, pp. 398–399.
[16] Aristotle, *Generation of Animals*, I:17, translated by Arthur Platt, in *The Basic Works of Aristotle*, edited by Richard McKeon (New York: Random House, 1941), p. 667.
[17] I. Kant, *Bestimmung des Begriffs einer Menschen-Rasse* [1785], quoted in Zirkle, *op. cit.*, pp. 422–423.

mental stress was applied consistently for dozens of hundreds of generations. The genetic psychologists, however, grasped Lamarck's elemental theory as a lifeline for upgrading the human species. Consider G. Stanley Hall's characteristically exhuberant declaration:

Only Lamarckianism in its most extreme form can explain the evolution of races, species, and their every diversity, great and small. . . . From this new viewpoint psychology must henceforth study all structural and functional adjustments as the key to all perspective and reflective adaptations.[18]

As unbridled enthusiasm inflated the theory of acquired characters from an explanation of hereditary variation to a doctrine for race improvement, fanciful speculations increased effusively. Hall, for example, asserted that children born of a man at age 40, after he had become a personage of affairs and acumen, will have intellectual traits superior to those of children born of the same man at age 20.[19] Redfield likewise insisted:

If we could induce the parents of each family to have one more child five years after they would normally cease reproduction, the children so produced might do more for the advancement of civilization and race progress than all the other children put together.[20]

Teleology

The concept of species mutability, while unifying individuals working in the organic sciences, impaled those committed to metaphysical values. Man appeared reduced to a trivial element in the natural scheme. He seemed not only to have evolved from soulless jungle brutes but to have shared their physical features since the birth of time. His body harmonized with nature in its chemical constituents, with all animals in basic physical functions, and with all vertebrates in physical structure. Bone-for-bone and ganglion-for-ganglion comparisons enervated the homo sapiens who dared pit human features against those in the animal kingdom! The homologies of man with his simian ancestors indicated clearly that he might be a senseless product of the forces governing mechanical variation. In sum, the theory of evolution threatened to dethrone man from a unique relation with the Creator and to deny him the promise of immortality.

The dilemma was heightened by the fact that the humanistic revival in Europe and the Reformation, while freeing individuals from ecclesiasti-

---

[18] Hall, op. cit., pp. 188–189.
[19] E. L. Thorndike, The Newest Psychology, Educational Review, 1904, 28, 217–227, p. 218.
[20] C. L. Redfield, Control of Heredity (Chicago: Monarch Books, 1903), p. 267.

cal dogmas and ceremonies, cemented firmly their fervent aspirations for relations with a personal deity and their faith in the everlasting immortality of the soul.[21] In the seventeenth century, a prudent and brilliant French philosopher and mathematician, René Descartes, showed that the physical universe could be viewed as a machine; animals, because they were governed by reflexive mechanisms, were bound by the physical dimensions, but man, by the fact of his consciousness, possessed a soul, a substance entirely independent of physical restrictions. Descartes' dualism promoted harmonious coexistence between metaphysical and mechanistic viewpoints. The pillars of science in the Middle Ages were bolstered in their pursuit of the mysteries of the physical world by the knowledge that, whatever they might discover, their special-creation, unique status in the universe, and assurance of immortality were free from jeopardy. The eminent plausibility of the theory of evolution, however, threw their complacence into disarray. The fear and anguish then voiced among churchman and scientist alike reverberates in Le Conte's distress:

> To many, both skeptics and Christians, evolution seems to be synonymous with blank materialism, and therefore cuts up by the roots every form of religion by denying the existence of God and the fact of immortality. . . . A little reflection will explain this. There can be no doubt that there is at present a strong and to many an overwhelming tendency toward materialism. The amazing achievements of modern science; the absorption of intellectual energy in the investigation of external nature and the laws of matter have created a current in that direction so strong that of those who feel its influence . . . it sweeps away and bears on its bosom all but the strongest and reflective minds.[22]

The predicament was neatly resolved when the evolutionists found a principle of development that allowed them to plant one foot firmly in the new determinism and the other foot equally firmly in the older metaphysics. A spate of investigations initiated by paleontologists immediately after the publication of Darwin's *Origin of Species* (1859) disclosed an evidentially striking parallel between the growth pattern of an individual organism and the historical evolution of the species to which it belonged. Suddenly it seemed that the rationale for the mighty processes of organic growth had been endowed with meaning and purpose. Evolution and growth encompassed vastly more than blind accommodation; the expedient, lawful relationship existing between the individual and his species revealed the perfecting work of a Creative Intelligence. Applied to organic growth, the law of recapitulation (see the section

[21] H. Hoffding, *A History of Modern Philosophy*, translated by B. E. Meyer, 2 vols. (London: Macmillan, 1900), Vol. I, pp. 59ff.
[22] J. Le Conte, *op. cit.*, pp. 284–285.

Synopsis below) professed to account for how a teleological force or perfecting principle might be acting within natural necessity or causality for ordained purposes or ends. The grand design of evolution, therefore, demonstrated that the individual development of man was at once natural and divine, involving a fixed sequence of growth patterns, the violation of which would be profane.[23] The principle of recapitulation established the guidelines for a science of human development, appropriately underwritten with supernatural sanctions, and genetic psychologists exhorted all who listened to heed its messianic promise. Consider the earnest supplications of Colonel Frances W. Parker, distinguished principal of the Cook County Normal School in Chicago:

. . . so much lies beyond in the interpretation of the child's instinctive activities, so much seems to exceed all present discovery. The question, my fellow-teachers is, what should these lessons teach us? The child instinctively begins all subjects known in the curriculum of the university. He begins them because he cannot help it; his very nature impels him. These tendencies, these spontaneous activities of the child, spring from the depths of its being, spring from all the past, for the child is the fruit of all the past, and the seed of all the future. These quiet, persistent, powerful tendencies we must examine and continue with great care. . . . The spontaneous tendencies of the child are the records of inborn divinity; we are here, my fellow-teachers, for one purpose, and that purpose is to understand these tendencies and continue them in all directions, following nature.[24]

Attend, too, to Maria Montessori, who insisted that animal and agricultural study aids "the psycho-physical development of the individual:"

The child follows the natural way of development of the human race. In short, such education makes the evolution of the individual harmonize with that of humanity. Man passed from the natural to the artificial state through agriculture: when he discovered the secret of intensifying the production of the soil, he obtained the reward of civilization. The same path must be traversed by the child who is destined to become a civilized man.[25]

And last, but hardly least, compare the quenchless fervor of G. Stanley Hall:

Along with the sense of the immense importance of further coordinating child and youth with the development of the race, has grown the conviction that only here can we hope to find true norms against the tendency to precocity in home, school, church, and civilization generally, and also to

[23] R. Hofstader, The Child and the World, *Daedalus*, 1962, **91**, 501–526.
[24] F. W. Parker, *Talks on Pedagogies* (New York: E. L. Kellogg, 1894), p. 23.
[25] M. Montessori, *The Montessori Method* (New York: Frederick A. Stokes, 1912), p. 160.

establish criteria by which to diagnose and measure arrest and retardation in the individual and the race.[26]

In the decades preceding widespread acceptance of the recapitulation theory, the posture of many first-generation evolutionists on teleology oscillated. The genetic psychologists were persuaded en masse to admit teleological elements into the science of human development, but their precursors, in the absence of strong support for recapitulation, emerged less resolute. Jean Lamarck sprinkled the pages of his celebrated *Philosophie Zoologique* with references to nature as purely mechanical, but he often succumbed to an apparently insatiable urge to speculate on the nature of causality; for example, "Everywhere and always the will of the Sublime Author of nature and of everything that exists is invariably carried out."[27] In connection with the first edition of the *Origin of Species*, Darwin militantly girded the mechanical necessity viewpoint: "The so-called improvement of our short-horn cattle, pigeons, etc., does not presuppose or require any aboriginal 'power of adaptation,' or 'principle of improvement.' "[28] By the sixth edition of *Origin of Species*, however, Darwin had become a seasoned teleologist: "We may look with some confidence to a secure future of great length . . . all corporeal and mental endowments will tend to progress towards perfection."[29] Ernst Haeckel claimed for fifty years that "modern cosmology and cosmogeny have found no trace whatever of the existence and activity of a personal and extramundane God,"[30] but in his efforts to solve the riddle of organic development, on frequent occasions, the temptation to view life in teleological terms proved overwhelming.[31]

The vacillations were burgeoned in part by Herbert Spencer, foremost intellectual of the late nineteenth century. His pronouncements galvanized evolutionary speculation, and his opinion on every principle and theory commanded sober attention. From the first edition of *Social Statics* in 1850 to the last in 1892, Spencer never waivered in his insistence that man eventually would become perfect, that evil and immorality would disappear, and that progress was a necessity rather than an accident. On recapitulation, however, Spencer reversed himself as paleonto-

[26] G. S. Hall, *Adolescence*, 2 vols. (New York: Appleton, 1904), Vol. I, p. viii.
[27] J. B. Lamarck, *Philosophy Zoological* [1809], translated by H. Elliott (New York: Hafner, 1963), p. 55.
[28] C. Darwin, *The Life and Letters of Charles Darwin* [1888], edited by F. Darwin, 2 vols. (New York: Basic Books, 1959), Vol. I, pp. 530–531.
[29] C. Darwin, *The Origin of Species*, Sixth Edition, 2 vols. (Akron, Ohio: Werner, 1872), Vol. II, p. 305.
[30] E. Haeckel, *The Wonders of Life* [1904], translated by J. McCabe (New York: Harper, 1905), p. 437.
[31] Nordenskiöld, *op. cit.*, pp. 505–528.

logical evidence accumulated. In the first edition of *Principles of Biology*, he rejected the idea that "during development each higher organism passes through stages in which it resembles the adult forms of lower organisms—that the embryo of man is at one time like a fish, and at another time like a reptile. This is not the fact."[32] In the final edition of *Principles*, completely negating his earlier judgment, Spencer states:

Each organism . . . must in a general way go through the particular line of forms which preceded it in all past times: there must be what has aptly [been] called a "recapitulation" of the successive ancestral structure.[33]

SYNOPSIS: GENETIC PSYCHOLOGY AND ADVANCES IN TAXONOMY

Refinement in genetic psychology crested at the moment when the doctrines of pangenesis, acquired characters, recapitulation, and teleology meshed with the theory of evolution. The collation of hoary principles described in the preceding section sketches the basic framework of genetic psychology, and the particular amalgam depicts a truly unique end product. Collating fails, however, to convey conception of the colossal taxonomic struggles antecedent to the birth of genetic psychology. Spectacular scientific progress is usually predicated upon increases in the systematization of knowledge, and the climax and nadir of genetic psychology, like the earlier culmination of special-creationism and the subsequent rise of contemporary developmental sciences, resulted largely from extensions in the taxonomy of the physical and natural sciences. The individuals whose contributions built genetic psychology are legion, and among them, certain pivotal figures loom large in the saga. It is at the efforts toward systematization of these select few—Aristotle, Linnaeus, Newton, Lamarck, Darwin, and Haeckel—that we must look for perspective on *why* genetic psychology happened to be stitched together as it was.

Taxonomy in antiquity was sporadic and fragmentary. No one foresaw order in the organic world; none thought to catalogue affinities and relationships among life-forms; none recognized in existing fossils clues to earlier changes and transmutations. Then, in the fourth century B.C., Aristotle, who was perhaps the most comprehensive scientist ever, completed a survey of the organic world so thorough that for a period longer than two millenia it persisted virtually unchallenged. Aristotle's significance, however, is less in his incredible pioneering achievements than in his domination of the Western Meccas of science until the European

[32] H. Spencer, *The Principles of Biology* [1864], 2 vols. (New York: Appleton, 1866), Vol. I, p. 143.

[33] H. Spencer, *The Principles of Biology*, revised and enlarged edition, 2 vols. (New York: Appleton, 1898), Vol. I, p. 453.

Renaissance. Scholars of the Middle Ages resolutely digested Aristotle's complete works. Appreciable advances in science occurred here and there, but these survived only if they could be assimilated into the Aristotelian encyclopedia.

Aristotle divided zoology, or the study of the animal kingdom, into three parts: natural history, anatomy-physiology, and generation. He identified more than 500 different species from personal observation, a few dissections, and the accounts of wandering fishermen, hunters, herdsmen, and sea voyagers. Aristotle recognized that living things differed too markedly from one another in external form, in anatomical structure, in presence or absence of particular organs, in sensibilities, and in intelligence to be easily arranged in any single graded sequence; hence he offered not one but two classificatory schemes. Both hierarchical systems were comprised of comprehensive classes or genera, which in turn were further subdivided into species of similar ranking. In *Generation of Animals*, Aristotle suggested an ordering of the animal kingdom based on degree of embryological development at birth. Man headed the list because his progeny are born as relatively more "perfect," whereas insects were sifted to the bottom because their young proceed through larval and egglike stages. Although this arrangement exerted tremendous influence on early embryologists, it is less germane to the present discussion than Aristotle's second view, which rests on teleological assumptions. In *De Anima*, Aristotle described the organic world as an ascending system of "Souls." A *nutritive* Soul inspires plants and animals to grow and reproduce themselves but lacks the capacity to impart feelings. Possession of any one Soul implies the possession of all those that precede it, and plants fall away as animals climb the scale in terms of *sentient*, *appetitive*, and *locomotive* Souls, which, together with the nutritive, cumulatively impart sensitivity, desire, and movement. The ultimate Soul, the *rational*, exists only in man and distinguishes him as the highest living-form on earth. Aristotle, lacking Newton's principle of inertia, accounted for motion in the universe and the energy for change and growth in terms of an *Unmoved Mover* or *Final Cause*—an immortal, changeless source of pure reason and energy, the greatest of essences, who fueled all activity in the heavens and earth. Every form of existence, except the Unmoved Mover, was embodied in matter and had within it characteristics of "privation," the nature of which was determined by the Souls the form possessed. Thus the growth of life-forms in the hierarchy may be viewed as a process by which the forms, endowed by the Unmoved Mover with an inner force, strove to realize their fullest potentiality.

It is noteworthy that Aristotle's conception of development is at once congruent and contrary to the evolutionary premises of genetic psychology. Aristotle indeed viewed everything in the universe as being in hierarchical order. His keen awareness of phenomena in astronomy and physics led him to perceive all quantities, lines, surfaces, solids, and motions as continuous, and he assumed also that everything in nature was composed of countless links, infinitesimally differentiated, starting with the most meager forms of existence and culminating on earth with man and in the heavens with the perfect Absolute. Moreover, Aristotle held the development of every organic existence to be strongly influenced by the end toward which it is self-actualizing. Teleological development is the essence of natural objects in Aristotelianism; nonetheless, in contrast to the nineteenth-century outlook, the world is presented as a continuous series of fixed, rigid, and changeless forms. The essential ingredient of evolutionary theory—that a form might be completely transformed into a different form—is wholly lacking. Aristotle defined the potentiality of a substance in terms of its status by privation, and growth for any substance, however positioned in the hierarchy, was limited to shifting the privation to positive form. Real change was possible in the Aristotelian system, but no life-form could realize qualities lacking in its potentiality.

While the Christian church was embroiled in rising out of the rubble of the Roman Empire, church theologians were obliged to either synthesize Aristotelian epistomology with church dogma or fall into disrepute among secular philosophers. During the absorption period, the Aristotelian doctrine of irreducible forms was successfully integrated with ecclesiastical suppositions about biological organization. Thomas Aquinas, or *Doctor Angelcus* as he was known in the theological schools of the thirteenth century, demonstrated that Christian revelation showed that Aristotle's *Unmoved Mover*, in addition to being pure energy and intelligence, was compassionate, demanding, and on occasion personally intervened in nature. In the sixteenth century, Francisco Suarez reasoned to everyone's satisfaction that the Aristotelian hierarchy of organic life was compatible with the Mosaic account of creation. The latter ignored the possibility that species could be transformed and it specifically denied, as an affront to the majesty and purpose of the Creator, that any creature could become extinct. Because Aristotle's scale was static and immutable, transformation and extinction were impossible. None need be upset; even though the simian might stand next to man, the hiatus between them was unbreachable. On creation itself, Suarez simply asserted that Aristotle's entire scale of organic life was created instantaneously when the Creator deemed it appropriate to establish life on earth.

The triumvirate created during the Middle Ages by the wholesale acceptance of the Aristotelian classification scheme, the ecclesiastical affirmation of special-creationism and immutableness, and the scientific advancement of preformationism appears to have pulverized further interest in investigating relations among life-forms. Instead it helped provoke enthusiasm for cataloging all members of the plant and animal kingdom. Attention focused especially on demonstrating the wondrous imagination of the Creator. Hoffding once observed that the educated man of the Middle Ages had at his disposal miserably inadequate materials. His poverty of realities, however, was embellished by formalities. "Thought developed a formal acuteness, a skill in drawing distinctions and building up arguments, which is altogether without parallel."[34] Taxonomy, as a result, took a quixotic turn. Scholars skilled in analytic methods, mindful of the possibility of finding links in the hierarchy unknown to Aristotle and of classifying the entire organic world, inadvertently brought themselves face-to-face with indisputable evidence for species mutability.

The vexation experienced by botanist Carl Linnaeus, perhaps the finest systematist of organic matter of all time—"a phenomenon rather than a man"[35]—is illustrative. Linnaeus proclaimed in the first edition of his renowned *Systema Natura* (1735) that species were originally created as we see them and are forever the permanent tracings of the plan of creation. Linnaeus' brilliant cataloging of the known botanical, zoological, and mineralogical species delighted the scientific world. His prestige augmented the authority with which he unqualifiedly sanctioned special-creation and immutability, and for a time the genetic viewpoint was never more inert. Linnaeus personally classified more than 19,000 plants, and in the process of reducing the botanical confusion to order, he perceived more clearly than any of his contemporaries that new species of plants might arise through cross-breeding. In 1759 he pondered: "Whether all these species are the children of time, or whether the Creator from the very beginning of the world had restricted this course of development to a definite number of species, I dare not decide with certainty."[36] Linnaeus, not one to honor a patently archaic theory, deleted in the final edition of *Systema* (1766) the statement that no new species can arise. As the eighteenth century closed, the precision and clarity with which medieval science and theology had endowed special-creation and immutability seemed irretrievably blurred.

The striking taxonomic achievements made by Aristotle and Linnaeus in botany and zoology were matched in astronomy by Copernicus and in physics by Newton. In the second century, Ptolemy, a masterful en-

[34] Hoffding, *op. cit.*, p. 5.
[35] L. Eiseley, *Darwin's Century* (Garden City, N.Y.: Doubleday), 1958, p. 16.
[36] K. Hagberg, *Carl Linnaeus*, translated by A. Blair (London: Jonathan Cape, 1952), p. 202.

cyclopedist of the magnitudes and motions of celestial bodies, reaffirmed the ancient "geocentric theory" that the earth was stationary at the center of the heavens. The theory insisted that the sun, moon, and planets revolve around the earth in concentric epicycles or orbits and, providing a boon to astrologers, that forces inherent in the stars both invigorate them and instill within them the capacity to intervene in the course of terrestrial events. Copernicus displaced the Ptolemaic system in the sixteenth century with the heliocentric theory of the universe, which deposed earth from the summit of the universe and relegated it to being a minute planet among many. Every astronomical body, including earth, Copernicus held to be in motion; as such, the theory paved the way for Kepler, Galileo, and Newton, who demonstrated that the concept of masses moving under their mutual forces was sufficient to explain motion throughout the universe. Known as the principle of inertia, and articulated with equations and laws in Newton's epochal *Principia* (1687), the simple assumption that particles of matter attract other particles with forces proportional to the product of their masses and inversely proportional to the square of distances between them revolutionized mathematical concepts of the universe.

With the universe in mechanical harmony, it was no longer necessary to believe, as had Aristotle and Ptolemy, that stars possessed arbitrary self-actuating energies. The extent to which capriciousness and miraculous intervention might influence natural occurrences had been reduced to insignificant proportions. Upon completion of Linnaeus' prestigious botanical classifications, the stage was set for learned men in the nineteenth century to marshal the facts of organic variation for an attempt at a naturalistic explanation of the origin of the myriad life-forms that inhabit the earth. First to appear on the scene was Jean Lamarck who explained, in *Philosophie Zoologique* (1809), the gradual formation of organic species by the interaction of two physiological functions—adaptation and heredity. Adaptation consisted of either the improvement of organs by use or the degeneration by disuse; heredity acted by transmitting the features thus acquired to posterity. A half century later, Haeckel acclaimed Lamarck's simple but powerful principles:

At their head [the French Nature-Philosophers] stands Jean Lamarck. . . . To him will always belong the immortal glory of having for the first time worked out the Theory of Descent, as an independent scientific theory of the first order, and as the philosophical foundation of the whole science of biology.[37]

[37] E. Haeckel, *The History of Creation* [1873, Fifth Edition], translated by E. R. Lankester, 2 vols. (New York: Appleton, 1912), Vol. I, p. 114.

Lamarck's views, however, encountered thunderous calumny early in the century. First and foremost, his precipitous break with special-creationism discomposed too many metaphysicians. Until Lamarck, it had been fashionable to attribute the origin of every form of organism to miraculous intervention, and public opinion still carped at anyone who dared flout this canon of church dogma. Second, his arguments were unconvincing to fellow scientists. He had failed to demonstrate how the acquisition of slight variations and their transmission to successive generations bring about, in the course of time, the transformation of some species and the extinction of others. Finally, Lamarck lacked convincing supporting evidence for his examples that showed that the environment of one generation determined the heredity of the next. To critics, Lamarck appeared to have argued from the relatively unknown to the relatively known. Indeed, Lamarck could only surmise that the derivation of the long hindlegs of jumping animals, the elongation of snakes, and the extended necks of giraffes, for example, had occurred through the influence of inherited habits.

Upon the publication of *Origin of Species* (1859), fifty years hence, Darwin had surmounted Lamarck's more serious fragilities. In an unceasing search that consumed all of twenty-eight years, Darwin wisely amassed mountains of data for the theory of evolution. In 1831, at age 22, when he sailed off on the *Beagle*, a ship sent by the English government to survey the southernmost coast of South America, Darwin was a confirmed special-creationist. But he returned at age 27 gripped by doubt:

I have been now, ever since my return, engaged in a very presumptuous work, and I know no one individual who would not say a very foolish one. I was so struck with the distribution of the Galapagos organisms, etc., and with the character of the American fossil mammifers, etc., that I determined to collect, blindly, every sort of fact, which could bear in any way on what are species. . . . At last, gleams of light have come, and I am almost convinced (quite contrary to the opinion I started with) that species are not (it is like confessing murder) immutable.[38]

As Darwin gathered data, the conviction that species were mutable evolved from his personal observations of plants and animals distributed throughout the world, from the experiments of domestic breeders in England, and from strong corroborative evidence based on recent studies of the earth's structure. Perhaps Darwin would have cumulated facts interminably except for the coincidence that in the late 1850s Alfred Russell Wallace informed Darwin that he was about to present a paper

[38] Darwin, *Life and Letters, Op. cit.*, Vol. I, p. 384.

promulgating a theory of species mutability. An English biologist, who had spent a year in Brazil and several years in the East Indian Archipelago, Wallace also possessed a certain amount of firsthand evidence. Because Darwin by now was shielding voluminous supportive materials, to resolve the preemptive dilemma amicably, they presented a paper jointly before the Linnean Society in 1858. A year later, replete with a quantity of facts that would have surpassed Lamarck's fondest expectations, and fearful of being overshadowed, Darwin published his incomparable magnum opus.

Darwin's procrastination was heightened less by the problem of documenting mutability than by that of satisfactorily explaining the appearance of variations among individuals and the rise of new species. Faced with the task of overthrowing the Linnean concept of species rigidity and lacking knowledge of the characteristics of chromosomes and genes, Darwin was hard pressed. In the earliest stages of his thinking he appears to have rejected Lamarck's theory of acquired characters mainly on two counts: one, that it failed to explain why some characteristics survived and others were extinguished; and two, that it provided entry for volitional dimensions in the adaptation process, which, given the mathematical harmony of the universe, ought not to be affected by such vagaries as "self-willing." Darwin's patient pursuit of a solution led him in 1838 to Thomas Malthus, *Essay on Population*. Here, at long last, Darwin found the clue he so earnestly sought. Malthus had maintained that because more individuals are produced than natural resources can support, sheer need will check population growth. The weakest would be certain to perish in a competition for limited resources. Similarly, Darwin then posited that the key to explaining why certain species survived and others perished was natural selection, or biological competition among organisms. Darwin's initial enthusiasm for natural selection led him, at one point, to assert dogmatically that only the plants and animals that possess superior qualities for adaptation would survive and endow certain of their offspring with even greater capacity to overcome competition. In a preliminary version of *Origin of Species* sent to Sir Joseph Hooker, a botanist friend, Darwin stated his point: "I believe Natural Selection will account for the production of every vertebrate animal."[39]

For three very important reasons, Darwin subsequently was compelled to forsake his total reliance on natural selection and to acknowledge that acquired characters influenced variation and mutability. First, his elaborate observations of the feats of domestic-animal breeders revealed to him that factors other than "artificial" natural selection—the process of selecting individuals with desired variations to produce offspring and

[39] Darwin, *Life and Letters, op. cit.,* Vol. I, p. 528.

of destroying the undesirable before they produce—were operating to produce change. Darwin conceded that climatic variations, abundance or scarcity of food, and changes in habitat might also stimulate alterations and mutations. Even by the time of the publication of the first edition of *Origin of Species*, the extent to which he made his evolutionary doctrine dependent on natural selection appears to have abated significantly: "I am convinced that Natural Selection has been the main, but not exclusive, means of modification."[40] Second, by chance or fortuitous variation, nature would have wasted countless progeny before one might emerge with a really serviceable advantage over its competitors. Geologist friends pointed out to Darwin that the terrestrial time clock had not been running long enough for natural selection alone to have fashioned the fantastic variety of life-forms presently populating the earth. Third, the majority of the natural scientists who rallied to support Darwin in the early 1860s had themselves linked natural selection and acquired characters as the major forces of evolutionary change. Darwin's perspective, consequently, continued its cautious but relentless shift toward Lamarckianism. As early as 1862 he wrote Lyell, "I hardly know why I am a little sorry, but my present work is leading me to believe more in the direct action of physical conditions."[41] In 1876 he said, "When I wrote the *Origin*, and for some years afterwards, I could find little good evidence of the direct action of the environment: now there is a large body of evidence."[42] In 1880, in the sixth and final edition of the *Origin of Species*, Darwin explicitly acknowledged the central role of Lamarck's law: species modification, he said, "has been effected chiefly through the natural selection of numerous, successive, slight, favourable variations; aided in an important manner by the inherited effects of the use and disuse of parts."[43]

Taxonomic achievements in the surface-variation sciences—botany, zoology, and husbandry—from which Darwin drew major support, massively buttressed the theory of evolution. Each, however, was assailable for exactly the same reason: each proffered support for evolution on the basis of observations of plants and animals now living, that is, on apparent correlations among living specimens. Purporting as each did to substantiate mutability from primordial to present time, each was vulnerable to the criticism of providing only oblique support. Adversaries claimed that Darwinism lacked genealogical trees showing the manner in which alterations had occurred in the transformation of species. The

[40] C. Darwin, *On the Origin of Species* (London: Murray, 1859), p. 6.
[41] Darwin, *Life and Letters, op. cit.*, Vol. II, p. 182.
[42] *Ibid.*, p. 338.
[43] Darwin, *Origin of Species*, Sixth Edition, *op. cit.*, Vol. II, p. 293.

growing impact of evolutionary theory scarcely faltered, however, as paleontologists rushed to Darwin's defense. Convinced that the clearest, most direct evidence for evolutionary change ought to exist in the record of fossilized organisms deposited in sedimentary formations, paleontologists painstakingly compared bones, remnants of body structures, and impressions left in stones to muster and to catalog the crucial proof.

The first in the outflow of the volumes upholding Darwinism was a tiny treatise appropriately named *Für Darwin* (1863). Prepared by Fritz Müller, it portrayed the evolutionary progress of the Crustacea, a species chosen largely because it seemed unlikely that the Creator would ever have interceded on behalf of such a lowly creature, so that its series of changes must obviously be its own doing. Following on Müller's heels, Ernst Haeckel promoted evolutionary principles with incomparable verve. With a steady stream of publications, extending for a half century, including *Generelle Morphologie* (1866), *History of Creation* (1868), and *The Wonders of Life* (1904), Haeckel established himself as "perhaps the chief source of the world's knowledge of Darwin."[44] Ernst Haeckel was also the first sage to distinguish functionally between the genetic development of species and that of individuals which belong to species. *Phylogeny* he set forth as the study of descent (or ascent, as more idealistic evolutionists preferred) of existing forms from antecedent forms. *Ontogeny* he designated as the study of individuals from their very earliest embryonic state through successive transformations or metamorphoses until maturity.

Haeckel was moved to make the distinction because he had become a confirmed recapitulationist. The name of the individual who deserves credit for being the first to allude to a recapitulatory relationship between the emergence of species and the growth of individuals is irrecoverable. Aristotle and Rousseau both spoke of a connection, and Lorenz Oken, in *Natur Philosophie* (1805), was among the first naturalist-philosophers to formulate a law holding that complex animals recapitulate stages in their development corresponding to the adult forms of simpler animals and their ancestors. Oken's most famous pupil, American naturalist Louis Agassiz, preserved the viewpoint in his carefully documented *Essay on Classification:*

It may therefore be considered as a general fact, very likely to be more fully illustrated as investigations cover a wider ground, that the phases of development of all living animals correspond to the order of succession of their extinct representatives in past geological times.[45]

[44] Nordenskiöld, *op. cit.*, p. 515.
[45] L. Agassiz, *Essay on Classification* [1858], edited by E. Lurie (Cambridge, Mass.: Harvard University Press, 1962), p. 114.

Agassiz, one of the more vigorous special-creationists whom Darwin faced, explained that the "marvelous relationships" simply demonstrated the omnipresence of the Creator. Haeckel swept aside Agassiz' incredulous adage and, instead, hailed the apparent fact of recapitulation as "the fundamental biogenetic law." He adduced that "ontogenesis is a brief and rapid recapitulation of phylogenesis, determined by the physiological functions of heredity and adaptation."[46] By viewing the recapitulation principle as an a priori law rather than as a theorem requiring demonstration, Haeckel believed that he had divined a principle that would unerringly direct science to all the troublesome gaps and developmental secrets left in anthropogenetic sequences by the inadequacies of comparative paleontology. He elevated recapitulation in the natural sciences as "the principal for the origin of life,"[47] and impatiently embarked on the task of constructing the grand genealogical tree for the entire animal world.

The significance to taxonomy of Haeckel's biogenetic law lay in the fact that it implied that the study of individuals in their embryonic, postnatal, childhood, and adolescent growth afforded a short and easy method of determining the ancestral history of every species. At first flush, it appeared that every differentiation in species evolution carried with it a corresponding and consequential differentiation in individual development. Advances in paleontology and embryology had disclosed "the stubborn power of permanency in whatever has once possessed reality!"[48] Further advances shortly thereafter, however, divulged that ontogenetic development seldom resembled perfect, unaltered recapitulation of phylogenetic evolution. The new evidence held for every species, from the worms and lampreys to the simians and homo sapiens. Haeckel already had acknowledged in his biogenetic law that ontogeny was affected both by heredity and adaptation; hence he proposed that the phyletic record was being effaced in ontogeny, in order to restrain the duration of the individual growth process, either by *palingenesis*, an abridged but exact repetition of the ancestral record, or by *cenogenesis*, a confounding of palingenetic abridgement and of adaptation to new environmental conditions.

However emphatically Haeckel declared himself to be a materialist, he apostatized his mechanistic outlook in discussions of the palingeny-cenogeny distinction. He believed wholeheartedly that ontogeny *ought* to pursue the palingenetic process. Inner mechanisms had been implanted in the individual by his phyletic ancestors; palingenetic growth merely

[46] Haeckel, *Wonders of Life, op. cit.,* p. 380.
[47] Nordenskiöld, *op. cit.,* p. 517.
[48] W. Goethe, quoted in L. F. Ward, *Haeckel's Genesis of Man or History of the Development of the Human Race* (Philadelphia: Edward Stern, 1879), p. 27.

foreshortened the retracing of the inherited phyletic stages, thus leaving the sacrosanct phylogeny-ontogeny sequence perfectly resonant. Because individuals had been shown to recapitulate phyletic stages throughout their developmental period, it followed, conversely, that cenogenetic trends defiled and distorted the foreordained growth pattern. He insisted, for example, that palingeny was positive whereas cenogeny was negative and that morphology would find the hidden path of phylogeny in ontogeny when it followed the palingenetic process and eliminated the cenogenetic.[49]

Haeckel possessed abundant precedence for adopting a teleological, nature-is-right doctrine. Aristotle had held that resistance of inorganic matter was thwarting the actualization of a perfect sequence of fixed organic forms. In the recommencement of evolutionary theory, Lamarck, while discarding the Aristotelian view of a fixed, finite quantity of forms awaiting realization and stressing instead the continuous creation of new, complex structures, concurred with Aristotle in holding that "nature has given to animal life the power of progressively consummating the organization [of the tree of evolution] and of developing and gradually perfecting it."[50] Ecological adaptations produce variations and evolve new kinds of life-forms in Lamarckianism, but these same events are anomalies that interfere with the realization of a flawlessly graded sequence in the evolutionary scheme:

The state in which we find any animals, is, on the one hand, the result of the increasing complexity of organisation, tending to form a regular gradation; and, on the other hand, of the influence of a multitude of very various conditions ever tending to destroy the regularity in the gradation of the increasing complexity of organisation.[51]

Taxonomies from the organic sciences converged in Ernst Haeckel's cogitations. Throbbing theoretical issues like spontaneous generation, pangenesis, acquired characters, and teleology fit snugly into the grandiose biogenetic law. Those who preceded Haeckel in contributing to the birth of genetic psychology are countless, but among the nineteenth-century evolutionists who stood on the foundation of the new discipline Haeckel looms signally prismatic. He was the first to divide growth processes into phylogenetic and ontogenetic aspects; his distinctions between palingeny and cenogeny and his stress on the venerable nature-is-right doctrine sustained the evangelical efforts of G. Stanley Hall and his contemporaries, who were about to raise the scaffold for a substantive genetic psychology.

---

[49] Haeckel, *Wonders of Life, op. cit.,* pp. 359–385.
[50] J. Lamarck, quoted in Nordenskiöld, *op. cit.,* p. 328.
[51] Lamarck, *Philosophy Zoological, op. cit.,* p. 107.

CHILDHOOD AND ADOLESCENCE

Genetic psychologists regarded the recapitulation principle and the nature-is-right doctrine as imperatives requiring pedagogues to abstain from interfering with children's growth propensities. Development should proceed as the inner, palingenetic impulses intend, and as Thorndike explained it, genetic psychologists steered their quest for the clues to human destiny by the following maxim:

No stage to which nature impels, should by human artifice be either hastened or prolonged, lest the magic order be disturbed. The ideal for humanity is to be sought in its natural outcome, in what it of itself tends to be, irrespective of training. Human effort should be to let the inner forces of development do their perfect work.[52]

Recapitulation theory, however, only prescribed that phylogeny should be enunciated in ontogeny. Extolling the virtues of the inner mechanisms of growth evaded the fundamental problem of ascertaining how to accelerate evolutionary progress. When should acquired characters be introduced in ontogeny in order to ensure phyletic advance? If evolution is to be carried forward, cenogenetic influences must be permitted their moment! Paleontologists again sifted their indispensable fossil-shell collections, which not unexpectedly gleaned nature's intention: recapitulation and variation, palingeny and cenogeny, were complementary processes. Whatever the species, as the child's development approached maturity, recapitulatory impulses appeared to lessen in urgency while plasticity, or capacity for acquisition of acquired characters, seemed to dilate tremendously. As Haeckel observed, alterations in ontogeny may occur at any stage of development; careful scrutiny of the paleontological records also had revealed that advances in the evolution of a species occurred when acquired characters emerged in the later phases of ontogenetic growth. This exceedingly important point was skillfully sewn together with the principle of abridgement by American paleontologist Alpheus Hyatt:

All modifications and variations in progressive series tend to appear first in the adolescent or adult stages of growth, and then to be inherited in successive descendants at earlier and earlier stages according to the law of acceleration, until they either become embryonic, or are crowded out of the organization, and replaced in the development by characteristics of later origin.[53]

[52] E. L. Thorndike, *The Original Nature of Man* (New York: Columbia University Press, 1913), pp. 271–272.
[53] A. Hyatt, Genesis of the Arietidae, *Smithsonian Contributions to Knowledge,* 1890, i-xi, 1–223, p. ix.

The paleontological distinction between the recapitulatory importance of childhood and the plastic significance of adolescence was corroborated by another line of investigation aimed at explaining why man developed intellectual capacities vastly superior to other species. Alfred R. Wallace, who with Darwin coauthored the first paper on natural selection, suggested in a series of essays that the emergence of the human species had been preceded by occasions during which natural selection worked on intellectual processes rather than on physical changes. It was Wallace's hypothesis that the point eventually was reached in evolution when intellectual variations were of more adaptive value than physical changes, and thus the transition from the apelike to the human condition was associated chiefly with the mind and nervous system.

To John Fiske, eminent Harvard philosopher and historian, the idea opened up "an entirely new world of speculation . . . struck out a most brilliant and pregnant suggestion. . . . If there is any one thing in which the human race is signally distinguished from other mammals, it is in the enormous duration of their infancy period."[54] Fiske reasoned that there must be a relationship between the length of infancy and intellectual development. A lower animal, he said, "when he comes to be born, he comes all ready to work."[55] Lower animals experience short infancy because their reflexive, instinctive behavior is easily impressed during the fetal period upon a fairly smooth brain. On the other hand, response patterns of higher vertebrates are too complex and too diverse to be registered entirely in the nervous system during fetal growth. Man "instead of being born with a certain number of definite developed capacities, has a number of potentialities which have got to be aroused according to his own individual experiences."[56] Contrasting the smooth simianlike brain surface of the newborn homo sapiens with the deeply furrowed, myriad-seamed terrain of the adult, Fiske recognized that the development of the intellectual characteristics of the human adult were long abeyant in the ontogenetic process and that the adolescent period was especially critical for evolutionary advancement:

The plastic period of adolescence, lengthened in civilized man until it has come to cover more than one third of his lifetime, is thus the guaranty of his boundless progressiveness.[57]

A little more than one hundred years earlier, Jean Jacques Rousseau had set forth in *Emile* (1762) a cogent analysis of the biological and

[54] J. Fiske, *A Century of Science* (Boston: Houghton Mifflin, 1900), pp. 104–106.
[55] *Ibid.*, p. 107.
[56] *Ibid.*, p. 108.
[57] J. Fiske, *The Destiny of Man Viewed in the Light of his Origin* (Boston: Houghton Mifflin, 1884), p. 57.

social aspects of children's growth. Written as a polemic against both crass materialism and unrestrained supernaturalism, Rousseau's dictum urged that self-preservation should be viewed as the base motive underlying human activity and that reasoning ought to be seen as a derivable faculty that imparts sentiments and higher meaning to emotions and feelings. These notions wielded powerful influence on the genetic psychologists as they shaped their hunches and the data of the natural sciences into principles and laws. The first echelon of evolutionists—Darwin, Wallace, Haeckel, Spencer—seldom assigned Rousseau more than passing reference and never referred to him in connection with the recapitulation theory. But the second order—John Fiske, G. Stanley Hall, and their students—found Rousseau a wellspring of profound insight when they recognized, as he had, that focus on development might well be diverged into childhood and adolescent stages.

Rousseau maintained that children should follow their instincts of self-preservation in acquiring enriching social experiences. In the process of development, emotional and reasoning functions interact with one another in relatively discrete, sequential stages. The first stage, from birth until age 5, Rousseau saw as animalistic and prehuman. Self-consciousness dawns around middle childhood. At around age 12, the rational faculties awaken, and at puberty, with the maturity of sexual capacities, social sentiments are ready to reign over the emotions. Rousseau would "allow the fundamental traits of savagery their fling till twelve;"[58] before then, children should be taught nothing that they can learn for themselves; intellectual development should be postponed, for its powers may be stunted by early use. Rousseau's view embodied perfectly the nature-is-right outlook: children are not to be inculcated by external sources; interests must be elicited by their needs, and thus children will grow up without prejudices, without habits—in sum, without any learning at all. Their growth would be free, unsuppressed, unarrested, unperverted, and undelayed! They would enter the adolescent arena immunized against unresolved animalistic cravings and would be ready and able to subordinate their spirits to the demands of a rational, socially responsible adult life.

The liaison created by recapitulation theory between the facts of the natural sciences and the products of Rousseau's perspicacious intuition enraptured genetic psychologists far into the twentieth century. John Fiske, for example, made a pilgrimage to Europe, seeking to be enthralled by the natural scenery that had charmed Rousseau's "marvellous powers of exposition."[59] More importantly, genetic psychologists searched chil-

---

[58] Hall, *Adolescence, op. cit.*, Vol. I, p. x.
[59] J. S. Clark, *The Life and Letters of John Fiske*, 2 vols. (Boston: Houghton Mifflin, 1917), Vol. I., p. 521.

dren's development for phyletic benchmarks, believing, in concert, that only by knowing the old racial stages and, thereby, knowing how to reconstruct a pristine environment would both evolutionary progress and individual development be nurtured. For very practical objectives, therefore, children and adolescents should be raised or socialized differently. One fashioned a fetterless environment for children; then, one stood back, watched, and never interfered. And for plausible reasons: "The child is naturally successively animal, anthropoid, half-barbarian, and then civilized."[60] "Every boy is pugnacious by inheritance. His remote ancestors were fighters; they had to fight for self-preservation."[61] "Like savages, children are both readily entertained and easily bored . . . in the primitive soul there is an insatiable longing for something new and exciting."[62] In sum:

. . . reason, true morality, religion, sympathy, love and esthetic enjoyment are but very slightly developed. Everything, in short, suggests the culmination of one stage of life as if it thus represented what was once, and for a very protracted and relatively stationary period, the age of maturity in some remote, perhaps pigmoid, stage of human evolution.[63]

Deference to recapitulatory impulses, however, prevailed only until adolescence. The recalcitrant child became the haplessly plastic and malleable adolescent. Hall expresses the undying conviction of genetic psychologists by way of his piquant vernacular: "In some respects, early adolescence is thus the infancy of man's higher nature, when he receives from the great all-mother his last capital of energy and evolutionary momentum."[64] And:

For those prophetic souls interested in the future of our race and desirous of advancing it, the field of adolescence is the quarry in which they must seek to find both goals and means. If such a higher stage is ever added to our race, it will not be by increments at any later plateau of adult life, but it will come by increased development of the adolescent stage, which is the bud of promise for the race.[65]

EPITAPH

The genetic psychology movement eventually tired as unremitting progress in science caused natural scientists to discredit pangenesis and

[60] J. M. Tyler, *Growth and Education* (Boston: Houghton Mifflin, 1907), p. 53.
[61] M. V. O'Shea, *The Trend of the Teens* (Chicago: Frederick Drake, 1920), p. 49.
[62] E. J. Swift, *Youth and the Race* (New York: Charles Scribner's Sons, 1916), pp. 30–31.
[63] Hall, *Adolescence, op. cit.*, Vol. I, p. ix.
[64] *Ibid.*, Vol. II, p. 71.
[65] *Ibid.*, Vol. I, p. 50.

acquired characters and to discard the theory of recapitulation. Among the undermining influences, two nineteenth-century episodes contributed especially to the collapse of the genetic approach. First, the problem of untangling palingenetic and cenogenetic stages in the biogenetic sequence ultimately overwhelmed the recapitulatory bastions. Who was to decide whether a given character was phylogenetic, hence ought to be repeated, or whether it was a recent aberration of nominal or even inhibitory significance? Neither Haeckel nor the paleontologists could offer criteria by which to distinguish the ancestral features from those that might account for suppression or arrest. Haeckel published more than 500 engravings of intricate structures in a valiant effort to identify the recapitulatory gaps in his phylogenetic trees. Where fossil shells of animals resembling presently living forms were lacking, Haeckel appears to have resorted to inventing fanciful ancestors. Certain Haeckelian drawings were so divergent from the reputable drawings of other naturalists that a sizable segment of the scientific community accused him of deliberate falsehood.[66] Skepticism mounted as scholars, one by one, reluctantly admitted that the ontogenetic-phylogenetic relationship was hopelessly confused. E. D. Cope, University of Pennsylvania zoologist, attempted to stem the growing confusion with a law of "inexact parallelism," which suggested that characters proven useful to the immature, growing form may have a tendency to be inherited at earlier ages than characters useful only to adults. Gradually, however, diehards succumbed to the irreconcilable fact that ontogeny failed to reveal more than grossly obvious clues to phylogeny. Years after genetic psychology had vanished, one of G. Stanley Hall's own students, looking back upon those years of ferment and enthusiasm, remarked irreverently: "There never would have been a recapitulation theory had as much attention been given to the dissimilarities as was given to the similarities."[67]

Second, a hardy band of intrepid evolutionists unceasingly attacked the ancient theories of pangenesis and acquired characters. Their notable spokesman in the 1860s, August Weismann, advanced the viewpoint that a sharp cleavage exists between general body tissue or somatoplasm and the reproductive tissue or germplasm. In Weismann's theory of heredity, external influences in general could not reach the germ cells, and throughout nature, from amoeba to homo sapiens, germ cells were elaborately protected from direct environmental influences. Weismann became an inveterate champion of the outlook that natural selection was the sole mechanism of hereditary change. As a result of Weismann's perseverance,

[66] Nordenskiöld, *op. cit.*, p. 517.
[67] E. Conklin, *Principles of Adolescent Psychology* (New York: Henry Holt, 1935), p. 15.

a division of naturalists into two schools occurred. Those who identified with Lamarck—Darwin, Haeckel, and Spencer—became known as Neo-Lamarckians; those who, with Weismann, denied that acquired characters could be inherited and laid emphasis on the Darwinian principle of natural selection as the only mechanism of hereditary variation were regarded as Neo-Darwinians.

Weismann's challenge stimulated vigorous research on the part of Neo-Darwinian theorists such as Carl Correns and Hugo De Vries, and more importantly, hastened the discovery in 1900 of two brief, epochal publications on the hybridization of the garden pea. Many naturalists, including Linnaeus, had investigated plant hybridization, but none had studied the problem as experimentally, as painstakingly, and with greater analytic ability than Gregor Mendel, an inconspicuous Austrian monk, who carried out his research in the seclusion of the cloister garden at the monastery in Brünn. Mendel crossed twenty-two varieties of garden pea in terms of such distinguishable characteristics as length, form, and color. By crossing contrasting characters, for example, those with long versus short stems or with round versus wrinkled seeds, he discovered in the plants thus developed that one character prevailed phenotypically or visibly to the exclusion of the other. The prevailing character Mendel called the dominant, the other being the recessive. By letting the cross-breds fertilize themselves, Mendel raised subsequent generations and discovered that in each generation, relative to preceding generations, the numerical proportion of dominants to recessives is predictably constant. With remarkable insight, Mendel recognized that hereditary genes do not mix; instead of seeming fluid, they acted as if they were particulate. In working out the numerical ratios between dominant and recessive traits as they were likely to appear in given generations, and in publishing, or burying, his results in the obscure *Proceedings of the Natural History Society of Brünn* in 1865, Mendel established himself as the forerunner of modern geneticists.

The Mendelian laws of heredity showed how inherited characters are actually distributed and, for the Neo-Lamarckians, demolished cherished hopes of advancing evolutionary goals by direct influence. Had Darwin's attention been directed toward Mendel's startling discoveries, he could have interpreted the effects of natural selection in terms of ratios and proportions rather than minuscule variations. Darwin could thereby have dispelled criticisms that the terrestrial time clock had not been running long enough for the evolution of man. He might have become a Mendelian instead of a Neo-Lamarckian. One point is certain; if Darwin had inclined toward the Darwinian cult, he would have disbarred himself from becoming one of the major protagonists in a drama recounting the history of genetic psychology. But being unaware of Mendel, Darwin turned to Lamarck. Thus genetic psychology blossomed impetuously, ignored Mendel, and drew blithely upon the more venerable of past dictums and the teeming, Lamarckian, nineteenth-century natural sciences.

The elevation of genetic psychology to eminence among the organic sciences in the nineteenth century began in Greek antiquity, reposed during the Dark and Middle Ages, and prospered auspiciously after a sequence of evolutionary pronouncements: the homo sapiens was a hereditary product of countless species who started their ascent from the simplest form of existence imaginable. At some primordial moment a fortuitous combination of prebiotic organic materials utilized external energy sources to make more complex entities of its own kind. Thenceforth, every offspring in his ontogenetic march toward maturity struggled to recapitulate the variations and adaptations of his parents and ancestors. The very fact that recapitulation apparently occurred signified that nature had decreed that it *ought* to occur; hence environmental pressures that might induce arrest and perversion of phyletic stages during the recapitulatory period—before maturity is attained—should be mitigated. Individuals obviously would be most malleable at the instant of the last expenditures of their phylogenetic legacy, and it was then, during adolescence, that new characters for advancing the species were to be acquired. Holding fatefully onto the assumption of pangenesis—that every cell, tissue, and organ of the body secretes hereditary particles—and that of acquired characters—that somatic variations in parents are preserved in reproduction and are inherited by progeny—the principle of teleologic growth via recapitulation seemed fastened securely to the realities of organic evolution and development. In this manner, genetic psychology developed and flourished.

PART ONE

Development and Change
in Classical Antiquity

NATURALISTIC explanations of organic life percolated in the first centuries that followed aeons of mythology. In ancient Greece, Egypt, Babylonia, and other early seats of civilization celestial or terrestrial happenings were initially interpreted as whimsical expressions of benign or angry deities. Thunder and lightning were weapons possessed by Zeus and Thor; light and darkness were coordinated by Phoebus whose flaming chariot ceaselessly roamed across the sky. Then, after what seems an interminable time span, rationality emerged, as units and rules of measurement, simple arithmetic, calendars, and measures of astronomical occurrences were developed.

The scholars of antiquity who first sought to explain diversity and multiplicity in earthly changes lived in the Greek community of Miletus about 600 B.C. The patriarch of the Milesian nature-philosophers, Thales, left no remnants of his writings; indeed, he probably could neither read nor write. He merits rank among ancient sages, however, for he seems to have been the first to formulate a naturalistic generalization about change. Thales pronounced diversity in the natural world to be the result of structural modifications in water, the one all-pervasive substance. The earth seemed like a flat disk surrounded everywhere by a vast, expansive sea. No one really knows why Thales chose water as the basic substance of the universe. Perhaps, as one authority[1] suggests, it was because water can easily be transfigured into the gaseous and solid states of steam and ice.

The notion that every form of existence originated from water disquieted Anaximander, fellow Milesian and son of an associate of Thales, who recognized that to endow water or any other seemingly basic substance, like fire or air, with primacy in the scheme of creation would

[1] W. K. C. Guthrie, *In the Beginning* (London: Methuen, 1957), p. 17.

be tantamount to admitting that it could consume and destroy other natural substances. Anaximander followed Thales in holding to a single, fundamental denominator of all existences, but to keep all the material substances on a par, he conceptualized them as constituting a special cosmos, at once with and without qualities, indeterminate, limitless, ethereal, and chaotic.

Anaximander supposed that every material and organic form had arisen from the shapeless mass and that eventually everything would be reabsorbed by it. Like the nineteenth-century evolutionary theorists, Anaximander saw the present world and its forms as a temporary phase in the cosmic mosaic, as a world once populated by now extinct forms and as one whose present characters faced certain replacement. Originally all was a seething caldron; then hot and cold masses arose. Water, pristine slime and mud, and earth were differentiated; finally, from the action of heat upon the damp, spongy masses, fire leaped into the heavens to enclose the colder substances in a great sphere of flame.

Anaximander's cosmic theory might have persisted unheralded had it not also encompassed the first explanation of how living beings developed. Plants and animals appeared first. Animal forms were spontaneously generated in the primordial moisture and mud. Man existed in fish guise until he cast off a prickly skin and abandoned water for dry land. Unfortunately, what is known of Anaximander's developmental theory has been preserved in only a few fragments from the works of later writers:

Animals came into being through vapours raised by the sun. Man, however, came into being from another animal, namely the fish, for at first he was like a fish.

Anaximander said that the first animals were generated in the moisture, and were covered with a prickly skin; and as they grew older, they became drier, and after the skin broke off from them, they lived for a little while.

Anaximander says that at the beginning man was generated from all sorts of animals, since all the rest can quickly get food for themselves, but man alone requires careful feeding for a long time; such a being at the beginning could not have preserved his existence.[2]

The fragmentary clues to Anaximander's thinking are hardly sufficient to qualify him unreservedly as a precursor of the genetic psychologists. Clearly, in postulating the procreating powers of vapors and moisture, he anticipated the doctrine of spontaneous generation. He observed that

[2] From M. C. Nahm, *Selections from Early Greek Philosophy* (New York: F. S. Crofts, 1935), p. 65. Copyright © 1964 by Meredith Publishing Co. Reprinted by permission of the publishers.

animals in their growth require opportunity to adjust to complex physical environs, and he preempted Fiske in pointing to the relationship between helplessness after birth and the prolongation of infancy.[3] A notion of adaptation was intimated in that the thorny, aquatic creatures were presumed to have shrugged their shells as the land mass dried; however, he did not suggest that survival is a function of adaptation to environmental conditions. Anaximander's theory of the origin of man, moreover, was reminiscent of earlier legends and myths. To his credit, teleological elements were lacking, but so were the issues of heredity and variation. He was untroubled by the physiological differences in internal organization necessary for shifting from watery to terrestrial life. Finally, the insight that there might be an evolutionary scale whereby higher species developed out of simpler forms was absent. Each species seemingly arose independently from sea slime, and man originated about as early as any other form of life.

The earliest gleaning of a relationship between adaptation and evolutionary progress appeared a century later in the work of Empedocles of Acragas, Sicily. Empedocles developed his particular theory of growth and change to resolve, in part, a basic philosophic issue that Parmenides had raised regarding the fact of existence (*Being*) and coming into existence (*Becoming*). Parmenides, from the Greek colony of Elea, argued that the Milesian viewpoint, with its emphasis on the perpetual flux and flow of a single material substance, denied real and permanent Becoming or change. Thales and Anaximander had, it seemed, assumed that the cosmic base maintained its identity throughout periods of change. Parmenides argued vigorously, therefore, that growth, destruction, change, and even motion were impossible. Particular forms presented to the senses as various substances were in reality of one immutable essence.

Empedocles protested Parmenides' unyielding insistence that the world, at its root, was in a suspended state of mere existence. To Empedocles, not one but four irreducible substances comprised the universe: fire, air, water, and earth. Each was assumed to be immortal, indestructible, and qualitatively permanent. Where the idea of four elements originated is unknown. It may have stemmed from observations of the action of fire. When green wood is burning, for example, fire may be seen by its light, air absorbs smoke, water pours out of the ends of the logs, and earth accumulates from ashes.[4] However, by recognizing four basic

---

[3] N. M. Butler, "Anaximander on the Prolongation of Infancy in Man," *Classical Studies in Honour of Henry Drisler* (New York: Macmillan, 1894), pp. 8–10.
[4] W. C. Dampier, *A History of Science* (Cambridge, England: Cambridge University Press, 1952), p. 21.

substances, Empedocles resolved Parmenides' dilemma in holding that movements or redistributions of the four immutable substances would leave their essential natures unaltered. Becoming or change would, therefore, be compatible with the processes governing existence itself.

Empedocles reasoned that in the distributive processes the elements were simply mixed or separated rather than transformed. Mixing led to origin and growth; separating, to decay and destruction. Because the elements themselves constituted being, they lacked the force or impulse to initiate the beginning, continuation, and cessation of mixture and separation. Thus Empedocles, on the basis of his observations of human behavior, derived the notion that two irreconcilable forces—Love and Hate—instigated change. Love compelled the elements to unite and combine; Hate, to divide and separate.[5] The two forces were imagined to dominate each other in cyclical fashion. When those of attraction became wholly dominant, the elements were indistinguishably fused in a great sphere. The penetration of Strife caused the elements to separate. When the disruptive forces were triumphant, the elements were separated into layers, with earth at the bottom followed by water, air, and fire above.

Empedocles felt that in the present world Strife was dominant but that, at least in respect to organic development, Love was gaining momentum, and his view of life corresponded to his cosmic philosophy. Strife had once been completely dominant and the four elements had been separated, but as Love exerted its unifying influence, the coming together of various elements also brought together separate body parts, limbs and organs, of men and animals. From the effects of Strife, different features of living creatures had been fashioned. Scattered about randomly, they eventually linked themselves together in all sorts of grotesque patterns. Extraordinary creatures arose from the ensuing chaos—heads without necks or bodies, arms bereft of shoulders, eyes minus sockets. Empedocles saw that spontaneous generation preceded procreation by sexual union, and he seemed to allude to the notion of hereditary transmission and to the possibility that the formation of life-forms might require ages. His most significant claim to eminence among developmental specialists was his belief that complete animals originated through the chance amalgamations of organs that adapted themselves to environmental conditions. The implication is clear that the unfit perished after several trials at living. Empedocles, however, neither suggested a hierarchy of life-forms nor saw plant life as preceding animal life. Furthermore, in his view, the unfit seemed to have been replaced summarily by the fittest rather than, as evolutionary doctrine presupposed, to have been gradually

---

[5] Nahm, *op. cit.*, p. 128.

succeeded by them. Empedocles has been hailed as "the father of the evolution idea,"[6] and the following excerpts from his writings suggest how roughly appropriate the distinction may be:

For all things are united, themselves with parts of themselves—the beaming sun and earth and sky and sea—whatever things are friendly but have separated in mortal things. And so, in the same way, whatever things are the more adapted for mixing, these are loved by each other and made alike by Aphrodite. But whatever things are hostile are separated as far as possible from each other, both in their origin and in their mixing and in the forms impressed on them, absolutely unwonted to unite and very baneful, at the suggestion of Strife, since it has wrought their birth.

Where many heads grew up without necks, and arms were wandering about naked, bereft of shoulders, and eyes roamed about alone with no foreheads.

This is indeed remarkable in the mass of human members; at one time all the limbs which form the body, united into one by Love, grow vigorously in the prime of life; but yet at another time, separated by evil Strife, they wander each in different directions along the breakers of the sea of life. Just so it is with plants and with fishes dwelling in watery halls, and beasts whose lair is in the mountains, and birds borne on wings.

But as divinity was mingled yet more with divinity, these things kept coming together in whatever way each might chance, and many others also in addition to these continually came into being.

Many creatures arose with double faces and double breasts, offspring of oxen with human faces, and again there sprang up children of men with oxen's heads; creatures, too, in which were mixed some parts from men and some of the nature of women, furnished with sterile members.

But come now, hear of these things; how fire separating caused the hidden offspring of men and weeping women to arise, for it is no tale apart from our subject, or witless. In the first place there sprang up out of the earth forms grown into one whole, having a share of both, of water and of fire.

These in truth fire caused to grow up, desiring to reach its like; but they showed as yet no lovely body formed out of the members, nor voice nor limb such as is natural to men.

In its warmer parts the womb is productive of the male, and on this account men are dark and more muscular and more hairy.

For it is by earth that we see earth, and by water water, and by air glorious air; so, too, by fire we see destroying fire, and love by love, and strife by baneful strife. For out of these (elements) all things are fitted together

[6] H. F. Osborn, *From the Greeks to Darwin* (New York: Macmillan, 1905), p. 37.

and their form is fixed, and by these men think and feel both pleasure and pain.[7]

The ideas of Anaximander and Empedocles pertaining to natural necessity, evolution, and growth, however crude, nestle well in postevolutionary-theory frames of reference. The two sages differed in defining the original "stuff" of the universe, but both are assumed to have believed that growth and change were a product of necessity, that is, of consequences following invariantly from antecedent events. Everything accrued by the rules of chance; furthermore, there was Empedocles' dark allusion that those whom fortuity favored were those who endured and survived. Empedocles never articulated a militant, nonteleological viewpoint, but it is relatively easy to believe that he might have held one.

Anaximander and Empedocles, however, were not viewed by genetic psychologists as major precursors of their discipline. The venerable sages, unlike G. Stanley Hall and his colleagues, presumed that the essence of nature, no matter how being and becoming were manifested, resembled a huge machine indifferent to the welfare of man and to his place in the universe. This particular view also disturbed ancient Greek scholars in the various city-states, who parried ideologies back and forth until the exaltation of man and Final Causes or ultimate purposes—so important in genetic psychology—finally emerged as important components of their cosmology. In the works of Aristotle of Stagira, systematist par excellence, Greek philosophy reached a zenith in its reconciliation of metaphysical and naturalistic thought systems. The knotty issues associated with being and becoming were settled until Darwin forced their reopening; then, while Aristotle's crude evolutionary arguments were discarded by the genetic psychologists, aspects of his system pertaining to Final Causes were warmly sanctioned.

Aristotle incorporated his works on biology and development in a series of treatises, *History of Animals, On the Parts of Animals*, the *Reproduction of Animals*, and *On the Soul* or *De Anima*, which encompassed virtually all existing knowledge about animal life in the fourth century B.C. Aristotle's biological works were inextricably interwoven with the wider philosophical questions that plagued Greek philosophers of his time. Like those facing Empedocles, these questions dealt largely with the form and substance of matter and reality, and like Empedocles', Aristotle's conclusions represented a synthesis of his predecessors' thinking. In his *Metaphysics*, Aristotle reviewed especially the theories of Democritus

[7] From M. C. Nahm, *Selections from Early Greek Philosophy*, (New York: F. S. Crofts, 1935). Copyright © 1964 by Meredith Publishing Co. Reprinted by permission of the publishers.

and Plato, and although he rejected them as a whole, on certain aspects of each he built the cosmology that was destined to dominate Western science for centuries.

Democritus of Meletus had simplified Empedocles' four elements by offering a theory of atoms based on the older and alternative single-element hypothesis. Change was a result of mingling and separating, but the basic denominator was reduced to a minuscule atom, which was eternal, unborn, and indestructible. Democritus perceived the world as having once been an infinite void comprised of individual atoms in motion. As the atoms collided, adhered, and fused, innumerable worlds ascended and crumbled. In those that survived, various life systems arose, which in turn survived if adapted to their environments. Atomism thus reduced the meaning of reality to concourses of minute particles lacking distinguishable qualities; becoming was as transitory to Democritus as it had been for Empedocles, and the concept of being had been diminished to the insensible atom.

Democritus' atomism and the earlier mechanistic theories were repugnant to scholars in Athens, who were less concerned with the issue of becoming than that of being or reality. Rather than a disinterested machine, reality was in essence something that approximated nature as it appears to the mind. The fundamental meaning of reality resided in a priori ideals and could be known only as the mind grasped the essence of the form of these archetypes. Change occurred in the natural world, agreed the Athenians, and it could be perceived, but such change conveyed only transitory meaning. Permanent reality or being resided in the ideals. Socrates, stressing that reality must be understood rather by inductive reasoning about the categories or classes of things than by perceptions of alterations in nature, led the counterattack in Athens on Democritus' naturalism. But it was Plato, his brilliant student, who most stringently adopted methods of Socratic thinking to direct man's attention away from events in the physical world. For Plato, the only reality was that constituted by the a priori ideals or universals, perfect and changeless, which could be imperfectly known through rational analyses. Thus, in contrast to materialism, a new philosophical idealism developed. The world was comprised not of a few seething substances yielding a phantasmagoria of material existences but of eternal universals or metaphysical entities. In deriving the notion of universals, Plato might have been guilty of unwarranted anthropomorphizing or deifying the objects of his own systems of thought, ethics, and morality and of reducing becoming to an illusion; nonetheless, he had glorified the fact of being by postulating immortal spiritual existences.

Aristotle, however, felt that both Democritus and Plato had erred, the former in forsaking the existence of universals and the latter in holding that the universals were entirely supernatural and thus above and beyond comprehension by sensory perception. Aristotle struggled heroically, therefore, to compromise the long-standing breach. The universals, he said, were imbedded in matter. In essence, Aristotle aligned both becoming and being by viewing matter, that which is perceived by the senses, as comprising only the potential, and by viewing reality as the end, form, or universal toward which a thing was growing. As a consequence of the alignment, Aristotle delimited the becoming of things to their foreordained forms, and thus departed radically from the concepts of unlimited structural change inherent in the systems of both Empedocles and Democritus. Specifically, he reasoned that every cognitive impression was filtered through four elementary qualities of the senses: hot, cold, wet, and dry. Rather than being divisible into atoms, the material world was, as Empedocles held, discernible in terms of four basic elements—earth, water, air, and fire—and knowledge of the a priori, eternal universals could be arrived at from sense perceptions of material objects and life-forms, constituting various combinations of the elements.

In the Aristotelian scheme, all things, even before they attained full status, were potentially whatever they had the capacity to become. The external environment, however, might prevent full realization of potential or becoming. Potentiality did not imply inevitability, for on many occasions the final form of an object or thing might not be representative of the Final Cause—the purpose or end for which the entity was brought into being. An acorn, for example, might be prevented from becoming an oak tree because nutriments were capriciously denied it by environmental conditions. The heavy hand of inorganic nature thus caused discontinuities in what the organic impulses toward perfection might achieve if unimpeded. The major theme contributed by Aristotle to the early developmental sciences was his belief that everything would realize its appointed end or Final Cause unless stunted by uncontrolled, inorganic, formless matter.

Aristotle provided a firm basis for the nature-is-right doctrine, and might have anticipated several other major principles of genetic psychology, except that he presented the world as a series of fixed, rigid, and changeless forms. All the forms in the universe were arranged in a hierarchical series, and the position of each on the ascending scale of existences depended on the highest level of soul inherent in it—ranging from nutritive through rational—because the souls furnished the inner impulse or thrust toward actualization. Aristotelianism was also congruent, therefore, with genetic psychology in reckoning the world to be comprised of an ascending series of life-forms. But Aristotle's idea of becoming, in the context of the hierarchical order, was highly constrained; the potential of matter was confined to its status by privation,· that is, the attributes it presently lacked relative to the realization of its Final Cause. Permanent transitions, structural alterations, and extinctions within the series of organic forms were impossible.

In trying to resolve the philosophical dilemma between form and matter, being and becoming, Aristotle established himself as the forerunner of modern science. He agreed with the Athenians to the point of acknowledging that reason, in terms of strengths and limitations of the human mind, must be the starting point for obtaining knowledge. He looked to matter, however, rather than to reasoning for basic information. In a collection of treatises known as the *Organon,* Aristotle set forth the processes of logical inference necessary for proving the validity of rational conclusions. Here Aristotle described his technique for building a science of trustworthy knowledge. One must start, he said, with a few essential axioms or truths which intuition has shown to be correct. These become theorems or self-evident truths and are used conjunctively with the syllogism. Thus one may argue deductively, from previously established rules or statements to particular instances, or conversely, from a collection of independently observed events toward general propositions. Aristotle hastened to exhort those who might employ his methods to be cautious, to be certain before application that the self-evident propositions cover the events deduced or that the generalizations developed are indeed representative of all the instances on which they are based.

Aristotle's magnificent *Organon* stands as the consummate masterpiece of logical processes. Few will achieve a more exalted rank among mortal men than Aristotle. Scientists from time immemorial will be indebted to him for this incomparable contribution to scientific methodology. Hardly anyone has ever been more clearly aware of the dangers of drawing sweeping conclusions from insufficient data than Aristotle, yet in his own practice he failed lamentably. In his effort to preserve a metaphysical explanation of the physical nature of the universe in partial harmony with Platonic ideals, Aristotle stumbled. He lacked techniques for rigorous research and he had to cope with crude scientific ideas and primitive data. Aristotle possessed too few facts to fulfill his audacious ambition to derive all the basic metaphysical and natural laws, and in his zeal he rushed into diffuse, inappropriate generalizations. Moreover, he beclouded his conceptual analyses with questions of Final Causes and failed, therefore, to focus clearly on purely scientific issues. Syllogistic reasoning, so helpful in stating formal proofs from accepted premises, was simply insufficient for establishing experimental sciences, where research and verification are especially critical factors. Problems such as these caused him to "depart from his own precepts, and led him a deluded captive through the labyrinth of metaphysical conjecture."[8] Consequently, Aristotle was condemned during the resurgence of science in the nineteenth century by all except the developmental specialists for founding "a system of stagnation and obedience to authority."[9]

Evolutionary theorists presumptively cast aside the Aristotelian concept of fixed forms, discarded the subjectivity rooted in metaphysical conjecture about the phenomenon of being, and, in part, returned to the simplicity and objectivity of Democritus' atomism. Many evolutionary theorists who adopted recapitulatory principles agreed with Aristotle, nonetheless, in superimposing a Final Cause upon the processes of becoming. They felt little urgency to find philosophical accommodation for questions about ultimate substances and problems of growth and development. The likelihood that everything that evolves and develops would eventually be reduced again to primary elements seemed irrelevant. The universe, now expanding, might someday reverse its apparent direction, but that faraway moment was incomprehensible. To these natural scientists, man could be seen in evolutionary and developmental perspective, and to them, the natural consequences of growth appeared limitless. Even in knowing that all existences might be degraded to ashes ultimately, one might be, as were Darwin, Spencer, and Hall, an inveterate optimist, hoping that for aeons hence the foreordained purposes of a supraintelligence would continue to be actualized.

The following excerpts from Aristotle's voluminous writings indicate the extent to which metaphysics dominated his thinking about growth and development. In the brief selection from *Physics*, Aristotle argued that an end or purpose was present in everything that developed in nature. Here are the rudiments of the nature-is-right doctrine. In the extract from *Parts of Animals*, Aristotle, in attempting to demolish Democritus' atomism, reiterated his teleological viewpoint that form is the essence of growth.

A definition of what it means to be a living organism was given in the selection from *De Anima;* further, both the hierarchical functions and the serial order of the *nutritive, sentient, appetitive, locomotive,* and *rational* souls was discussed. The latter discourse in *De Anima* is especially noteworthy for its implications to genetic psychology when read in the

---

[8] G. H. Lewes, *Aristotle* (London: Smith Elder, 1864), p. 113.
[9] E. Nordenskiöld, *The History of Biology* (New York: Tudor, 1935), p. 43; H. Hoffding, *A History of Modern Philosophy* (New York: Macmillan, 1900); Vol. I, pp. 7–9.

context of these brief passages alluding to recapitulation from *Generation of Animals:*

For nobody would put down the unfertilized embryo as soulless or in every sense bereft of life (since both the semen and the embryo of an animal have every bit as much life as a plant). . . . As they [embryos] develop they also acquire the sensitive soul in virtue of which an animal is an animal. For e.g. an animal does not become at the same time an animal and a man or a horse or any other particular animal. For the end is developed last, and the peculiar character of the species is the end of the generation in each individual. . . . For at first all such embryos seem to live the life of a plant. And it is clear that we must be guided by this in speaking of the sensitive and the rational soul. For all three kinds of soul, not only the nutritive, must be possessed potentially before they are possessed in actuality.[10]

ARISTOTLE (384–322 B.C.)

ON THE CAUSES OF DEVELOPMENT

PHYSICS, BOOK II, CHAPTER 8

WE must explain then that Nature belongs to the class of causes which act for the sake of something. . . .

A difficulty presents itself: why should not nature work, not for the sake of something, nor because it is better so, but just as the sky rains, not in order to make the corn grow, but of necessity? What is drawn up must cool, and what has been cooled must become water and descend, the result of this being that the corn grows. Similarly if a man's crop is spoiled on the threshing-floor, the rain did not fall for the sake of this—in order that the crop might be spoiled—but that result just followed. Why then should it not be the same with the parts in nature, e.g., that our teeth should come up *of necessity*—the front teeth sharp,

[10] Aristotle, *Generation of Animals*, II:3, translated by Arthur Platt, in *The Works of Aristotle*, Edited by W. D. Ross (Oxford: Clarendon Press, 1912). Reprinted by permission of the publisher.
SOURCE: The excerpts are from *The Works of Aristotle*, translated into English under the editorship of W. D. Ross (Oxford: Clarendon Press, 1930). (*a*) Volume II, *Physica*, Book II, Chapter 8. Translated by R. P. Hardie and R. K. Gaye. (*b*) Volume V, *De Partibus Animalium*, Book I, Chapter 1. Translated by William Ogle. (*c*) Volume III, *De Anima*, Book II, Chapters 2–4. Translated by J. A. Smith. All selections are abridged and footnotes are deleted. Reprinted by permission of the publisher.

fitted for tearing, the molars broad and useful for grinding down the food—since they did not arise for this end, but it was merely a coincident result; and so with all other parts in which we suppose that there is purpose? Wherever then all the parts came about just what they would have been if they had come to be for an end, such things survived, being organized spontaneously in a fitting way; whereas those which grew otherwise perished and continue to perish, as Empedocles says his "man-faced ox-progeny" did.

Such are the arguments (and others of the kind) which may cause difficulty on this point. Yet it is impossible that this should be the true view. For teeth and all other natural things either invariably or normally come about in a given way; but of not one of the results of chance or spontaneity is this true. We do not ascribe to chance or mere coincidence the frequency of rain in winter, but frequent rain in summer we do; nor heat in the dog-days, but only if we have it in winter. If then, it is agreed that things are either the result of coincidence or for an end, and these cannot be the result of coincidence or spontaneity, it follows that they must be for an end; and that such things are all due to nature even the champions of the theory which is before us would agree. Therefore action for an end is present in things which come to be and are by nature.

Further, where a series has a completion, all the preceding steps are for the sake of that. Now surely as in intelligent action, so in nature; and as in nature, so it is in each action, if nothing interferes. Now intelligent action is for the sake of an end; therefore the nature of things also is so. Thus if a house, e.g., had been a thing made by nature, it would have been made in the same way as it is now by art; and if things made by nature were made also by art, they would come to be in the same way as by nature. Each step then in the series is for the sake of the next; and generally art partly completes what nature cannot bring to a finish, and partly imitates her. If, therefore, artificial products are for the sake of an end, so clearly also are natural products. The relation of the later to the earlier terms of the series is the same in both.

This is most obvious in the animals other than man: they make things neither by art nor after inquiry or deliberation. Wherefore people discuss whether it is by intelligence or by some other faculty that these creatures work—spiders, ants, and the like. By gradual advance in this direction we come to see clearly that in plants too that is produced which is conducive to the end—leaves, e.g., grow to provide shade for the fruit. If then it is both by nature and for an end that the swallow makes its nest and the spider its web, and plants grow leaves for the sake of the fruit and send their roots down (not up) for the sake of nourishment, it is plain that this kind of cause is operative in things which come to be and are by nature. And since "nature" means two things, the matter and the form, of which the latter is the end, and since all the rest is for the sake of the end, the form must be the cause in the sense of "that for the sake of which."

Now mistakes come to pass even in the operations of art: the grammarian makes a mistake in writing and the doctor pours out the wrong dose. Hence clearly mistakes are possible in the operations of nature also. If then in art there are cases in which what is rightly produced serves a purpose, and if where mistakes occur there was a purpose in what was attempted, only it was not attained, so must it be also in natural products, and monstrosities will be failures in the purposive effort.

PARTS OF ANIMALS, BOOK I, CHAPTER 1

. . . For the process of evolution is for the sake of the thing finally evolved, and not this for the sake of the process. Empedocles, then, was in error when he said that many of the characters presented by animals were merely the results of incidental occurrences during their development; for instance, that the backbone was divided as it is into vertebrae, because it happened to be broken owing to the contorted position of the foetus in the womb. In so saying he overlooked the fact that propagation implies a creative seed endowed with certain formative properties. Secondly, he neglected another fact, namely, that the parent animal pre-exists, not only in idea, but actually in time. For man is generated from man; and thus it is the possession of certain characters by the parent that determines the development of like characters in the child. The same statement holds good also for the operations of art, and even for those which are apparently spontaneous. For the same result as is produced by art may occur spontaneously. Spontaneity, for instance, may bring about the restoration of health. The products of art, however, require the pre-existence of an efficient cause homogeneous with themselves, such as the statuary's art, which must necessarily precede the statue; for this cannot possibly be produced spontaneously. Art indeed consists in the conception of the result to be produced before its realization in the material. As with spontaneity, so with chance; for this also produces the same result as art, and by the same process.

The fittest mode, then, of treatment is to say, a man has such and such parts, because the conception of a man includes their presence, and because they are necessary conditions of his existence, or, if we cannot quite say this, which would be best of all, then the next thing to it, namely, that it is either quite impossible for him to exist without them, or, at any rate, that it is better for him that they should be there; and their existence involves the existence of other antecedents. Thus we should say, because man is an animal with such and such characters, therefore is the process of his development necessarily such as it is; and therefore is it accomplished in such and such an order, this part being formed first, that next, and so on in succession; and after a like fashion should we explain the evolution of all other works of nature.

Now that with which the ancient writers, who first philosophized about Nature, busied themselves, was the material principle and the material cause. They inquired what this is, and what its character; how the universe is generated out of it, and by what motor influence, whether, for instance, by antagonism or friendship, whether by intelligence or spontaneous action, the substratum of matter being assumed to have certain inseparable properties; fire, for instance, to have a hot nature, earth a cold one; the former to be light, the latter heavy. For even the genesis of the universe is thus explained by them. After a like fashion do they deal also with the development of plants and of animals. They say, for instance, that the water contained in the body causes by its currents the formation of the stomach and the other receptacles of food or of excretion; and that the breath by its passage breaks open the outlets of the nostrils; air and water being the materials of which bodies are made; for all represent nature as composed of such or similar substances.

But if men and animals and their several parts are natural phenomena, then the natural philosopher must take into consideration not merely the ultimate substances of which they are made, but also flesh, bone, blood, and all the other homogeneous parts; not only these, but also the heterogeneous parts, such as face, hand, foot; and must examine how each of these comes to be what it is, and in virtue of what force. For to say what are the ultimate substances out of which an animal is formed, to state, for instance, that it is made of fire or earth, is no more sufficient than would be a similar account in the case of a couch or the like. For we should not be content with saying that the couch was made of bronze or wood or whatever it might be, but should try to describe its design or mode of composition in preference to the material; or, if we did deal with the material, it would at any rate be with the concretion of material and form. For a couch is such and such a form embodied in this or that matter, or such and such a matter with this or that form; so that its shape and structure must be included in our description. For the formal nature is of greater importance than the material nature.

Does, then, configuration and colour constitute the essence of the various animals and of their several parts? For if so, what Democritus says will be strictly correct. For such appears to have been his notion. At any rate he says that it is evident to every one what form it is that makes the man, seeing that he is recognizable by his shape and colour. And yet a dead body has exactly the same configuration as a living one; but for all that is not a man. So also no hand of bronze or wood or constituted in any but the appropriate way can possibly be a hand in more than name. For like a physician in a painting, or like a flute in a sculpture, in spite of its name it will be unable to do the office which that name implies. Precisely in the same way no part of a dead body, such I mean as its eye or its hand, is really an eye or a hand. To say, then, that shape and colour constitutes the animal is an inadequate statement, and is much the same as if a woodcarver were to insist that the hand he had cut out was really a hand. Yet the physiologists, when they give an account of the development and causes of the animal form, speak very much like such a craftsman. What, however, I would ask, are the forces by which the hand or the body was fashioned into its shape? The woodcarver will perhaps say, by the axe or the auger; the physiologist, by air and by earth. Of these two answers the artificer's is the better, but it is nevertheless insufficient. For it is not enough for him to say that by the stroke of his tool this part was formed into a concavity, that into a flat surface; but he must state the reasons why he struck his blow in such a way as to effect this, and what his final object was; namely, that the piece of wood should develop eventually into this or that shape. It is plain, then, that the teaching of the old physiologists is inadequate, and that the true method is to state what the definitive characters are that distinguish the animal as a whole; to explain what it is both in substance and in form, and to deal after the same fashion with its several organs; in fact, to proceed in exactly the same way as we should do, were we giving a complete description of a couch.

If now this something that constitutes the form of the living being be the soul, or part of the soul, or something that without the soul cannot exist; as would seem to be the case, seeing at any rate that when the soul departs, what is left is no longer a living animal, and that none of the parts remain what they were before, excepting in mere configuration, like the animals that in the fable are turned into stone; if, I say, this be so, then it will come within the province of the natural philosopher to inform himself concerning the soul, and to treat of it, either in its entirety, or, at any rate, of that part of it which constitutes the essential character of an animal; and it will be his duty to say what this soul or this part of a soul is; and to discuss the attributes that attach to this essential character, especially as nature is spoken of in two senses, and the nature of a thing is either its matter or its essence; nature as essence including both the motor cause and the final cause. Now it is in the latter of these two senses that either the whole soul or some part of it constitutes the nature of an animal; and inasmuch as it is the presence of the soul that enables matter to constitute the animal nature, much more than it is the presence of matter which so enables the soul, the inquirer into nature is bound on every ground to treat of the soul rather than of the matter. For though the wood of which they are made constitutes the couch and the tripod, it only does so because it is capable of receiving such and such a form.

ON THE SOUL, BOOK II, CHAPTERS 2 TO 4

We resume our inquiry from a fresh starting-point by calling attention to the fact that what has soul in it differs from what has not in that the former displays life. Now this word has more than one sense, and provided any one alone of these is found in a thing we say that thing is living. Living, that is, may mean thinking or perception or local movement and rest, or movement in the sense of nutrition, decay and growth. Hence we think of plants also as living, for they are observed to possess in themselves an originative power through which they increase or decrease in all spatial directions; they grow up *and* down, and everything that grows increases its bulk alike in both directions or indeed in all, and continues to live so long as it can absorb nutriment.

This power of self-nutrition can be isolated from the other powers mentioned, but not they from it—in mortal beings at least. The fact is obvious in plants; for it is the only psychic power they possess.

This is the originative power the possession of which leads us to speak of things as *living* at all, but it is the possession of sensation that leads us for the first time to speak of living things as animals; for even those beings which possess no power of local movement but do possess the power of sensation we call animals and not merely living things.

The primary form of sense is touch, which belongs to all animals. Just as the power of self-nutrition can be isolated from touch and sensation generally, so touch can be isolated from all other forms of sense. (By the power of self-nutrition we mean that departmental power of the soul which is common to plants and animals: all animals whatsoever are observed to have the sense of touch.) What the explanation of these two facts is, we must discuss later. At present we must confine ourselves to saying that soul is the source of this phenomena and is characterized by them, viz., by the powers of self-nutrition, sensation, thinking, and motivity.

Is each of these a soul or a part of a soul? And if a part, a part in what sense? A part merely distinguishable by definition or a part distinct in local situation as well? In the case of certain of these powers, the answers to these questions are easy, in the case of others we are puzzled what to say. Just as in the case of plants which when divided are observed to continue to live though removed to a distance from one another (thus showing that in *their* case the soul of each individual plant before division was actually one, potentially many), so we notice a similar result in other varieties of soul, i.e., in insects which have been cut in two; each of the segments possesses both sensation and local movement; and if sensation, necessarily also imagination and appetition; for, where there is sensation, there is also pleasure and pain, and, where these, necessarily also desire.

We have no evidence as yet about mind or the power to think; it seems to be a widely different kind of soul, differing as what is eternal from what is perishable; it alone is capable of existence in isolation from all other psychic powers. All the other parts of soul, it is evident from what we have said, are, in spite of certain statements to the contrary, incapable of separate existence though, of course, distinguishable by definition. If opining is distinct from perceiving, to be capable of opining and to be capable of perceiving must be distinct, and so with all the other forms of living above enumerated. Further, some animals possess all these parts of soul, some certain of them only, others one only (this is what enables us to classify animals). A similar arrangement is found also within the field of the senses; some classes of animals have all the senses, some only certain of them, others only one, the most indispensable, touch. . . .

Of the psychic powers above enumerated some kinds of living things, as we have said, possess all, some less than all, others one only. Those we have mentioned are the nutritive, the appetitive, the sensory, the locomotive, and the power of thinking. Plants have none but the first, the nutritive, while another order of living things has this *plus* the sensory. If any order of living things has the sensory, it must also have the appetitive; for appetite is the genus of which desire, passion, and wish are the species; now all animals have one sense at least, viz., touch, and whatever has a sense has the capacity for pleasure and pain and therefore has pleasant and painful objects present to it, and wherever these are present, there is desire, for desire is just appetition of what is pleasant. Further, all animals have the sense for food (for touch is the sense for food); the food of all living things consists of what is dry, moist, hot, cold, and these are the qualities apprehended by touch; all other sensible qualities are apprehended by touch only indirectly. Sounds, colours, and odours contribute nothing to nutriment; flavours fall within the field of tangible qualities. Hunger and thirst are forms of desire, hunger a desire for what is dry and hot, thirst a desire for what is cold and moist; flavour is a sort of seasoning added to both. . . . All animals that possess the sense of touch have also appetition. . . . Certain kinds of animals possess in addition the power of locomotion, and still another order of animate beings, i.e., man and possibly another order like man or superior to him, the power of thinking, i.e., mind. It is now evident that a single definition can be given of soul only in the same sense as one can be given of figure. For, as in that case there is no figure distinguishable and apart from triangle, so here there is no soul apart from the forms of soul just enumerated. It is true that a highly general definition can be given for figure which will fit all figures without expressing the peculiar nature of any figure. So here in the case of soul and its specific forms. Hence it is absurd in this and similar cases to demand an absolutely general definition which will fail to express the peculiar nature of anything that *is*, or again, omitting this, to look for separate definitions corresponding to each *infima species*. The cases of figure and soul are exactly parallel; for the particulars subsumed under the common name in both cases—figures and living beings—constitute a series, each successive term of which potentially contains its predecessor, e.g., the square the triangle, the sensory power the self-nutritive. Hence we must ask in the case of each order of living things, What is its soul, i.e., What is the soul of plant, animal, man? Why the terms are related in this serial way must form the subject of later examination. But the facts are that the power of perception is never found apart from the power of self-nutrition, while—in plants—the latter is found isolated from the former. Again, no sense is found apart from that of touch, while touch *is* found by itself; many animals have neither sight, hearing, nor smell. Again, among living things that possess sense some have the power of locomotion, some not. Lastly, certain living beings—a small minority—possess calculation and thought, for (among mortal beings) those which possess calculation have all the other powers above mentioned, while the converse does not hold—indeed some live by imagination alone, while others have not even imagination. . . .

The soul is the cause or source of the living body. The terms cause and source have many senses. But the soul is the cause of its body alike in all three senses which we explicitly recognize. It is (*a*) the source or origin of movement, it is (*b*) the end, it is (*c*) the essence of the whole living body.

That it is the last, is clear; for in everything the essence is identical with the ground of its being, and here, in the case of living things, their being is to live, and of their being and their living the soul in them is the cause or source. Further, the actuality of whatever is potential is identical with its formulable essence.

It is manifest that the soul is also the final cause of its body. For Nature, like mind, always does whatever it does for the sake of something, which something is its end. To that something corresponds in the case of animals the soul and in this it follows the order of nature; all natural bodies are organs of the soul. This is true of those that enter into the constitution of plants as well as of those which enter into that of animals.

PART TWO

Variation and Heredity

When schools and universities first rose to eminence in the later centuries of the Middle Ages, science instructors, such as they were, rigidly adhered to ecclesiastical doctrines and relentlessly maintained a vigilance against heretical inroads. The cosmic world view offered by Aristotle, with its stress on a supreme intelligence, its denial of material or natural causality, and its emphasis on final ends, formed an acceptable scientific base for the rationalistic viewpoint of the medieval church, which doted on the fine points of self-evident truths. Slavish expositions of Aristotelianism thus served to counter every secular threat.

Above the ceaseless din of theological debate a shout could occasionally be heard proclaiming a new insight into the natural order, but unless the new principle could be reconciled with the dominant metaphysics, it was unceremoniously put down. In the sixteenth century, for example, Francis Bacon attacked Aristotelianism, insisting that variations in experience may be produced experimentally and that systems of knowledge must be constructed with accumulated data and mathematically conclusive proofs. As a forthright critic, Bacon performed an exemplary service to science; in his overall outlook, however, Bacon held, as did Aristotle, that natural philosophy must be kept subordinate to metaphysical causes. Galileo, Bacon's contemporary, with a homemade telescope discovered sunspots, various comets, and other anomalies in astronomical events which conflicted with Aristotle's conception of heavenly spheres possessing perfect characteristics. More importantly, Galileo sought in vain to convince Aristotelian philosophers that the Copernican rather than the Ptolemaic theory of the universe explained the phenomena. None dared look through Galileo's telescope at the vexatious spectacles; instead, the extraordinary scientist was forced upon his knees and compelled to perjure himself by recanting his incommeasurable theories.

Galileo's inspired approach, "to measure what can be measured and to make measurable what cannot be measured,"[1] nonetheless, led William

[1] E. Nordenskiöld, *The History of Biology* (New York: Tudor, 1935), p. 117.

Harvey early in the seventeenth century to make the first scientific study of living beings. Harvey discovered the basic principles governing the circulation of blood and the mechanical operations of the heart and offered a creditable description of embryonic development in lower and higher animals. Although Harvey laid the groundwork for upturning ancient concepts of biology, in harmony with the thought modes of his day he never relinquished the archaic, teleological belief that the heart, as the seat of intelligence, dilated and expanded in accordance with the fancy of a resident life spirit. The impact of Harvey's scientific views was blunted for two centuries also by the invention of the microscope, which led to wholesale acceptance of preformationism and the rise of a period during which naturalistic investigations yielded to perusals of the whimsical homunculi.

At the headwaters of the major streams of medieval thought in the centuries preceding the articulation of the theory of species evolution, the Mosaic account of creation dammed every tributary of scientific progress in the organic sciences. That account, which was so completely dominant in the finest minds of early Renaissance scientists, has been outlined briefly by Thomas H. Huxley, brilliant nineteenth-century champion of Darwinism:

The world was made in six natural days. On the first of these days the *materia prima* was made out of nothing, to receive afterwards those "substantial forms" which moulded it into the universe of things; on the third day, the ancestors of all living plants suddenly came into being, full-grown, perfect, and possessed of all the properties which now distinguish them; while, on the fifth and sixth days, the ancestors of all existing animals were similarly caused to exist in their complete and perfect state, by the infusion of their appropriate material substantial forms into the matter which had already been created. Finally, on the sixth day, the *anima rationalis*—that rational and immortal substantial form which is peculiar to man—was created out of nothing, and "breathed into" a mass of matter which, till then, was mere dust of the earth, and so man arose. But the species man was represented by a solitary male individual, until the Creator took out one of his ribs and fashioned it into a female.[2]

The first man who publicly offered a plausible alternative to the testy special-creation doctrine was Jean Baptiste Pierre Antoine de Monet, Chevalier de Lamarck. After rejecting the priesthood and forsaking a commission in the French Army, Lamarck gained the friendship of George de Buffon, distinguished French biologist, who helped him climb from penniless literary hack to impoverished botanist and, at age 50, to professor of zoology in a Paris academy. At age 65, which is the

[2] T. H. Huxley, *Darwiniana Essays* [1871] (New York: Appleton, 1893), p. 144.

twilight period in most men's professional careers, Lamarck published his masterful *Philosophie Zoologique*. The Aristotelian and medieval concept of development held that the form or shape of living beings gave rise to habits and behaviors; Lamarck argued, diametrically, that new habits and behaviors, acquired over time as adaptations to changing modes of life and environment, foisted special shapes on organs and forms. Lamarck's striking break with tradition established him as a precursor of modern zoology, a subject he never studied formally.

Lamarck explained variations among life-forms by two assumptions: (1) the law of use and disuse and (2) the law of inheritance of acquired characters. Lamarck looked "down" the evolutionary scale, by arranging animals and plants from complexity to simplicity, and positively convinced naturalists—seventy-five years later—not only that gradations existed but that he had recognized why they occurred. Here was the bedrock of genetic psychology, and in return for his profound insights, Ernst Haeckel, Herbert Spencer, and G. Stanley Hall literally venerated Lamarck. Nonetheless, however credibly Lamarck expressed his laws and however frequently he asserted that nature was consummating the divine will in eradicating irregularities in the animal scale, his notions of continuity among species and of alterations in forms being a function of attempts to fulfill nothing more sacred than material cravings elicited little but excruciating ridicule from his contemporaries.

Lamarck's severest critic, George Cuvier, except for his unflinching dedication to special-creationism, might well have earned the eulogies of the Haeckel and Hall cohort too. Cuvier commanded all the advantages of the French intelligentsia. As Inspector General of the Department of Education in France, he reformed the French educational system and founded several new universities in France, Italy, and Holland. In the Napoleonic era, he became an authority on both science and education, indispensable to the French Government. Cuvier was the first great comparative scientist to extend Aristotle's relatively crude zoological work on affinities among animals. He pioneered in starting the disciplines of comparative anatomy, zoology, and paleontology, and introduced to zoology the study of fossilized remains. His endeavors, however, led him squarely to the question of the relations between forms of earlier animals and of those presently living. From peeling successive geological strata off the French countryside, Cuvier recognized disconcertedly that earlier fauna differed from present-day animals in proportion to the depth of the stratum in which they lay. Faced with the necessity of reconciling this puzzling discovery with special-creationism, Cuvier boldly proclaimed that a successive series of natural catastrophes had destroyed all life in their wake and had created layers of strata by sudden, violent upheavals in the crust of the earth. To preserve the belief of there having been only one special-creation, Cuvier added the assumption that in each instance of a disaster isolated parts of the earth were spared. Distinct faunas were created when surviving creatures migrated and propagated themselves. With Lamarck's raspish theory of evolution as the only alternative, Cuvier was untroubled by the many vulnerabilities in his "catastrophic theory;" furthermore, his brilliant laboratory studies together with his unsurpassable critical acumen marshaled the French natural scientists at the turn of the nineteenth century.

In the following selection from Chapter 7 of *Philosophie Zoologique*, Lamarck described how environmental influences and learned habits alter the structure of species. The last sentence of this commanding work is formulated as a question: "Can there be any more important conclusion in the range of natural history?" Cuvier and his legion cried "yes," but they were the hapless prisoners of metaphysical dogma. As a result of their censure, the self-educated zoologist was jeered in the learned academies of Paris, reduced to abject poverty, and at his death buried in an unmarked pauper's grave. Today, in sharp contrast to the scorn of the early French savants for environment and learning, is the comprehensive interest of natural and social scientists in these matters. Although one may not agree with Lamarck on the fine points of the theory of acquired characters, his remarkable endeavor stirs loud applause.

JEAN BAPTISTE LAMARCK (1744–1829)

ON ACQUIRED CHARACTERS

WE are not here concerned with an argument, but with the examination of a positive fact—a fact which is of more general application than is supposed, and which has not received the attention that it deserves, no doubt because it is usually very difficult to recognise. This fact consists in the influence that is exerted by the environment on the various living bodies exposed to it.

It is indeed long since the influence of the various states of our organisation on our character, inclinations, activities and even ideas has been

SOURCE: J. B. Lamarck. *Zoological Philosophy* (London: Macmillan, 1914). Translated by Hugh Elliot. Originally published 1809. "Of the Influence of the Environment on the Activities and Habits of Animals, and the Influence of the Activities and Habits of These Living Bodies in Modifying Their Organisation and Structure, Chapter 7, pp. 106–127. Abridged. Footnotes deleted. Reprinted by permission of the publisher.

recognised; but I do not think that anyone has yet drawn attention to the influence of our activities and habits even on our organisation. Now since these activities and habits depend entirely on the environment in which we are habitually placed, I shall endeavour to show how great is the influence exerted by that environment on the general shape, state of the parts and even organisation of living bodies. It is, then, with this very positive fact that we have to do in the present chapter.

If we had not had many opportunities of clearly recognising the result of this influence on certain living bodies that we have transported into an environment altogether new and very different from that in which they were previously placed, and if we had not seen the resulting effects and alterations take place almost under our very eyes, the important fact in question would have remained forever unknown to us.

The influence of the environment as a matter of fact is in all times and places operative on living bodies; but what makes this influence difficult to perceive is that its effects only become perceptible or recognisable (especially in animals) after a long period of time.

Before setting forth to examine the proofs of this fact, which deserves our attention and is so important for zoological philosophy, let us sum up the thread of the discussions that we have already begun.

In the preceding chapter we saw that it is now an unquestionable fact that on passing along the animal scale in the opposite direction from that of nature, we discover the existence, in the groups composing this scale, of a continuous but irregular degradation in the organisation of animals, an increasing simplification in their organisation, and, lastly, a corresponding diminution in the number of their faculties.

This well-ascertained fact may throw the strongest light over the actual order followed by nature in the production of all the animals that she has brought into existence, but it does not show us why the increasing complexity of the organisation of animals from the most imperfect to the most perfect exhibits only an *irregular gradation*, in the course of which there occur numerous anomalies or deviations with a variety in which no order is apparent.

Now on seeking the reason of this strange irregularity in the increasing complexity of animal organisation, if we consider the influence that is exerted by the infinitely varied environments of all parts of the world on the general shape, structure and even organisation of these animals, all will then be clearly explained.

It will in fact become clear that the state in which we find any animal, is, on the one hand, the result of the increasing complexity of organisation tending to form a regular gradation; and, on the other hand, of the influence of a multitude of very various conditions ever tending to destroy the regularity in the gradation of the increasing complexity of organisation.

I must now explain what I mean by this statement: *the environment affects the shape and organisation of animals*, that is to say that when the environment becomes very different, it produces in course of time corresponding modifications in the shape and organisation of animals.

It is true if this statement were to be taken literally, I should be convicted of an error; for, whatever the environment may do, it does not work any direct modification whatever in the shape and organisation of animals.

But great alterations in the environment of animals lead to great alterations in their needs, and these alterations in their needs necessarily lead to others in their activities. Now if the new needs become permanent, the animals then adopt new habits which last as long as the needs that evoked them. This is easy to demonstrate, and indeed requires no amplification.

It is then obvious that a great and permanent alteration in the environment of any race of animals induces new habits in these animals.

Now, if a new environment, which has become permanent for some race of animals, induces new habits in these animals, that is to say, leads them to new activities which become habitual, the result will be the use of some one part in preference to some other part, and in some cases the total disuse of some part no longer necessary.

Nothing of all this can be considered as hypothesis or private opinion; on the contrary, they are truths which, in order to be made clear, only require attention and the observation of facts.

We shall shortly see by the citation of known facts in evidence, in the first place, that new needs which establish a necessity for some part really bring about the existence of that part, as a result of efforts; and that subsequently its continued use gradually strengthens, develops and finally greatly enlarges it; in the second place, we shall see that in some cases, when the new environment and the new needs have altogether destroyed the utility of some part, the total disuse of that part has resulted in its gradually ceasing to share in the development of the other parts of the animal; it shrinks and wastes little by little, and ultimately, when there has been total disuse for a long period, the part in question ends by disappearing. All this is positive; I propose to furnish the most convincing proofs of it.

In plants, where there are no activities and consequently no habits, properly so-called great changes of environment none the less lead to great differences in the development of their parts; so that these differences cause the origin and development of some, and the shrinkage and disappearance of others. But all this is here brought about by the changes sustained in the nutrition of the plant, in its absorption and transpiration, in the quantity of caloric. light, air and moisture that it habitually receives; lastly, in the dominance that some of the various vital movements acquire over others.

Among individuals of the same species, some of which are continually well fed and in an environment favourable to their development, while others are in an opposite environment, there arises a difference in the state of the individuals which gradually becomes very remarkable. How many examples I might cite both in animals and plants which bear out the truth of this principle! Now if the environment remains constant, so that the condition of the ill-fed, suffering or sickly individuals becomes permanent, their internal organisation is ultimately modified, and these acquired modifications are preserved by reproduction among the individuals in question, and finally give rise to a race quite distinct from that in which the individuals have been continuously in an environment favourable to their development.

A very dry spring causes the grasses of a meadow to grow very little, and remain lean and puny; so that they flower and fruit after accomplishing very little growth.

A spring intermingled with warm and rainy days causes a strong growth in this same grass, and the crop is then excellent.

But if anything causes a continuance of the unfavourable environment, a corresponding variation takes place in the plants: first in their general appearance and condition, and then in some of their special characters.

Suppose, for instance, that a seed of one of the meadow grasses in question is transported to an elevated place on a dry, barren and stony plot much exposed to the winds, and is there left to germinate; if the plant can live in such a place, it will always be badly nourished, and if the individuals reproduced from it continue to exist in this bad environment, there will result a race fundamentally different from that which lives in the meadows and from which it originated. The individuals of this new race will have small and meagre parts; some of their organs will have developed more than others, and will then be of unusual proportions.

Those who have observed much and studied large collections, have acquired the conviction that according as changes occur in environment, situation, climate, food, habits of life, etc., corresponding changes in the animals likewise occur in size, shape, proportions of the parts, colour, consistency, swiftness and skill.

What nature does in the course of long periods we do every day when we suddenly change the environment in which some species of living plant is situated.

Every botanist knows that plants which are transported from their native places to gardens for purposes of cultivation, gradually undergo changes which ultimately make them unrecognisable. Many plants, by nature hairy, become glabrous or nearly so; a number of those which used to lie and creep on the ground, become erect; others lose their thorns or excrescences; others again whose stem was perennial and woody in their native hot climates, become herbaceous in our own climates and some of them become annuals; lastly, the size of their parts itself undergoes very considerable changes. These effects of alterations of environment are so widely recognised, that botanists do not like to describe garden plants unless they have been recently brought into cultivation.

Is it not the case that cultivated wheat (*Triticum sativum*) is a plant which man has brought to the state in which we now see it? I should like to know in what country such a plant lives in nature, otherwise than as the result of cultivation.

Where in nature do we find our cabbages, lettuces, etc., in the same state as in our kitchen gardens? and is not the case the same with regard to many animals which have been altered or greatly modified by domestication?

How many different races of our domestic fowls and pigeons have we obtained by rearing them in various environments and different countries; birds which we should now vainly seek in nature?

Those which have changed the least, doubtless because their domestication is of shorter standing and because they do not live in a foreign climate, nonetheless display great differences in some of their parts, as a result of the habits which we have made them contract. Thus our domestic ducks and geese are of the same type as wild ducks and geese; but ours have lost the power of rising into high regions of the air and flying across large tracts of country; moreover, a real change has come about in the state of their parts, as compared with those of the animals of the race from which they come.

Who does not know that if we rear some bird of our own climate in a cage and it lives there for five or six years, and if we then return it to nature by setting it at liberty, it is no longer able to fly like its fellows, which have always been free? The slight change of environment for this individual has indeed only diminished its power of flight, and doubtless has worked no change in its structure; but if a long succession of generations of individuals of the same race had been kept in captivity for a considerable period, there is no doubt that even the structure of these individuals would gradually have undergone notable changes. Still more, if instead of a mere continuous captivity, this environmental factor had been further accompanied by a change to a very different climate; and if these individuals had by degrees been habituated to other kinds of food and other activities for seizing it, these factors when combined together and become permanent would have unquestionably given rise imperceptibly to a new race with quite special characters.

Where in natural conditions do we find that multitude of races of dogs which now actually exist, owing to the domestication to which we have reduced them? Where do we find those bull-dogs, greyhounds, water-spaniels, spaniels, lap-dogs, etc., etc.; races which show wider differences than those which we call specific when they occur among animals of one genus living in natural freedom?

No doubt a single, original race, closely resembling the wolf, if indeed it was not actually the wolf, was at some period reduced by man to domestication. That race, of which all the individuals were then alike, was gradually scattered with man into different countries and climates; and after they had been subjected for some time to the influences of their environment and of the various habits which had been forced upon them in each country, they underwent remarkable alterations and formed various special races. Now man travels about to very great distances, either for trade or any other purpose; and thus brings into thickly populated places, such as a great capital, various races of dogs formed in very distant countries. The crossing of these races by reproduction then gave rise in turn to all those that we now know.

The following fact proves in the case of plants how the change of some important factor leads to alteration in the parts of these living bodies.

So long as *Ranunculus aquatilis* is submerged in the water, all its leaves are finely divided into minute segments; but when the stem of this plant reaches the surface of the water, the leaves which develop in the air are large, round and simply lobed. If several feet of the same plant succeed in growing in a soil that is merely damp without any immersion, their stems are then short, and none of their leaves are broken up into minute divisions, so that we get *Ranunculus hederaceus*, which botanists regard as a separate species.

There is no doubt that in the case of animals, extensive alterations in their customary environment produce corresponding alterations in their parts; but here the transformations take place much more slowly than in the case of plants; and for us therefore they are less perceptible and their cause less readily identified.

As to the conditions which have so much power in modifying the organs of living bodies, the most potent doubtless consist in the diversity of the places where they live, but there are many others as well which exercise considerable influence in producing the effects in question.

It is known that localities differ as to their character and quality, by reason of their position, construction and climate: as is readily perceived on passing through various localities distinguished by special qualities; this is one cause of variation for animals and plants living in these various places. But what is not known so well and indeed what is not generally believed, is that every locality itself changes in time as to exposure, climate, character and quality, although with such extreme slowness, according to our notions, that we ascribe to it complete stability.

Now in both cases these altered localities involve a corresponding alteration in the environment of the living bodies that dwell there, and this again brings a new influence to bear on these same bodies.

Hence it follows that if there are extremes in these alterations, there are also finer differences: that is to say, intermediate stages which fill up the interval. Consequently there are also fine distinctions between what we call species.

It is obvious then that as regards the character and situation of the substances which occupy the various parts of the earth's surface, there exists a variety of environmental factors which induces a corresponding variety in the shapes and structure of animals, independent of that special variety which necessarily results from the progress of the complexity of organisation in each animal.

In every locality where animals can live, the conditions constituting any one order of things remain the same for long periods: indeed they alter so slowly that man cannot directly observe it. It is only by an inspection of ancient monuments that he becomes convinced that in each of these localities the order of things which he now finds has not always been existent; he may thence infer that it will go on changing.

Races of animals living in any of these localities must then retain their habits equally long: hence the apparent constancy of the races that we call species—a constancy which has raised in us the belief that these races are as old as nature.

But in the various habitable parts of the earth's surface, the character and situation of places and climates constitute both for animals and plants environmental influences of extreme variability. The animals living in these various localities must therefore differ among themselves, not only by reason of the state of complexity of organisation attained in each race, but also by reason of the habits which each race is forced to acquire; thus when the observing naturalist travels over large portions of the earth's surface and sees conspicuous changes occurring in the environment, he invariably finds that the characters of species undergo a corresponding change.

Now the true principle to be noted in all this is as follows:

1. Every fairly considerable and permanent alteration in the environment of any race of animals works a real alteration in the needs of that race.

2. Every change in the needs of animals necessitates new activities on their part for the satisfaction of those needs, and hence new habits.

3. Every new need, necessitating new activities for its satisfaction, requires the animal, either to make more frequent use of some of its parts which it previously used less, and thus greatly to develop and enlarge them; or else to make use of entirely new parts, to which the needs have imperceptibly given birth by efforts of its inner feeling; this I shall shortly prove by means of known facts.

Thus to obtain a knowledge of the true causes of that great diversity of shapes and habits found in the various known animals, we must reflect that the infinitely diversified but slowly changing environment in which the animals of each race have successively been placed, has involved each of them in new needs and corresponding alterations in their habits. This is a truth which, once recognised, cannot be disputed. Now we shall easily discern how the new needs may have been satisfied, and the new habits acquired, if we pay attention to the two following laws of nature, which are always verified by observation.

First Law

In every animal which has not passed the limit of its development, a more frequent and continuous use of any organ gradually strengthens, develops and enlarges that organ, and gives it a power proportional to the length of time it has been so used; while the permanent disuse of any organ imperceptibly weakens and deteriorates it, and progressively diminishes its functional capacity, until it finally disappears.

Second Law

All the acquisitions or losses wrought by nature on individuals, through the influence of the environment in which their race has long been placed, and hence through the influence of the predominant use or permanent disuse of any organ; all these are preserved by reproduction to the new individuals which arise, provided that the acquired modifications are common to both sexes, or at least to the individuals which produce the young.

Here we have two permanent truths, which can only be doubted by those who have never observed or followed the operations of nature, or by those who have allowed themselves to be drawn into the error which I shall now proceed to combat.

Naturalists have remarked that the structure of animals is always in perfect adaptation to their functions, and have inferred that the shape and condition of their parts have determined the use of them. Now this is a mistake: for it may be easily proved by observation that it is on the contrary the needs and uses of the parts which have caused the development of these same parts, which have even given birth to them when they did not exist, and which consequently have given rise to the condition that we find in each animal.

If this were not so, nature would have had to create as many different kinds of structure in animals, as there are different kinds of environment in which they have to live; and neither structure nor environment would ever have varied.

This is indeed far from the true order of things. If things were really so, we should not have race-horses shaped like those in England; we should not have big draught-horses so heavy and so different from the former, for none such are produced in nature; in the same way we should not have basset-hounds with crooked legs, nor grey-hounds so fleet of foot, nor water-spaniels, etc.; we should not have fowls without tails, fantail pigeons, etc.; finally, we should be able to cultivate wild plants as long as we liked in the rich and fertile soil of our gardens, without the fear of seeing them change under long cultivation.

A feeling of the truth in this respect has long existed; since the following maxim has passed into a proverb and is known by all, *Habits form a second nature.*

Assuredly if the habits and nature of each animal could never vary, the proverb would have been false and would not have come into existence, nor been preserved in the event of any one suggesting it.

If we seriously reflect upon all that I have just set forth, it will be seen that I was entirely justified when in my work entitled *Recherches sur les corps vivants*, I established the following proposition:

"It is not the organs, that is to say, the nature and shape of the parts of an animal's body, that have given rise to its special habits and faculties; but it is, on the contrary, its habits, mode of life and environment that have in course of time controlled the shape of its body, the number and state of its organs and, lastly, the faculties which it possesses."

If this proposition is carefully weighed and compared with all the observations that nature and circumstances are incessantly throwing in our way, we shall see that its importance and accuracy are substantiated in the highest degree.

Time and a favourable environment are as I have already said nature's two chief methods of bringing all her productions into existence: for her, time has no limits and can be drawn upon to any extent.

As to the various factors which she has required and still constantly uses for introducing variations in everything that she produces, they may be described as practically inexhaustible.

The principal factors consist in the influence of climate, of the varying temperatures of the atmosphere and the whole environment, of the variety of localities and their situation, of habits, the commonest movements, the most frequent activities, and, lastly, of the means of self-preservation, the mode of life and the methods of defence and multiplication.

Now as a result of these various influences, the faculties become extended and strengthened by use, and diversified by new habits that are long kept up. The conformation, consistency and, in short, the character and state of the parts, as well as of the organs, are imperceptibly affected by these influences and are preserved and propagated by reproduction.

These truths, which are merely effects of the two natural laws stated above, receive in every instance striking confirmation from facts; for the facts afford a clear indication of nature's procedure in the diversity of her productions.

But instead of being contented with generalities which might be considered hypothetical, let us investigate the facts directly, and consider the effects in animals of the use or disuse of their organs on these same organs, in accordance with the habits that each race has been forced to contract.

Now I am going to prove that the permanent disuse of any organ first decreases its functional capacity, and then gradually reduces the organ and causes it to disappear or even become extinct, if this disuse lasts for a very long period throughout successive generations of animals of the same race.

I shall then show that the habit of using any organ, on the contrary, in any animal which has not reached the limit of the decline of its functions, not only perfects and increases the functions of that organ, but causes it in addition to take on a size and development which imperceptibly alter it; so that in course of time it becomes very different from the same organ in some other animal which uses it far less.

The permanent disuse of an organ, arising from a change of habits, causes a gradual shrinkage and ultimately the disappearance and even extinction of that organ.

Since such a proposition could only be accepted on proof, and not on mere authority, let us endeavour to make it clear by citing the chief known facts which substantiate it.

The vertebrates, whose plan of organisation is almost the same throughout, though with much variety in their parts, have their jaws armed with teeth; some of them, however, whose environment has induced the habit of swallowing the objects they feed on without any preliminary mastication, are so affected that their teeth do not develop. The teeth then remain hidden in the bony framework of the jaws, without being able to appear outside; or indeed they actually become extinct down to their last rudiments.

In the right-whale, which was supposed to be completely destitute of teeth, M. Geoffroy has nevertheless discovered teeth concealed in the jaws of the foetus of this animal. The professor has moreover discovered in birds the groove in which the teeth should be placed, though they are no longer to be found there.

Even in the class of mammals, comprising the most perfect animals, where the vertebrate plan of organisation is carried to its highest completion, not only is the right-whale devoid of teeth, but the ant-eater (*Myrmecophaga*) is also found to be in the same condition, since it has acquired a habit of carrying out no mastication, and has long preserved this habit in its race.

Eyes in the head are characteristic of a great number of different animals, and essentially constitute a part of the plan of organisation of the vertebrates.

Yet the mole, whose habits require a very small use of sight, has only minute and hardly visible eyes, because it uses that organ so little.

Olivier's *Spalax* (*Voyage en Égypte et en Perse*), which lives underground like the mole, and is apparently exposed to daylight even less than the mole, has altogether lost the use of sight: so that it shows nothing more than vestiges of this organ. Even these vestiges are entirely hidden under the skin and other parts, which cover them up and do not leave the slightest access to light.

The *Proteus*, an aquatic reptile allied to the salamanders, and living in deep dark caves under the water, has, like the *Spalax*, only vestiges of the organ of sight, vestiges which are covered up and hidden in the same way.

The following consideration is decisive on the question which I am now discussing:

Light does not penetrate everywhere; consequently animals which habitually live in places where it does not penetrate, have no opportunity of exercising their organ of sight, if nature has endowed them with one. Now animals belonging to a plan of organisation of which eyes were a necessary part, must have originally had them. Since, however, there are found among them some which have lost the use of this organ and which show nothing more than hidden and covered up vestiges of them, it becomes clear that the shrinkage and even disappearance of the organ in question are the results of a permanent disuse of that organ.

This is proved by the fact that the organ of hearing is never in this condition, but is always found in animals whose organisation is of the kind that includes it: and for the following reason.

The substance of sound, that namely which, when set in motion by the shock or the vibration of bodies, transmits to the organ of hearing the impression received, penetrates everywhere and passes through any medium, including even the densest bodies: it follows that every animal, belonging to a plan of organisation of which hearing is an essential part, always has some opportunity for the exercise of this organ wherever it may live. Hence among the vertebrates we do not find any that are destitute of the organ of hearing; and after them, when this same organ has come to an end, it does not subsequently recur in any animal of the posterior classes.

It is not so with the organ of sight; for this organ is found to disappear, re-appear and disappear again according to the use that the animal makes of it.

In the acephalic molluscs, the great development of the mantle would make their eyes and even their head altogether useless. The permanent disuse of these organs has thus brought about their disappearance and extinction, although molluscs belong to a plan of organisation which should comprise them.

Lastly, it was part of the plan of organisation of the reptiles, as of other vertebrates, to have four legs in dependence on their skeleton. Snakes ought consequently to have four legs, especially since they are by no means the last order of the reptiles and are farther from the fishes than are the batrachians (frogs, salamanders, etc.).

Snakes, however, have adopted the habit of crawling on the ground and hiding in the grass; so that their body, as a result of continually repeated efforts at elongation for the purpose of passing through narrow spaces, has acquired a considerable length, quite out of proportion to its size. Now, legs would have been quite useless to these animals and consequently unused. Long legs would have interfered with their need of crawling, and very short legs would have been incapable of moving their body, since they could only have had four. The disuse of these parts thus became permanent in the various races of these animals, and resulted in the complete disappearance of these same parts, although legs really belong to the plan of organisation of the animals of this class.

Many insects, which should have wings according to the natural characteristics of their order and even of their genus, are more or less completely devoid of them through disuse. Instances are furnished by many Coleoptera, Orthoptera, Hymenoptera and Hemiptera, etc., where the habits of these animals never involve them in the necessity of using their wings.

But it is not enough to give an explanation of the cause which has brought about the present condition of the organs of the various animals—a condition that is always found to be the same in animals of the same species; we have in addition to cite instances of changes wrought in the organs of a single individual during its life, as the exclusive result of a great mutation in the habits of the individuals of its species. The following very remarkable fact will complete the proof of the influence of habits on the condition of the organs, and of the way in which permanent changes in the habits of an individual lead to others in the condition of the organs, which come into action during the exercise of these habits.

M. Tenon, a member of the Institute, has notified to the class of sciences, that he had examined the intestinal canal of several men who had been great drinkers for a large part of their lives, and in every case he had found it shortened to an extraordinary degree, as compared with the same organ in all those who had not adopted the like habit.

It is known that great drinkers, or those who are addicted to drunkenness, take very little solid food, and eat hardly anything; since the drink which they consume so copiously and frequently is sufficient to feed them.

Now since fluid foods, especially spirits, do not long remain either in the stomach or intestine, the stomach and the rest of the intestinal canal lose among drinkers the habit of being distended, just as among sedentary persons, who are continually engaged on mental work and are accustomed to take very little food; for in their case also the stomach slowly shrinks and the intestine shortens.

This has nothing to do with any shrinkage or shortening due to a binding of the parts which would permit of the ordinary extension, if instead of remaining empty these viscera were again filled; we have to do with a real shrinkage and shortening of considerable extent, and such that these organs would burst rather than yield at once to any demand for the ordinary extension.

Compare two men of equal ages, one of whom has contracted the habit of eating very little, since his habitual studies and mental work have made digestion difficult, while the other habitually takes much exercise, is often out-of-doors, and eats well; the stomach of the first will have very little capacity left and will be filled up by a very small quantity of food, while that of the second will have preserved and even increased its capacity.

Here then is an organ which undergoes profound modification in size and capacity, purely on account of a change of habits during the life of the individual.

The frequent use of any organ, when confirmed by habit, increases the functions of that organ, leads to its development and endows it with a size and power that it does not possess in animals which exercise it less.

We have seen that the disuse of any organ modifies, reduces and finally extinguishes it. I shall now prove that the constant use of any organ, accompanied by efforts to get the most out of it, strengthens and enlarges that organ, or creates new ones to carry on functions that have become necessary.

The bird which is drawn to the water by its need of finding there the prey on which it lives, separates the digits of its feet in trying to strike the water and move about on the surface. The skin which unites these digits at their base acquires the habit of being stretched by these continually repeated separations of the digits; thus in course of time there are formed large webs which unite the digits of ducks, geese, etc., as we actually find them. In the same way efforts to swim, that is to push against the water so as to move about in it, have stretched the membranes between the digits of frogs, sea-tortoises, the otter, beaver, etc.

On the other hand, a bird which is accustomed to perch on trees and which springs from individuals all of whom had acquired this habit, necessarily has longer digits on its feet and differently shaped from those of the aquatic animals that I have just named. Its claws in time become lengthened, sharpened and curved into hooks, to clasp the branches on which the animal so often rests.

We find in the same way that the bird of the water-side which does not like swimming and yet is in need of going to the water's edge to secure its prey, is continually liable to sink in the mud. Now this bird tries to act in such a way that its body should not be immersed in the liquid, and hence makes its best efforts to stretch and lengthen its legs. The long-established habit acquired by this bird and all its race of continually stretching and lengthening its legs, results in the individuals of this race becoming raised as though on stilts, and gradually obtaining long, bare legs, denuded of feathers up to the thighs and often higher still.

We note again that this same bird wants to fish without wetting its body, and is thus obliged to make continual efforts to lengthen its neck. Now these habitual efforts in this individual and its race must have resulted in course of time in a remarkable lengthening, as indeed we actually find in the long necks of all water-side birds.

If some swimming birds like the swan and goose have short legs and yet a very long neck, the reason is that these birds while moving about on the water acquire the habit of plunging their head as deeply as they can into it in order to get the aquatic larvae and various animals on which they feed; whereas they make no effort to lengthen their legs.

If an animal, for the satisfaction of its needs, makes repeated efforts to lengthen its tongue, it will acquire a considerable length (ant-eater, green-woodpecker); if it requires to seize anything with this same organ, its tongue will then divide and become forked. Proofs of my statement are found in the humming-birds which use their tongues for grasping things, and in lizards and snakes which use theirs to palpate and identify objects in front of them.

Needs which are always brought about by the environment, and the subsequent continued efforts to satisfy them, are not limited in their results to a mere modification, that is to say, an increase or decrease of the size and capacity of organs; but they may even go so far as to extinguish organs, when any of these needs make such a course necessary.

Fishes, which habitually swim in large masses of water, have need of lateral vision; and, as a matter of fact, their eyes are placed on the sides of their head. Their body, which is more or less flattened according to the species, has its edges perpendicular to the plane of the water; and their eyes are placed so that there is one on each flattened side. But such fishes as are forced by their habits to be constantly approaching the shore, and especially slightly inclined or gently sloping beaches, have been compelled to swim on their flattened surfaces in order to make a close approach to the water's edge. In this position, they receive more light from above than below and stand in special need of paying constant attention to what is passing above them; this requirement has forced one of their eyes to undergo a sort of displacement, and to assume the very remarkable position found in the soles, turbots, dabs, etc. (*Pleuronectes* and *Achirus*). The position of these eyes is not symmetrical, because it results from an incomplete mutation. Now this mutation is entirely completed in the skates, in which the transverse flattening of the body is altogether horizontal, like the head. Accordingly the eyes of skates are both situated on the upper surface and have become symmetrical.

Snakes, which crawl on the surface of the earth, chiefly need to see objects that are raised or above them. This need must have had its effect on the position of the organ of sight in these animals, and accordingly their eyes are situated in the lateral and upper parts of their head, so as easily to perceive what is above them or at their sides; but they scarcely see at all at a very short distance in front of them. They are, however, compelled to make good the deficiency of sight as regards objects in front of them which might injure them as they move forward. For this purpose they can only use their tongue, which they are obliged to thrust out with all their might. This habit has not only contributed to making their tongue slender and very long and contractile, but it has even forced it to undergo division in the greater number of species, so as to feel several objects at the same time; it has even permitted of the formation of an aperture at the extremity of their snout, to allow the tongue to pass without having to separate the jaws.

Nothing is more remarkable than the effects of habit in herbivorous mammals.

A quadruped, whose environment and consequent needs have for long past inculcated the habit of browsing on grass, does nothing but walk about on the ground; and for the greater part of its life is obliged to stand on its four feet, generally making only few or moderate movements. The large portion of each day that this kind of animal has to pass in filling itself with the only kind of food that it cares for, has the result that it moves but little and only uses its feet for support in walking or running on the ground, and never for holding on, or climbing trees.

From this habit of continually consuming large quantities of food-material, which distend the organs receiving it, and from the habit of making only moderate movements, it has come about that the body of these animals has greatly thickened, become heavy and massive and acquired a very great size: as is seen in elephants, rhinoceroses, oxen, buffaloes, horses, etc.

The habit of standing on their four feet during the greater part of the day, for the purpose of browsing, has brought into existence a thick horn which invests the extremity of their digits; and since these digits have no exercise and are never moved and serve no other purpose than that of support like the rest of the foot, most of them have become shortened, dwindled and, finally, even disappeared.

Thus in the pachyderms, some have five digits on their feet invested in horn, and their hoof is consequently divided into five parts; others have only four, and others again not more than three; but in the ruminants, which are apparently the oldest of the mammals that are permanently confined to the ground, there are not more than two digits on the feet and indeed, in the solipeds, there is only one (horse, donkey).

Nevertheless some of these herbivorous animals, especially the ruminants, are incessantly exposed to the attacks of carnivorous animals in the desert countries that they inhabit, and they can only find safety in headlong flight. Necessity has in these cases forced them to exert themselves in swift running, and from this habit their body has become more slender and their legs much finer; instances are furnished by the antelopes, gazelles, etc.

In our own climates, there are other dangers, such as those constituted by man, with his continual pursuit of red deer, roe deer and fallow deer; this has reduced them to the same necessity, has impelled them into similar habits, and had corresponding effects.

Since ruminants can only use their feet for support, and have little strength in their jaws, which only obtain exercise by cutting and browsing on the grass, they can only fight by blows with their heads, attacking one another with their crowns.

In the frequent fits of anger to which the males especially are subject, the efforts of their inner feeling cause the fluids to flow more strongly towards that part of their head; in some there is hence deposited a secretion of horny matter, and in others of bony matter mixed with horny matter, which gives rise to solid protuberances: thus we have the origin of horns and antlers, with which the head of most of these animals is armed.

It is interesting to observe the result of habit in the peculiar shape and size of the giraffe (*Camelo-pardalis*): this animal, the largest of the mammals, is known to live in the interior of Africa in places where the soil is nearly always arid and barren, so that it is obliged to browse on the leaves of trees and to make constant efforts to reach them. From this habit long maintained in all its race, it has resulted that the animal's fore-legs have become longer than its hind legs, and that its neck is lengthened to such a degree that the giraffe, without standing up on its hind legs, attains a height of six metres (nearly 20 feet).

Among birds, ostriches, which have no power of flight and are raised on very long legs, probably owe their singular shape to analogous circumstances.

The effect of habit is quite as remarkable in the carnivorous mammals as in the herbivores; but it exhibits results of a different kind.

Those carnivores, for instance, which have become accustomed to climbing, or to scratching the ground for digging holes, or to tearing their prey, have been under the necessity of using the digits of their feet: now this habit has promoted the separation of their digits, and given rise to the formation of the claws with which they are armed.

But some of the carnivores are obliged to have recourse to pursuit in order to catch their prey: now some of these animals were compelled by their needs to contract the habit of tearing with their claws, which they are constantly burying deep in the body of another animal in order to lay hold of it, and then make efforts to tear out the part seized. These repeated efforts must have resulted in its claws reaching a size and curvature which would have greatly impeded them in walking or running on stony ground: in such cases the animal has been compelled to make further efforts to draw back its claws, which are so projecting and hooked as to get in its way. From this there has gradually resulted the formation of those peculiar sheaths, into which cats, tigers, lions, etc. withdraw their claws when they are not using them.

Hence we see that efforts in a given direction, when they are long sustained or habitually made by certain parts of a living body, for the satisfaction of needs established by nature or environment, cause an enlargement of these parts and the acquisition of a size and shape that they would never have obtained, if these efforts had not become the normal activities of the animals exerting them. Instances are everywhere furnished by observations on all known animals.

Can there be any more striking instance than that which we find in the kangaroo? This animal, which carries its young in a pouch under the abdomen, has acquired the habit of standing upright, so as to rest only on its hind legs and tail; and of moving only by means of a succession of leaps, during which it maintains its erect attitude in order not to disturb its young. And the following is the result:

1. Its fore legs, which it uses very little and on which it only supports itself for a moment on abandoning its erect attitude, have never acquired a development proportional to that of the other parts, and have remained meagre, very short and with very little strength.

2. The hind legs, on the contrary, which are almost continually in action either for supporting the whole body or for making leaps, have acquired a great development and become very large and strong.

3. Lastly, the tail, which is in this case much used for supporting the animal and carrying out its chief movements, has acquired an extremely remarkable thickness and strength at its base.

These well-known facts are surely quite sufficient to establish the results of habitual use on an organ or any other part of animals. If on observing in an animal any organ particularly well-developed, strong, and powerful, it is alleged that its habitual use has nothing to do with it, that its continued disuse involves it in no loss, and finally, that this organ has always been the same since the creation of the species to which the animal belongs, then I ask, Why can our domestic ducks no longer fly like wild ducks? I can, in short, cite a multitude of instances among ourselves, which bear witness to the differences that accrue to us from the use or disuse of any of our organs, although these differences are not preserved in the new individuals which arise by reproduction: for if they were their effects would be far greater.

When the will guides an animal to any action, the organs which have to carry out that action are immediately stimulated to it by the influx of subtle fluids (the nervous fluid), which become the determining factor of the movements required. This fact is verified by many observations, and cannot now be called in question.

Hence it follows that numerous repetitions of these organised activities strengthen, stretch, develop and even create the organs necessary to them. We have only to watch attentively what is happening all around us, to be convinced that this is the true cause of organic development and changes.

Now every change that is wrought in an organ through a habit of frequently using it, is subsequently preserved by reproduction, if it is common to the individuals who unite together in fertilisation for the propagation of their species. Such a change is thus handed on to all succeeding individuals in the same environment, without their having to acquire it in the same way that it was actually created.

Furthermore, in reproductive unions, the crossing of individuals who have different qualities or structures is necessarily opposed to the permanent propagation of these qualities and structures. Hence it is that in man, who is exposed to so great a diversity of environment, the accidental qualities or defects which he acquires are not preserved and propagated by reproduction. If, when certain peculiarities of shape or certain defects have been acquired, two individuals who are both affected were always to unite together, they would hand on the same peculiarities; and if successive generations were limited to such unions, a special and distinct race would then be formed. But perpetual crossings between individuals, who have not the same peculiarities of shape, cause the disappearance of all peculiarities acquired by special action of the environment. Hence, we may be sure that if men were not kept apart by the distances of their habitations, the crossing in reproduction would soon bring about the disappearance of the general characteristics distinguishing different nations.

If I intended here to pass in review all the classes, orders, genera and species of existing animals, I should be able to show that the conformation and structure of individuals, their organs, faculties, etc., etc., are everywhere a pure result of the environment to which each species is exposed by its nature, and by the habits that the individuals composing it have been compelled to acquire; I should be able to show that they are not the result of a shape which existed from the beginning, and has driven animals into the habits they are known to possess.

It is known that the animal called the *ai* or sloth (*Bradypustridactylus*) is permanently in a state of such extreme weakness that it only executes very slow and limited movements, and walks on the ground with difficulty. So slow are its movements that it is alleged that it can only take fifty steps in a day. It is known, moreover, that the organisation of this animal is entirely in harmony with its state of feebleness and incapacity for walking; and that if it wished to make other movements than those which it actually does make it could not do so.

Hence on the supposition that this animal had received its organisation from nature, it has been asserted that this organisation forced it into the habits and miserable state in which it exists.

This is very far from being my opinion; for I am convinced that the habits which the ai was originally forced to contract must necessarily have brought its organisation to its present condition.

If continual dangers in former times have led the individuals of this species to take refuge in trees, to live there habitually and feed on their leaves, it is clear that they must have given up a great number of movements which animals living on the ground are in a position to perform. All the needs of the ai will then be reduced to clinging to branches and crawling and dragging themselves among them, in order to reach the leaves, and then to remaining on the tree in a state of inactivity in order to avoid falling off. This kind of inactivity, moreover, must have been continually induced by the heat of the climate; for among warm-blooded animals, heat is more conducive to rest than to movement.

Now the individuals of the race of the ai have long maintained this habit of remaining in the trees, and of performing only those slow and little varied movements which suffice for their needs. Hence their organisation will gradually have come into accordance with their new habits; and from this it must follow:

1. That the arms of these animals, which are making continual efforts to clasp the branches of trees, will be lengthened;
2. That the claws of their digits will have acquired a great length and a hooked shape, through the continued efforts of the animal to hold on;
3. That their digits, which are never used in making independent movements, will have entirely lost their mobility, become united and have preserved only the faculty of flexion or extension all together;
4. That their thighs, which are continually clasping either the trunk or large branches of trees, will have contracted a habit of always being

separated, so as to lead to an enlargement of the pelvis and a backward direction of the cotyloid cavities;

5. Lastly, that a great many of their bones will be welded together, and that parts of their skeleton will consequently have assumed an arrangement and form adapted to the habits of these animals, and different from those which they would require for other habits.

This is a fact that can never be disputed; since nature shows us in innumerable other instances the power of environment over habit and that of habit over the shape, arrangement and proportions of the parts of animals.

Since there is no necessity to cite any further examples, we may now turn to the main point elaborated in this discussion.

It is a fact that all animals have special habits corresponding to their genus and species, and always possess an organisation that is completely in harmony with those habits.

It seems from the study of this fact that we may adopt one or other of the two following conclusions, and that neither of them can be verified.

Conclusion adopted hitherto: Nature (or her Author) in creating animals, foresaw all the possible kinds of environment in which they would have to live, and endowed each species with a fixed organisation and with a definite and invariable shape, which compel each species to live in the places and climates where we actually find them, and there to maintain the habits which we know in them.

My individual conclusion: Nature has produced all the species of animals in succession, beginning with the most imperfect or simplest, and ending her work with the most perfect, so as to create a gradually increasing complexity in their organisation; these animals have spread at large throughout all the habitable regions of the globe, and every species has derived from its environment the habits that we find in it and the structural modifications which observation shows us.

The former of these two conclusions is that which has been drawn hitherto, at least by nearly everyone: it attributes to every animal a fixed organisation and structure which never have varied and never do vary; it assumes, moreover, that none of the localities inhabited by animals ever vary; for if they were to vary, the same animals could no longer survive, and the possibility of finding other localities and transporting themselves thither would not be open to them.

The second conclusion is my own: it assumes that by the influence of environment on habit, and thereafter by that of habit on the state of the parts and even on organisation, the structure and organisation of any animal may undergo modifications, possibly very great, and capable of accounting for the actual condition in which all animals are found.

In order to show that this second conclusion is baseless, it must first be proved that no point on the surface of the earth ever undergoes variation as to its nature, exposure, high or low situation, climate, etc., etc.; it must then be proved that no part of animals undergoes even after long periods of time any modification due to a change of environment or to the necessity which forces them into a different kind of life and activity from what has been customary to them.

Now if a single case is sufficient to prove that an animal which has long been in domestication differs from the wild species whence it sprang, and if in any such domesticated species, great differences of conformation are found between the individuals exposed to such a habit and those which are forced into different habits, it will then be certain that the first conclusion is not consistent with the laws of nature, while the second, on the contrary, is entirely in accordance with them.

Everything then combines to prove my statement, namely: that it is not the shape either of the body or its parts which gives rise to the habits of animals and their mode of life; but that it is, on the contrary, the habits, mode of life and all the other influences of the environment which have in course of time built up the shape of the body and of the parts of animals. With new shapes, new faculties have been acquired, and little by little nature has succeeded in fashioning animals such as we actually see them.

Can there by any more important conclusion in the range of natural history, or any to which more attention should be paid than that which I have set forth?

Comment

FEW scientific theories have suffered the tribulations that beset Lamarck's theory of acquired characters. Almost aborted by Cuvier's derision, it survived to predominate in late–nineteenth-century biology until, upon the discovery of Mendel's papers pertaining to the particulate theory of heredity, it again fell into disrepute.

Lamarckianism enjoyed its brightest day when Darwin, in explaining hereditary variations during the evolution of species, admitted that acquired characters augmented natural selection. He had invested a quarter century in mustering incontrovertible evidence for organic affinity. The scientific community, long dominated by ecclesiastics, buckled under the persuasion of his argument and the mass of his data. In the *Origin of Species* Darwin had shown the world that plants and animals were interrelated, and with the incorporation of Lamarckianism, he had satisfied misgivings regarding the limitations of natural selection as the sole force in accounting for hereditary variations. And Darwin, more clearly than anyone else, recognized that the premise of evolution must ultimately rest on an adequate explanation of hereditary transmission. In Darwin's words:

How, it may be asked, have species arisen in a state of nature? The differences between natural varieties are slight; whereas the differences are considerable between the species of the same genus, and great between the species of distinct genera. How do these lesser differences become augmented into the greater difference? How do varieties, or as I have called them incipient species, become converted into true and well-defined species? How has each new species been adapted to the surrounding physical conditions, and to the other forms of life on which it in any way depends?[3]

After the publication of the *Origin of Species*, Darwin turned resolutely toward developing the theoretical base that was necessary for showing how very simple organs have been converted by small and graduated steps into highly perfect, complex organs. In 1868 he advanced the first version of the provisional hypothesis of pangenesis in his *Variation of Animals and Plants under Domestication* and established it as a major theory in the second edition of the work in 1875. Darwin's heady excursion into cytology, an area in which he was totally inexperienced, is explicable. He was anxious to produce a universally applicable theory of heredity, and given the primitive state of cytology—genes and chromosomes were still undiscovered—Darwin quite naturally looked to the ancient sages for ideas that would be compatible with the theory of evolution. Darwin was compelled in terms of his two basic assumptions—acquired characters and natural selection—to derive a theory of heredity that would endow the germ or reproductive cells with the power to give rise, in the course of development, to variations that the parents had acquired during their lifetime as a consequence of adapting to external conditions. Darwin presumed, therefore, that in every body cell a host of atomlike gemmules arose, which possessed the qualities for reproducing that specific cell in progeny. The gemmules migrated via the bloodstream to the myriad parts of the body. Eventually they reached the ovaries and testes, and finally they penetrated the reproductive cells where they accumulated, awaiting fecundation.

On pangenesis Darwin appears to have wandered from the precepts of the natural scientist and to have engaged in speculation as erratic

[3] C. Darwin, *The Variation of Plants and Animals Under Domestication* [1868], 2 vols. (New York: Appleton, 1896), Vol. I, p. 5.

as that of some of his critics. He regarded his pangenesis hypothesis to be provisional, but he did descry it as describing the facts of hereditary transmission better than did any other theory. For Darwin, the more comprehensive and the more explanatory a theory, the more convincing it seemed.[4] The pangenesis hypothesis necessitated the assumption that each particle or gemmule derived from a given part of the organism would find its way through the circulatory system to its exact niche in the growing embryo. To dispassionate observers, this seemed a fantastic feat; moreover, pangenesis seemed akin to the older preformationism

Darwin, however, enjoyed considerable company. During the second half of the nineteenth century metaphysical speculation abounded in discussions of hereditary transmission. Ernst Haeckel in 1876 offered a modification of Darwin's theory, which he called the theory of peregenesis. Haeckel sensed a sort of hereditary motion to be inherent in the chemistry of the molecular motion of the reproductive cells. Body alterations result, he said, when variations in the motions incurred as a consequence of environmental pressures are passed on to progeny.

W. K. Brooks in 1883 offered a Law of Inheritance, which differed from Darwin's pangenesis theory only to the extent that cells were viewed as throwing off minute gemmules not continuously but when body organization and environmental stress were in disharmony. Brooks affirmed the Darwinian outlook that male sperm cells possess more abundant supplies of gemmules than female egg cells and that the sperm cells represent the more progressive and the egg cells the more conservative elements in propagation and inheritance of change.

In 1884 Carl Naegeli offered a theory of idioplasm in which both natural selection and acquired characters were discarded as mechanisms of variation for what he termed an inborn, divine, growth propensity. Naegeli, a highly esteemed biologist in spite of his extreme metaphysical bent, assumed that idioplasms, those portions of body cells capable of transmitting inheritable qualities, were connected internally in an invisible network. The network, Naegeli insisted, was unaffected by external influences such as exercise, climate, nutrition, and natural selection; change was an outcome of divine purpose. Naegeli's peculiar theory of pangenesis was avowedly the most teleological of those formulated.

One of the more sophisticated of the pangenetic theories was that offered by Hugo de Vries who, in 1889, suggested a theory of intracellular pangenesis. De Vries' theory paralleled Darwin's except that he omitted the supposition about the transportation of minute gemmules throughout the body. De Vries assumed that every cell possessed all the transmissible qualities of the individual. He argued further that the

[4] Nordenskiöld, op. cit., p. 473.

slight variations that occur in the life of a species from generation to generation exerted an insignificant influence on evolution; heredity changes occurred only when dramatic environmental alterations resulted in sudden new modifications. De Vries' analyses of the hereditary qualities of gemmules, which he called pangens, provided a fairly reasonable muta- tion theory based on relatively large rather than imperceptibly small variations. The viewpoint was regarded favorably and helped lay a firm basis for the overwhelming acceptance of Mendel's laws of hereditary transmission.

Mendelism dealt the deathblow to the theories of pangenesis. Darwin's two-volume treatise on pangenesis and the facsimiles it inspired are treated today as the products of visionary folly; in twentieth-century perspective, however, the important fact is obscured that Lamarckianism, hence ge- netic psychology, could not have survived without them.

Charles Darwin (1809–1882)
THE PROVISIONAL HYPOTHESIS OF PANGENESIS

Every one would wish to explain to himself, even in an imperfect man- ner, how it is possible for a character possessed by some remote ancestor suddenly to reappear in the offspring; how the effects of increased or decreased use of a limb can be transmitted to the child; how the male sexual element can act not solely on the ovules, but occasionally on the mother-form; how a hybrid can be produced by the union of the cellular tissue of two plants independently of the organs of generation; how a limb can be reproduced on the exact line of amputation, with neither too much nor too little added; how the same organism may be produced by such widely different processes, as budding and true seminal genera- tion; and, lastly, how of two allied forms, one passes in the course of its development through the most complex metamorphoses, and the other does not do so, though when mature both are alike in every detail of structure. I am aware that my view is merely a provisional hypothesis or speculation; but until a better one can be advanced, it will serve to bring together a multitude of facts which are at present left disconnected

SOURCE: C. Darwin. *The Variation of Animals and Plants Under Domestication,* Second Edition, 2 vols. (New York: Appleton, 1896). Originally published 1868. Volume II. Selections from "Provisional Hypothesis of Pangenesis," Chapter 27, pp. 349–399. Abridged. Footnotes deleted.

by any efficient cause. As Whewell, the historian of the inductive sciences, remarks: "Hypotheses may often be of service to science, when they involve a certain portion of incompleteness, and even of error." Under this point of view I venture to advance the hypothesis of Pangenesis, which implies that every separate part of the whole organisation reproduces itself. So that ovules, spermatozoa, and pollen-grains—the fertilised egg or seed, as well as buds—include and consist of a multitude of germs thrown off from each separate part or unit. . . .

THE FUNCTIONAL INDEPENDENCE OF THE ELEMENTS OR UNITS OF THE BODY

Physiologists agree that the whole organism consists of a multitude of elemental parts, which are to a great extent independent of one another. Each organ, says Claude Bernard, has its proper life, its autonomy; it can develop and reproduce itself independently of the adjoining tissues. A great German authority, Virchow, asserts still more emphatically that each system consists of an "enormous mass of minute centres of action. . . . Every element has its own special action, and even though it derives its stimulus to activity from other parts, yet alone effects the actual performance of duties. . . . Every single epithelial and muscular fibre-cell leads a sort of parasitical existence in relation to the rest of the body. . . . Every single bone-corpuscle really possesses conditions of nutrition peculiar to itself." Each element, as Sir J. Paget remarks, lives its appointed time and then dies, and is replaced after being cast off or absorbed. I presume that no physiologist doubts that, for instance, each bone-corpuscle of the finger differs from the corresponding corpuscle in the corresponding joint of the toe; and there can hardly be a doubt that even those on the corresponding sides of the body differ, though almost identical in nature. This near approach to identity is curiously shown in many diseases in which the same exact points on the right and left sides of the body are similarly affected; thus Sir J. Paget gives a drawing of a diseased pelvis, in which the bone has grown into a most complicated pattern, but "there is not one spot or line on one side which is not represented, as exactly as it would be in a mirror, on the other."

Many facts support this view of the independent life of each minute element of the body. Virchow insists that a single bone-corpuscle or a single cell in the skin may become diseased. The spur of a cock, after being inserted into the ear of an ox, lived for eight years, and acquired a weight of 396 grammes (nearly fourteen ounces), and the astonishing length of twenty-four centimetres, or about nine inches; so that the head of the ox appeared to bear three horns. The tail of a pig has been grafted into the middle of its back, and reacquired sensibility. Dr. Ollier inserted a piece of periosteum from the bone of a young dog under the skin of a rabbit, and true bone was developed. A multitude of similar facts could be given. The frequent presence of hairs and of perfectly developed teeth, even teeth of the second dentition, in ovarian tumours, are facts leading to the same conclusion. Mr. Lawson Tait refers to a tumour in which "over 300 teeth were found, resembling in many respects milk-teeth;" and to another tumour, "full of hair which had grown and been shed from one little spot of skin not bigger than the tip of my little finger. The amount of hair in the sac, had it grown from a similarly sized area of the scalp, would have taken almost a lifetime to grow and be shed."

Whether each of the innumerable autonomous elements of the body is a cell or the modified product of a cell, is a more doubtful question, even if so wide a definition be given to the term, as to include cell-like bodies without walls and without nuclei. The doctrine of *omnis cellula e cellulâ* is admitted for plants, and widely prevails with respect to animals. Thus Virchow, the great supporter of the cellular theory, whilst allowing that difficulties exist, maintains that every atom of tissue is derived from cells, and these from pre-existing cells, and these primarily from the egg, which he regards as a great cell. That cells, still retaining the same nature, increase by self-division or proliferation, is admitted by every one. But when an organism undergoes great changes of structure during development, the cells, which at each stage are supposed to be directly derived from previously existing cells, must likewise be greatly changed in nature; this change is attributed by the supporters of the cellular doctrine to some inherent power which the cells possess, and not to any external agency. Others maintain that cells and tissues of all kinds may be formed, independently of pre-existing cells, from plastic lymph or blastema. Whichever view may be correct, every one admits that the body consists of a multitude of organic units, all of which possess their own proper attributes, and are to a certain extent independent of all others. Hence it will be convenient to use indifferently the terms cells or organic units, or simply units.

VARIABILITY AND INHERITANCE

Variability is not a principle co-ordinate with life or reproduction, but results from special causes, generally from changed conditions acting during successive generations. The fluctuating variability thus induced is apparently due in part to the sexual system being easily affected, so that it is often rendered impotent; and when not so seriously affected, it often fails in its proper function of transmitting truly the characters of the parents to the offspring. But variability is not necessarily connected with the sexual system, as we see in the cases of bud-variation. Although we are seldom able to trace the nature of the connection, many deviations of structure no doubt result from changed conditions acting directly on the organisation, independently of the reproductive system. In some instances we may feel sure of this, when all, or nearly all the individuals which have been similarly exposed are similarly and definitely affected, of which several instances have been given. But it is by no means clear why the offspring should be affected by the exposure of the parents to new conditions, and why it is necessary in most cases that several generations should have been thus exposed.

How, again, can we explain the inherited effects of the use or disuse of particular organs? The domesticated duck flies less and walks more than the wild duck, and its limb-bones have become diminished and increased in a corresponding manner in comparison with those of the wild duck. A horse is trained to certain paces, and the colt inherits similar consensual movements. The domesticated rabbit becomes tame from close confinement; the dog, intelligent from associating with man; the retriever is taught to fetch and carry; and these mental endowments and bodily powers are all inherited. Nothing in the whole circuit of physiology is more wonderful. How can the use or disuse of a particular limb or of the brain affect a small aggregate of reproductive cells, seated in a distant part of the body, in such a manner that the being developed from these cells inherits the characters of either one or both parents? Even an imperfect answer to this question would be satisfactory.

A multitude of newly-acquired characters, whether injurious or bene-ficial, whether of the lowest or highest vital importance, are often faith-fully transmitted—frequently even when one parent alone possesses some new peculiarity; and we may on the whole conclude that inheritance is the rule, and non-inheritance the anomaly. In some instances a character is not inherited, from the conditions of life being directly opposed to its development; in many instances, from the conditions incessantly induc-ing fresh variability, as with grafted fruit-trees and highly-cultivated flowers. In the remaining cases the failure may be attributed to reversion, by which the child resembles its grandparents or more remote progeni-tors, instead of its parents.

Inheritance is governed by various laws. Characters which first appear at any particular age tend to reappear at a corresponding age. They often become associated with certain seasons of the year, and reappear in the offspring at a corresponding season. If they appear rather late in life in one sex, they tend to reappear exclusively in the same sex at the same period of life. . . .

I have now enumerated the chief facts which every one would desire to see connected by some intelligible bond. This can be done, if we make the following assumptions, and much may be advanced in favour of the chief one. The secondary assumptions can likewise be supported by various physiological considerations. It is universally admitted that the cells or units of the body increase by self-division or proliferation, retaining the same nature, and that they ultimately become converted into the various tissues and substances of the body. But besides this means of increase I assume that the units throw off minute granules which are dispersed throughout the whole system; that these, when supplied with proper nutriment, multiply by self-division, and are ultimately developed into units like those from which they were originally derived. These granules may be called gemmules. They are collected from all parts of the system to constitute the sexual elements, and their development in the next generation forms a new being; but they are likewise capable of transmission in a dormant state to future generations and may then be developed. Their development depends on their union with other partially developed or nascent cells which precede them in the regular course of growth. Why I use the term union will be seen when we discuss the direct action of pollen on the tissues of the mother-plant. Gemmules are supposed to be thrown off by every unit, not only during the adult state, but during each stage of development of every organism; but not necessarily during the continued existence of the same unit. Lastly, I assume that the gemmules in their dormant state have a mutual affinity for each other, leading to their aggregation into buds or into the sexual elements. Hence, it is not the reproductive organs or buds which generate new organisms, but the units of which each individual is composed. These assumptions constitute the provisional hypothesis which I have called Pangenesis.

Before proceeding to show, firstly, how far these assumptions are in themselves probable, and secondly, how far they connect and explain the various groups of facts with which we are concerned, it may be useful to give an illustration, as simple as possible, of the hypothesis. If one of the Protozoa be formed, as it appears under the microscope, of a small mass of homogeneous gelatinous matter, a minute particle or gemmule thrown off from any part and nourished under favourable circumstances would reproduce the whole; but if the upper and lower surfaces were to differ in texture from each other and from the central portion, then all three parts would have to throw off gemmules, which when aggregated by mutual affinity would form either buds or the sexual elements, and would ultimately be developed into a similar organism. Precisely the same view may be extended to one of the higher animals; although in this case many thousand gemmules must be thrown off from the various parts of the body at each stage of development; these gemmules being developed in union with pre-existing nascent cells in due order of succession.

Physiologists maintain, as we have seen, that each unit of the body, though to a large extent dependent on others, is likewise to a certain extent independent or autonomous, and has the power of increasing by self-division. I go one step further, and assume that each unit casts off free gemmules which are dispersed throughout the system, and are capable under proper conditions of being developed into similar units. Nor can this assumption be considered as gratuitous and improbable. It is manifest that the sexual elements and buds include formative matter of some kind, capable of development; and we now know from the production of graft-hybrids that similar matter is dispersed throughout the tissues of plants, and can combine with that of another and distinct plant, giving rise to a new being, intermediate in character. We know also that the male element can act directly on the partially developed tissues of the mother-plant, and on the future progeny of female animals. The formative matter which is thus dispersed throughout the tissues of plants, and which is capable of being developed into each unit or part, must be generated there by some means; and my chief assumption is that this matter consists of minute particles or gemmules cast off from each unit or cell.

But I have further to assume that the gemmules in their undeveloped state are capable of largely multiplying themselves by self-division, like independent organisms. Delpino insists that to "admit of multiplication by fissiparity in corpuscles, analogous to seeds or buds . . . is repugnant to all analogy." But this seems a strange objection, as Thuret has seen the zoospore of an alga divide itself, and each half germinated. Haeckel divided the segmented ovum of a siphonophora into many pieces, and these were developed. Nor does the extreme minuteness of the gemmules, which can hardly differ much in nature from the lowest and simplest organisms, render it improbable that they should grow and multiply. A great authority, Dr. Beale, says "that minute yeast cells are capable of throwing off buds or gemmules, much less than the 1/100,000 of an inch in diameter;" and these he thinks "are capable of subdivision practically ad infinitum."

A particle of small-pox matter, so minute as to be borne by the wind, must multiply itself many thousandfold in a person thus inoculated; and so with the contagious matter of scarlet fever. It has recently been ascertained that a minute portion of the mucous discharge from an animal affected with rinderpest, if placed in the blood of a healthy ox, increases so fast that in a short space of time "the whole.mass of blood, weighing many pounds, is infected, and every small particle of that blood contain enough poison to give, within less than forty-eight hours, the disease to another animal."

The retention of free and undeveloped gemmules in the same body from early youth to old age will appear improbable, but we should remember how long seeds lie dormant in the earth and buds in the bark of a tree. Their transmission from generation to generation will appear still more improbable; but here again we should remember that many rudimentary and useless organs have been transmitted during an indefinite number of generations. We shall presently see how well the long-continued transmission of undeveloped gemmules explains many facts.

As each unit, or group of similar units, throughout the body, casts off its gemmules, and as all are contained within the smallest ovule, and within each spermatozoon or pollen-grain, and as some animals and plants produce an astonishing number of pollen-grains and ovules, the number and minuteness of the gemmules must be something inconceivable. But considering how minute the molecules are, and how many go to the formation of the smallest granule of any ordinary substance, this difficulty with respect to the gemmules is not insuperable. From the data arrived at by Sir W. Thomson, my son George finds that a cube of 1/10,000 of an inch of glass or water must consist of between 16 million millions, and 131 thousand million million molecules. No doubt the molecules of which an organism is formed are larger, from being more complex, than those of an inorganic substance, and probably many molecules go to the formation of a gemmule; but when we bear in mind that a cube of 1/10,000 of an inch is much smaller than any pollen-grain, ovule or bud, we can see what a vast number of gemmules one of these bodies might contain.

The gemmules derived from each part or organ must be thoroughly dispersed throughout the whole system. We know, for instance, that even a minute fragment of a leaf of a Begonia will reproduce the whole plant; and that if a fresh-water worm is chopped into small pieces, each will reproduce the whole animal. Considering also the minuteness of the gemmules and the permeability of all organic tissues, the thorough dispersion of the gemmules is not surprising. That matter may be readily transferred without the aid of vessels from part to part of the body, we have a good instance in a case recorded by Sir J. Paget of a lady, whose hair lost its colour at each successive attack of neuralgia and recovered it again in the course of a few days. With plants, however, and probably with compound animals, such as corals, the gemmules do not ordinarily spread from bud to bud, but are confined to the parts developed from each separate bud; and of this fact no explanation can be given.

The assumed elective affinity of each gemmule for that particular cell which precedes it in due order of development is supported by many analogies. In all ordinary cases of sexual reproduction, the male and female elements certainly have a mutual affinity for each other: thus, it is believed that about ten thousand species of Compositæ exist, and there can be no doubt that if the pollen of all these species could be simultaneously or successively placed on the stigma of any one species, this one would elect with unerring certainty its own pollen. This elective capacity is all the more wonderful, as it must have been acquired since the many species of this great group of plants branched off from a common progenitor. On any view of the nature of sexual reproduction, the formative matter of each part contained within the ovules and the male element act on each other by some law of special affinity, so that corresponding parts affect one another; thus, a calf produced from a short-horned cow by a long-horned bull has its horns affected by the union of the two forms, and the offspring from two birds with differently coloured tails have their tails affected.

The various tissues of the body plainly show, as many physiologists have insisted, an affinity for special organic substances, whether natural or foreign to the body. We see this in the cells of the kidneys attracting urea from the blood; in curare affecting certain nerves; *Lytta vesicatoria* the kidneys; and the poisonous matter of various diseases, as small-pox, scarlet-fever, hooping-cough, glanders, and hydrophobia, affecting certain definite parts of the body.

It has also been assumed that the development of each gemmule depends on its union with another cell or unit which has just commenced its development, and which precedes it in due order of growth. That the formative matter within the pollen of plants, which by our hypothesis consists of gemmules, can unite with and modify the partially developed cells of the mother-plant, we have clearly seen in the section devoted to this subject. As the tissues of plants are formed, as far as is known, only by the proliferation of pre-existing cells, we must conclude that the gemmules derived from the foreign pollen do not become developed into new and separate cells, but penetrate and modify the nascent cells of the mother-plant. This process may be compared with what takes place in the act of ordinary fertilisation, during which the contents of the pollen-tubes penetrate the closed embryonic sac within the ovule, and determine the development of the embryo. According to this view, the cells of the mother-plant may almost literally be said to be fertilised by the gemmules derived from the foreign pollen. In this case and in all others the proper gemmules must combine in due order with pre-existing nascent cells, owing to their elective affinities. A slight difference in nature between the gemmules and the nascent cells would be far from interfering with their mutual union and development, for we well know in the case of ordinary reproduction that such slight differentiation in the sexual elements favours in a marked manner their union and subsequent development, as well as the vigour of the offspring thus produced. . . .

CONCLUSION

The hypothesis of Pangenesis, as applied to the several great classes of facts just discussed, no doubt is extremely complex, but so are the facts. The chief assumption is that all the units of the body, besides having the universally admitted power of growing by self-division, throw off minute gemmules which are dispersed through the system. Nor can this assumption be considered as too bold, for we know from the cases of graft-hybridisation that formative matter of some kind is present in the tissues of plants, which is capable of combining with that included in another individual, and of reproducing every unit of the whole organism. But we have further to assume that the gemmules grow, multiply, and aggregate themselves into buds and the sexual elements; their development depending on their union with other nascent cells or units. They are also believed to be capable of transmission in a dormant state, like seeds in the ground, to successive generations.

In a highly-organised animal, the gemmules thrown off from each different unit throughout the body must be inconceivably numerous and minute. Each unit of each part, as it changes during development, and we know that some insects undergo at least twenty metamorphoses, must throw off its gemmules. But the same cells may long continue to increase by self-division, and even become modified by absorbing peculiar nutriment, without necessarily throwing off modified gemmules. All organic beings, moreover, include many dormant gemmules derived from their grandparents and more remote progenitors, but not from all their progenitors. These almost infinitely numerous and minute gemmules are contained within each bud, ovule, spermatozoon, and pollen-grain. Such an admission will be declared impossible; but number and size are only relative difficulties. Independent organisms exist which are barely visible under the highest powers of the microscope, and their germs must be excessively minute. Particles of infectious matter, so small as to be wafted by the wind or to adhere to smooth paper, will multiply so rapidly as to infect within a short time the whole body of a large animal. We should also reflect on the admitted number and minuteness of the molecules composing a particle of ordinary matter. The difficulty, therefore, which at first appears insurmountable, of believing in the existence of gemmules so numerous and small as they must be according to our hypothesis, has no great weight.

The units of the body are generally admitted by physiologists to be autonomous. I go one step further and assume that they throw off reproductive gemmules. Thus an organism does not generate its kind as a whole, but each separate unit generates its kind. It has often been said by naturalists that each cell of a plant has the potential capacity of reproducing the whole plant; but it has this power only in virtue of containing gemmules derived from every part. When a cell or unit is from some cause modified, the gemmules derived from it will be in like manner modified. If our hypothesis be provisionally accepted, we must look at all the forms of asexual reproduction, whether occurring at maturity or during youth, as fundamentally the same, and dependent on the mutual aggregation and multiplication of the gemmules. The regrowth of an amputated limb and the healing of a wound is the same process partially carried out. Buds apparently include nascent cells, belonging to that stage of development at which the budding occurs, and these cells are ready to unite with the gemmules derived from the next succeeding cells. The sexual elements, on the other hand, do not include such nascent cells; and the male and female elements taken separately do not contain a sufficient number of gemmules for independent development, except in the cases of parthenogenesis. The development of each being, including all the forms of metamorphosis and metagenesis, depends on the presence of gemmules thrown off at each period of life, and on their development, at a corresponding period, in union with preceding cells. Such cells may be said to be fertilised by the gemmules which come next in due order of development. Thus the act of ordinary impregnation and the development of each part in each being are closely analogous processes. The child, strictly speaking, does not grow into the man, but includes germs which slowly and successively become developed and form the man. In the child, as well as in the adult, each part generates the same part. Inheritance must be looked at as merely a form of growth, like the self-division of a lowly-organised uni-cellular organism. Reversion depends on the transmission from the forefather to his descendants of dormant gemmules, which occasionally become developed under certain known or unknown conditions. Each animal and plant may be compared with a bed of soil full of seeds, some of which soon germinate, some lie dormant for a period, whilst others perish. When we hear it said that a man carries in his constitution the seeds of an inherited disease, there is much truth in the expression. No other attempt, as far as I am aware, has been made, imperfect as this confessedly is, to connect under one point of view these several grand classes of facts. An organic being is a microcosm—a little universe, formed of a host of self-propagating organisms, inconceivably minute and numerous as the stars in heaven.

PART THREE

The Theory of Recapitulation

THE theory of evolution swiftly unshackled the nineteenth-century natural sciences as supporting hands from every scientific discipline hastened to link with Darwin. Alfred Russell Wallace lent compatible insights and fresh, independent data. Charles Lyell strengthened Darwinism from the viewpoint of geology, and Thomas H. Huxley mustered skeptical philosophers and beat back theological uprisings. None of Darwin's support, however, proved as indispensable as that furnished by a band of paleontologists and biologists who recognized that in the genealogy of embryological forms they might verify Darwin's hypothesis of species descent and simultaneously inaugurate a science of individual development.

The first significant bolster for evolutionary theory appeared within five years after the publication of *The Origin of Species*. Fritz Müller, in 1864, published tiny *Für Darwin*, a carefully organized zoological exposition that exerted seminal influence on his generation. Müller "verified" the theory of evolution by comparing closely related embryonic forms among the Crustacea—a class of invertebrates, including shrimps, crabs, barnacles, and lobsters. He thought at first that the undertaking might consume "the strength and life of an individual," but within a few years he felt that not only had he thrown a "sand-grain" on the scale against Darwin's opponents but that, additionally, he had supplied a few basic generalizations on individual development. Resemblances between the larvae of more complex crustacea and the adults of less complex forms engrossed Müller. Crustacea higher on the evolutionary scale seemingly recapitulated the early forms of their species in their embryonic growth. The probability that individual development contained a historical record of major significance to paleontology cheered Ernst Haeckel, who set forth on a venture that, indeed, would sap anyone's strength. On the basis of his interpretation of Müller's law of recapitulation Haeckel proposed to construct the genealogy of the entire animal kingdom, including man. Haeckel's lofty aspirations were complemented by those of

American paleontologists Edward D. Cope and Alpheus Hyatt, who toiled arduously with fossil-shell studies of marine mollusks, brachiopods, and crustaceans to show that when corollaries were tacked to the recapitulation theory it could be construed as a universally applicable developmental principle. Haeckel, Cope, and Hyatt, however, were subsequently upstaged by Herbert Spencer. An authentic "Victorian Aristotle,"[1] Spencer, after shifting from the stance of a critic to that of a stout recapitulationist, raised the theory to its most estimable stature.

The components for a crude science of individual development were fashioned initially by Müller and then assembled by Haeckel, Cope, Hyatt, and Spencer. Each championed Neo-Lamarckianism. Because each seized on recapitulation from the perspective of his particular discipline, sophisticated modifications were systematically fastened to the theory. The selections presented in this part—drawn from the books of harbingers, Müller, Haeckel, Cope, and Spencer—are aimed at showing these decisive modifications in the recapitulation theory and, thus, how its integrity was preserved and enhanced until ultimately the second echelon of evolutionists, headed by G. Stanley Hall, revered it as the first principle of genetic psychology.[2]

Fritz Müller's rudimentary science of individual development commenced in ambiguity. Development, he said in *Für Darwin*, may proceed in either of two patterns: (*a*) progeny may deviate from ancestral forms early in embryonic growth toward adult forms, or (*b*) progeny may faithfully pass through the developmental phases of their progenitors. The first instance would render the ontogenetic record void of clues to the phylogenetic sequence; the second instance would unfold individual growth as a delineation of species evolution. Müller avoided committing himself on the question of whether one of the routes was predestined. He turned his back on individuals craving a "mysterious inherent impulse" in growth or evolutionary destiny, but in his painstaking efforts to describe how the historical record is both "effaced" and "sophisticated" in ontogenetic growth, he betrayed an inclination to view evolutionary progress as contingent on progeny pursuing a modified recapitulatory pattern.

Ernst Haeckel boldly proclaimed that Müller's second pattern represented *the* law of development. Every organism, according to Haeckel, from the unicellular protista to the sponges, plants, and vertebrates, reproduced the conserving influence of heredity: "In the very

[1] R. Hofstadter, *Social Darwinism in American Thought*, Revised Edition (Boston: Beacon Press, 1955), p. 32.
[2] An extended selection from Hyatt's writings is omitted because he and Cope adopted similar positions.

name, 'fundamental law of biogeny,' which I have given to my recapitulation theory, I claim that it is universal."[3] Not a single scientific discovery is attributable to Haeckel; the ideas that he promulgated were largely borrowed, and his works were conclusively antiquated with the advent of modern genetics. Haeckel, however, was at once the most colorful and the most puzzling natural scientist on the European Continent during the heady rise of evolutionary theory. Speculative, intrepid, idealistic, and peevish, Haeckel both commanded fierce loyalties and drew bitter detractions. Trained in botany, anatomy, and microscopy, Haeckel entered from a devout childhood into an adult world fomenting with political liberalism and social reform. Political freethinking induced him to abandon his religious piety and to venerate humanity itself. The theory of recapitulation, as Haeckel interpreted it, offered a reason for suggesting a mechanical, frankly antimetaphysical, explanation of nature.

In most of his writings, including the selection offered here from *History of Creation*, Haeckel spoke of ontogeny and phylogeny as standing in "the closest causal connection" and asserted that man "passes through the same series of transformations which its animal progenitors have passed through."[4] Haeckel professed to abhor the Aristotelian idea of Final Causes and, consequently, struggled to apply the theory of recapitulation without metaphysical assumptions; however, resemblances all along the phylogenetic scale intimated foreordained order and purpose. Haeckel never was capable of developing a detached viewpoint toward his spiritualistic background, and his works in general are perforated with contradictions. He leaned, as the occasion suited him, on either transcendental or materialistic underpinnings. Although seduced by a mechanical interpretation of the theory of recapitulation, Haeckel failed to suppress his wistfulness to find a divine meaning in growth processes.

Haeckel's opening remarks in Chapter 13 of *History of Creation* indicate why he thought that his particular litany on the processes of man's development would provide a naturalistic and philosophic basis for understanding growth and evolution. Always less concerned with substantiating a hypothesis than with proving a point, Haeckel loudly claimed that his particular view of individual development supported both the theory of evolution and a monistic, or mechanically harmonious, conception of the universe. Restless, impatient, and grieved that too few individuals had appraised his outlook, Haeckel digressed in these initial remarks, flailing theologians, philosophers, and natural scientists alike for their tra-

---

[3] E. Haeckel, *Wonders of Life* [1904], translated by J. McCabe (New York: Harper, 1905), p. 381.
[4] E. Haeckel, *The History of Creation* [1873, Eighth German Edition], translated by E. R. Lankester, 2 vols. (New York: Appleton, 1906). Vol. I, pp. 355–356.

ditional, conservative educational practices. Once back to his major concern, Haeckel set forth a series of ontogenic comparisons, the knowledge of which he hoped would "promote the intellectual advance, and thereby the mental perfecting of the human race." Although Haeckel hinted that a complete phylogeny of man, showing his succession from the fishes and amphibians would be forthcoming, for lack of data more useful than mere conjecture, his actual comparisons were constrained to ancestors whose embryogeny was similar to that of man.

The manner in which Haeckel wrestled with the observation that changing environmental conditions somehow simplify the primordial processes of development betrayed his everlasting difficulties with causal relations. His clumsy discourse on the modifications of recapitulation theory, his comment on the "law of abridged inheritance," and his roving idea for making comparative anatomical studies at different paleontological periods failed to clarify precisely how he regarded the nexus between phylogeny and ontogeny. He indicated that he followed Müller in accepting both palingenetic and cenogenetic consequences as equally crucial phases of progressive evolution; on numerous occasions, however, Haeckel also deserted Müller. A half century later, for example, in *Wonders of Life*, he asserted, "I have insisted from the first that the biogenetic law consists of two parts, one positive and palingenetic and the other restrictively negative and cenogenetic."[5]

Edward D. Cope, in the selection included from *The Primary Factors of Organic Evolution*, acknowledged his indebtedness to Haeckel for distinguishing between palingeny and cenogeny. Cope, the foremost paleontologist and authority on comparative anatomy in the United States during the late nineteenth century, at the same time recognized that several subsidiary processes seemed to be operative. Moreover, by extending the scope of paleontological investigations to include higher vertebrates and man, Cope greatly increased both the plausibility and the generalizability of the theory of recapitulation. Cope and fellow-American paleontologist, Alpheus Hyatt, were among the first to recognize that the cenogenetic influences must have their day at some point in ontogeny if progressive, phylogenetic evolution is to occur. Both Cope and Hyatt saw that organisms of greater complexity necessarily underwent many ontogenetic changes in their recapitulation toward maturity, and they sensed, therefore, that newly acquired characters might eventually replace the older. The process whereby the antiquated aspects of phylogeny were foreshortened in ontogeny they termed "acceleration." In Hyatt's words:

[5] Haeckel, *Wonders of Life, op. cit.*, pp. 381–382.

There is one phase of the law of acceleration which requires to be dwelt upon as the best means of conveying its full meaning to those not yet accustomed to note its action in their researches. It expresses the mode by which the continual replacement of the older by newer and later acquired characteristics takes place in every genetic series, and therefore *explains the mechanism of gradation, whether progressive or retrogressive. Changes in environment, which introduce new adaptive characteristics in the nealogic or adult stages, necessarily add these to the hereditary stages of the younger periods of growth,* and thus shorten the development of the latter by direct replacement.[6]

Thus the two paleontologists recognized the likelihood that the more progressive life-forms might acquire the characters that were crucial to survival earlier than those that were no longer useful. In progressive evolution, then, cenogeny or "inexact parallelism" would be the rule rather than the exception. Finally, Cope deduced the principle of "retardation," which warned that retrogressive evolutionary factors might arise that would lead to the extinction of newly acquired characters. In a law, which was the converse of acceleration, Cope proclaimed that progeny would lose their evolutionary momentum if higher organisms should be arrested in their ontogenetic growth before reaching the farthest stage in their phylogenetic history. The law ominously implied that should the arrest become widespread, a given species might deteriorate to the point of extinction.

The venerable nature-is-right doctrine, which held that development proceeded as the inner, palingenetic impulses intended, remained undiminished by Cope's laws of acceleration, inexact parallelism, and retardation. These laws mainly clarified how the inner impulses worked in the context of cenogenetic influences. Even though unadulterated palingenesis was shown realistically to be exceedingly rare in higher organisms, perspective on "inexactness" now existed, and recapitulatory phenomena still appeared, at first glance, as predictably ordered as if they were purely palingenetic.

A second look at Cope's laws, however, reveals the compilation of flaws that eventually doomed recapitulation theory. The processes of acceleration compounded with those of inexact parallelism in the short ontogenetic growing period could not help but hopelessly confuse the record of phylogenetic recapitulation. During various phylogenetic periods, some characters might have been abbreviated while others were unduly prolonged, and after these alterations they would be cast together and developed simultaneously in ontogeny. Even more disconcerting,

[6] A. Hyatt, Genesis of the Arietidae, *Smithsonian Contributions to Knowledge,* 1890, 26, 1–223, p. 44.

stages in growth might be disarrayed so that highly useful characters might begin their growth earlier in ontogeny than those less important, although the latter might have been acquired in an earlier chronological period. The possibility that the phylogenetic record might be jumbled and reversed, as Cope's law of "inexact parallelism" suggested, jeopardized every precept of recapitulation theory. Cope responded to critics by retreating to the assumption that the laws of phylogenetic order held when comparisons were made at the level of separate characters or body parts rather than at that of orders and classes of species, but his new assumptions were hardly more convincing.

Amid the confusion of biologists and paleontologists struggling to interpret the bewildering facts of recapitulation, Herbert Spencer unobtrusively thrust the theory to its zenith. Having acquired a breadth of scholarship unequaled in the nineteenth century and a prudent, disciplined acumen, Spencer possessed qualifications requisite to bridging the hiatus between the developmental concepts of the nineteenth-century natural sciences and the basic principles of genetic psychology. Beginning in 1860 and continuing at a prolific pace for more than thirty years, Spencer published a ten-volume series on the *System of Synthetic Philosophy*. The series began with *First Principles*, a philosophic treatise, and continued with volumes on the *Principles of Biology, Psychology, Sociology,* and *Ethics*, respectively.

Spencer's fully articulated recapitulation theory is presented in the fifth edition (1898) of *Principles of Biology*. As the selection reprinted here reveals, Spencer's logical analyses of recapitulation theory began with Karl Ernst Von Baer's general law, which describes growth as proceeding from indefinite homogeneity to definite heterogeneity. Early in the century, Von Baer had set forth principles that accounted for the genesis of principal organs from cells and germ layers, and in general had stimulated considerable interest in the origin of body tissue and growth. Along with nearly everyone in that era, Von Baer had committed himself to special-creationism. His scholarly pursuits, nonetheless, led him to make embryological comparisons of several different animals, whereupon he was duteously impressed by their similarities and by the probability that all animals passed through similar embryological stages in their development. Indeed, Von Baer confessed, at the risk of being branded heretical, that he was unable to distinguish positively between reptile, bird, and mammal embryos during early stages of growth. Von Baer once ridiculed the theory of recapitulation. Spencer suggested that he was misguided by the doctrine of special-creation and that he had overlooked the apparent parallelism among animal forms, because then such a viewpoint would have been meaningless. To Spencer, who was driven by a compulsion to link everything in nature to Final Causes, the recapitulation theory abounded in meaning:

> On the hypothesis of evolution this parallelism has a meaning—indicates that primordial kinship of all organisms, and that progressive differentiation of them, which the hypothesis alleges. But on any other hypothesis the parallelism is meaningless; or rather, it raises a difficulty; since it implies either an effect without a cause or a design without a purpose.[7]

The befogged attempts of Haeckel, Cope, and Hyatt to disentangle historical events in ontogeny neither abetted nor impeded Spencer's own extension of recapitulation theory. Spencer surely must have been aware of these prestigious disciples of Darwin, but it seems that he chose to overlook their contributions. He preferred to work independently, reasoning from a basic premise to a conclusion without resorting to the works and writings of others. Nonetheless, there exist several points at which the views of Haeckel, Cope, and Hyatt were congruent with Spencer's system. For example, Spencer believed that a principle of proclivity operated continuously to keep growth oriented toward original, primordial forms. The tendency toward proclivity was confronted at every developmental turn by a corresponding tendency toward acquired characters imposed by the environment. Initial and terminal forms thus war constantly, each attempting to establish its primacy during growth. The driving force of proclivity maintained the classic palingenetic-cenogenetic conflict; however, Spencer extended the issue by insisting that the recapitulating embryo was in danger of arrest as a consequence not only of perversions at various stages of cenogenetic growth, which might be environmentally induced, but also of pressures from very primitive phylogenetic forms.

Spencer further recognized that evolutionary progress was contingent on whether "terminal types" established themselves. Spencer thought not from the viewpoint of abridgement, acceleration, and inexact parallelism but in terms of *economy*. Under what conditions might cenogenetic or environmental influences on acquired characters propitiously further evolutionary progress? He saw the folly of thinking that mammalian embryos, enroute to their terminal forms, became successively complete fish, complete amphibians, complete simians, and so on. It was extravagantly wasteful of time and materials. Spencer reasoned, therefore, that special evolutionary advantages would accrue if circumstances permitted an embryo to reach maturity without waste. Descendents would inherit

---

[7] H. Spencer, *The Principles of Biology* [1864], revised and enlarged edition, 2 vols. (New York: Appleton, 1898), Vol. I, p. 453.

a longer life span and beneficial competitive traits, which would better enable them to carry forward the baton of progress. For Spencer, efficient ontogenetic growth encompassed functional economy as well as simple acceleration.

From the primary premise of economy, Spencer derived several secondary principles to account for the variations so readily apparent in the recapitulatory sequence. These might have been as unsatisfactory to skeptics as Cope's notion of "inexact parallelism," but Spencer's awesome prestige and splendid logic extinguished uncertainties. In countless minds, as regards recapitulation theory, faith in Spencer sufficed for substantive proof. In brief, Spencer's economy theory held that primitive organs might be obliterated in later stages of development if highly complicated, newly acquired characters require a longer developmental period. The lack of uniformity thus introduced might be compounded by the disappearance of disused organs, whose demise would be hastened if they consumed crucial nutriments. Sometimes a structure might continue in an organism long after its usefulness had been expended if the processes of economy should be preoccupied in accomplishing purposes in another aspect of growth; occasionally disused organs might persist, should their parts be utilized in newly acquired, thriving structures. In sum, Spencer's elaborate principles elevated the theory of recapitulation to its apogee; never again would it seem as sacrosanct and inviolable.

FRITZ MÜLLER (1821–1897)

THE PROGRESS OF EVOLUTION

WHEN I had read Charles Darwin's book *On the Origin of Species*, it seemed to me that there was one mode, and that perhaps the most certain, of testing the correctness of the views developed in it, namely, to attempt to apply them as specially as possible to some particular group of animals. Such an attempt to establish a genealogical tree, whether for the families of a class, the genera of a large family, or for the species of an extensive genus, and to produce pictures as complete and intelligible as possible of the common ancestors of the various smaller and larger circles, might furnish a result in three different ways.

SOURCE: F. Müller. *Facts and Arguments for Darwin* (London: John Murray, 1869). Translated by W. S. Dallas. Originally published 1863. Selections from "Introductory," Chapter 1, pp. 1–6, and "On the Progress of Evolution," Chapter 11, pp. 110–121. Abridged. Footnotes deleted.

1. In the first place, Darwin's suppositions when thus applied might lead to irreconcilable and contradictory conclusions, from which the erroneousness of the suppositions might be inferred. If Darwin's opinions are false, it was to be expected that contradictions would accompany their detailed application at every step, and that these, by their cumulative force, would entirely destroy the suppositions from which they proceeded, even though the deductions derived from each particular case might possess little of the unconditional nature of mathematical proof.

2. Secondly, the attempt might be successful to a greater or less extent. If it was possible upon the foundation and with the aid of the Darwinian theory, to show in what sequence the various smaller and larger circles had separated from the common fundamental form and from each other, in what sequence they had acquired the peculiarities which now characterise them, and what transformations they had undergone in the lapse of ages—if the establishment of such a genealogical tree, of a primitive history of the group under consideration, free from internal contradictions, was possible—then this conception, the more completely it took up all the species within itself, and the more deeply it enabled us to descend into the details of their structure, must in the same proportion bear in itself the warrant of its truth, and the more convincingly prove that the foundation upon which it is built is no loose sand, and that it is more than merely "an intellectual dream."

3. In the third place, however, it was possible, and this could not but appear, *prima facie*, the most probable case, that the attempt might be frustrated by the difficulties standing in its way, without settling the question, either way, in a perfectly satisfactory manner. But if it were only possible in this way to arrive for oneself at a moderately certain independent judgment upon a matter affecting the highest questions so deeply, even this alone could not but be esteemed a great gain.

Having determined to make the attempt, I had in the first place to decide upon some particular class. The choice was necessarily limited to those the chief forms of which were easily to be obtained alive in some abundance. The Crabs and Macrurous Crustacea, the Stomapoda, the Diastylidæ, the Amphipoda and Isopoda, the Ostracoda and Daphnidæ, the Copepoda and Parasita, the Cirripedes and Rhizocephala of our coast, representing the class of Crustacea with the deficiency only of the Phyllopoda and Xiphosura, furnished a long and varied, and at the same time intimately connected series, such as was at my command in no other class. But even independently of this circumstance the selection of the Crustacea could hardly have been doubtful. Nowhere else, as has already been indicated by various writers, is the temptation stronger

to give to the expressions "relationship, production from a common fundamental form," and the like, more than a mere figurative signification,
than in the case of the lower Crustacea. Among the parasitic Crustacea,
especially, everybody has long been accustomed to speak, in a manner
scarcely admitting of a figurative meaning, of their arrest of development
by parasitism, as if the transformation of species were a matter of course.
It would certainly never appear to any one to be a pastime worthy
of the Deity, to amuse himself with the contrivance of these marvellous
cripplings, and so they were supposed to have fallen by their own fault,
like Adam, from their previous state of perfection. . . .

When I thus began to study our Crustacea more closely from this
new stand-point of the Darwinian theory—when I attempted to bring
their arrangements into the form of a genealogical tree, and to form
some idea of the probable structure of their ancestors—I speedily saw
(as indeed I expected) that it would require years of preliminary work
before the essential problem could be seriously handled. The extant systematic works generally laid more weight upon the characters separating
the genera, families and orders, than upon those which unite the members
of each group, and consequently often furnished but little employable
material. But above all things a thorough knowledge of development
was indispensable, and every one knows how imperfect is our present
knowledge of this subject. . . .

But although the satisfactory completion of the "Genealogical tree
of the Crustacea" appeared to be an undertaking for which the strength
and life of an individual would hardly suffice, even under more favourable
circumstances than could be presented by a distant island, far removed
from the great market of scientific life, far from libraries and museums—
nevertheless its practicability became daily less doubtful in my eyes,
and fresh observations daily made me more favourably inclined towards
the Darwinian theory.

In determining to state the arguments which I derived from the consideration of our Crustacea in favour of Darwin's views, and which (together with more general considerations and observations in other departments), essentially aided in making the correctness of those views seem
more and more palpable to me, I am chiefly influenced by an expression
of Darwin's: "Whoever," says he, "is led to believe that species are
mutable, will do a good service by conscientiously expressing his conviction." To the desire expressed in these words I respond, for my own
part, with the more pleasure, as this furnishes me with an opportunity
of publicly giving expression in words to the thanks which I feel most
deeply to be due from me to Darwin for the instructions and suggestions
for which I am so deeply indebted to his book. Accordingly I throw

this sand-grain with confidence into the scale against "the load of prejudice by which this subject is overwhelmed," without troubling myself
as to whether the priests of orthodox science will reckon me amongst
dreamers and children in knowledge of the laws of nature.

ON THE PROGRESS OF EVOLUTION

From this scarcely unavoidable but unsatisfactory sideglance upon the
old school, which looks down with so great an air of superiority upon
Darwin's "intellectual dream" and the "giddy enthusiasm" of its friends,
I turn to the more congenial task of considering the developmental history
of the Crustacea from the point of view of the Darwinian theory.

Darwin himself, in the thirteenth chapter of his book, has already
discussed the conclusions derived from his hypotheses in the domain of
developmental history. For a more detailed application of them, however,
it is necessary in the first place to trace these general conclusions a little
further than he has there done.

The changes by which young animals depart from their parents, and
the gradual accumulation of which causes the production of new species,
genera, and families, may occur at an earlier or later period of life—in
the young state, or at the period of sexual maturity. For the latter is
by no means always, as in the Insecta, a period of repose; most other
animals even then continue to grow and to undergo changes. Some variations, indeed, from their very nature, can only occur when the young
animal has attained the adult stage of development. Thus the Sea Caterpil-
lars (*Polynoë*) at first possess only a few body-segments, which, during
development, gradually increase to a number which is different in different species, but constant in the same species; now before a young animal
could exceed the number of segments of its parents, it must of course
have attained that number. We may assume a similar supplementary
progress wherever the deviation of the descendants consists in an addition
of new segments and limbs.

*Descendants therefore reach a new goal, either by deviating sooner
or later whilst still on the way towards the form of their parents, or
by passing along this course without deviation, but then, instead of standing still, advance still farther.*

The former mode will have had a predominant action where the posterity of common ancestors constitutes a group of forms standing upon
the same level in essential features, as the whole of the Amphipoda,
Crabs, or Birds. On the other hand we are led to the assumption of
the second mode of progress, when we seek to deduce from a common
original form, animals some of which agree with young states of others.

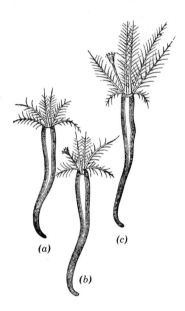

Figure 1 Young Tubicolar worms, magnified with the simple lens about 6 diam.: (*a*) without operculum, *Protula*-stage; (*b*) with a barbate opercular peduncle, *Filograna*-stage; (*c*) with a naked opercular peduncle, *Serpula*-stage. (The figure is drawn from memory, as the little animals, which I at first took for young *Protulae*, only attracted my attention when I remarked the appearance of the operculum, which induced me to draw them.)

In the former case the developmental history of the descendants can only agree with that of their ancestors up to a certain point at which their courses separate—as to their structure in the adult state it will teach us nothing. *In the second case the entire development of the progenitors is also passed through by the descendants, and, therefore, so far as the production of a species depends upon this second mode of progress, the historical development of the species will be mirrored in its developmental history.* In the short period of a few weeks or months, the changing forms of the embryo and larvæ will pass before us, a more or less complete and more or less true picture of the transformations through which the species, in the course of untold thousands of years, has struggled up to its present state. . . .

The historical record preserved in developmental history is gradually EFFACED *as the development strikes into a constantly straighter course from the egg to the perfect animal, and it is frequently* SOPHISTICATED *by the struggle for existence which the free-living larvæ have to undergo*

Thus as the law of inheritance is by no means strict, as it gives room for individual variations with regard to the form of the parents, this is also the case with the succession in time of the developmental processes. Every father of a family who has taken notice of such matters is well aware that even in children of the same parents, the teeth, for example, are not cut or changed, either at the same age, or in the same order. Now in general it will be useful to an animal to obtain as early as possible those advantages by which it sustains itself in the struggle for existence. A precocious appearance of peculiarities originally acquired at a later period will generally be advantageous, and their retarded appearance disadvantageous; the former, when it appears accidentally, will be preserved by natural selection. It is the same with every change which gives to the larval stages, rendered multifarious by crossed and oblique characters, a more straightforward direction, simplifies and abridges the process of development, and forces it back to an earlier period of life, and finally into the life of the egg.

As this conversion of a development passing through different young states into a more direct one, is not the consequence of a mysterious inherent impulse, but dependent upon advances accidentally presenting themselves, it may take place in the most nearly allied animals in the most various ways, and require very different periods of time for its completion. There is one thing, however, that must not be overlooked here. The historical development of a species can hardly ever have taken place in a continuously uniform flow; periods of rest will have alternated with periods of rapid progress. But forms, which in periods of rapid progress were severed from others after a short duration, must have impressed themselves less deeply upon the developmental history of their descendants, than those which repeated themselves unchanged, through a long series of successive generations in periods of rest. These more fixed forms, less inclined to variation, will present a more tenacious resistance in the transition to direct development, and will maintain themselves in a more uniform manner and to the last, however different may be the course of this process in other respects. . . .

That besides this gradual extinction of the primitive history, a *falsification* of the record preserved in the developmental history takes place by means of the struggle for existence which the free-living young states have to undergo, requires no further exposition. For it is perfectly evident that the struggle for existence and natural selection combined with this, must act in the same way, in change and development, upon larvæ which have to provide for themselves, as upon adult animals. The changes of the larvæ, independent of the progress of the adult animal, will become the more considerable, the longer the duration of the life of the larva in comparison to that of the adult animal, the greater the difference in their mode of life, and the more sharply marked the division of labour between the different stages of development. These processes have to a certain extent an action opposed to the gradual extinction of the primitive history; they increase the differences between the individual stages of development, and it will be easily seen how even a straightforward course of development may be again converted by them into a development with metamorphosis. . . .

Which of the different modes of development at present occurring in a class of animals may claim to be that approaching most nearly to the original one, is easy to judge from the above statements.

The primitive history of a species will be preserved in its developmental history the more perfectly, the longer the series of young states through which it passes by uniform steps; and the more truly, the less the mode of life of the young departs from that of the adults, and the less the peculiarities of the individual young states can be conceived as transferred back from later ones in previous periods of life, or as independently acquired.

ERNST HAECKEL (1834–1919)
THE INDIVIDUAL DEVELOPMENT
OF ORGANISMS

THE greater number of educated persons who nowadays show more or less interest in our theories of development unfortunately know next to nothing of the facts of organic development from actual observation. Man, like other mammals, appears at birth in an already developed form. The chicken, like other birds, creeps out of the egg in a completely developed form. But the wonderful processes by which these completed animal forms arise are entirely unknown to most persons. And yet these but little considered processes contain a fund of knowledge, which is unsurpassed by any other in general importance. For we here have the development before our eyes as a tangible fact, and we need only place a number of hen's eggs in an incubator, and watch their development for three weeks carefully with a microscope, in order to understand

SOURCE: E. Haeckel. *The History of Creation*, Eighth German Edition, 2 vols. (New York: Appleton, 1906). Translated by E. R. Lankester. Originally published 1873. Volume I. "The Individual Development of Organisms. The History of the Development of the Animal Tribes," Chapter 13, pp. 332–362. Abridged. Footnotes deleted.

the mystery by which a highly organized bird develops out of a single simple cell. Step by step we can trace this wonderful transformation, and step by step point out how one organ is developed out of the other.

And for this reason alone—because, in fact, it is in this domain only that the facts of development are presented to us in tangible reality. I consider it of paramount consequence to direct the reader's careful attention to those infinitely important and interesting processes in the *individual development of organisms*, viz. to *ontogeny*, and above all to the *ontogeny* of *the vertebrate animals*, including *man*. I wish specially to recommend these exceedingly remarkable and instructive phenomena to the reader's most careful consideration; for, on the one hand, they form one of our strongest supports for the theory of descent, and for the monistic conception of the universe generally; and, on the other hand, because hitherto it is only a few privileged persons who have properly estimated their immense general importance.

We cannot, indeed, but be astonished when we consider the deep ignorance which still prevails, in the widest circles, about the facts of the individual development of man and organisms in general. These facts, the universal importance of which cannot be estimated too highly, were established, in their most important outlines, even more than a hundred years ago, in 1759, by the great German naturalist Caspar Friedrich Wolff, in his classical *Theoria Generationis*. But, just as Lamarck's Theory of Descent, founded in 1809, lay dormant for half a century, and was only awakened to new and imperishable life in 1859, by Darwin, in like manner Wolff's Theory of Epigenesis remained unknown for nearly half a century; and it was only after Oken, in 1806, had published his history of the development of the intestinal tube, and after Meckel, in 1812, had translated Wolff's work (written in Latin) on the same subject into German, that Wolff's theory of epigenesis became more generally known, and has since formed the foundation of all subsequent investigations of the history of individual development. The study of ontogenesis thus received a great stimulus, and soon there appeared the classical investigations of the two friends, Christian Pander (1817) and Carl Ernst Bär (1819). Bär, in his remarkable *Entwickelungsgeschichte der Thiere*, worked out the ontogeny of vertebrate animals in all its important facts. He carried out a series of such excellent observations, and illustrated them by such profound philosophical reflections, that his work became the foundation for a thorough understanding of this important group of animals, to which, of course, man also belongs. The facts of embryology alone would be sufficient to solve the question of man's position in nature, which is the highest of all problems. Look attentively at and compare the eight figures which are represented on the adjoining

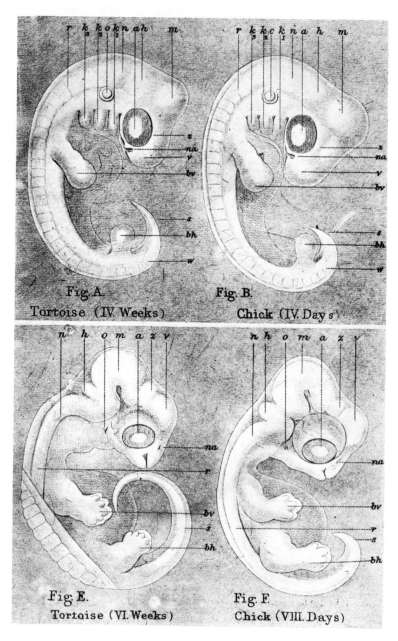

Plate I Germs or embryos of four vertebrates. *v*, Fore brain; *z*, twixt brain; *m*, mid brain; *h*, hind brain; *n*, after brain; *w*, spine; *r*, spinal cord; *na*, nose; *a*, eyes; *o*, ear; $k_1k_2k_3$, gill-arches; *s*, tail; *bv*, fore leg; *bh*, hind leg.

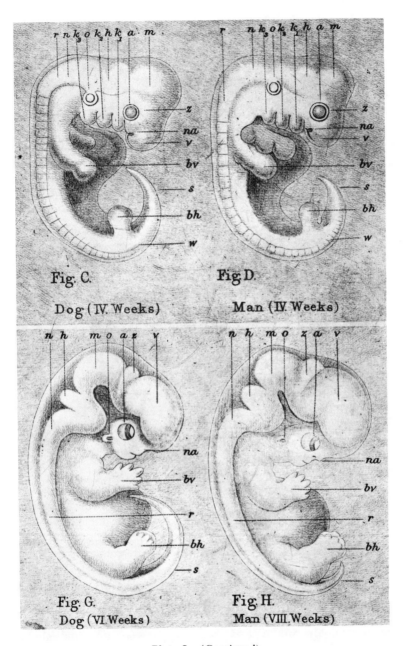

Fig. C.
Dog (IV. Weeks)

Fig D.
Man (IV. Weeks)

Fig. G.
Dog (VI. Weeks)

Fig. H.
Man (VIII. Weeks)

Plate I   (*Continued*)

Plate I, and it will be seen that the philosophical importance of embryology cannot be too highly estimated.

We may well ask, What do our so-called "educated" circles, who think so much of the high civilization of the nineteenth century, know of these most important biological facts, of these indispensable foundations for understanding their own organization? How much do our speculative philosophers and theologians know about them, who fancy they can arrive at an understanding of the human organism by mere guesswork or divine inspiration? What indeed do the majority of naturalists, even so-called "zoologists" (including the entomologists!), know about them?

The answer to this question tells much to the shame of the persons above indicated, and we must confess, willingly or unwillingly, that these invaluable facts of human ontogeny are, even at the present day, utterly unknown to most people, or are in no way valued as they deserve to be. It is the face of such a condition of things as this that we see clearly upon what a wrong and one-sided road the much-vaunted culture of the nineteenth century still moves. Ignorance and superstition are the foundations upon which most men construct their conception of their own organization, and its relation to the totality of things; and the palpable facts of the history of development, which might throw the light of truth upon them, are wholly ignored.

The chief cause of this lamentable and mischievous state of things is unquestionably owing to the education given in our higher schools, and, above all, owing to our so-called "classical education." For as it is still deeply imbued with the scholasticism of the Middle Ages, it is still unable to digest the enormous advances which natural science has made in our century. It still does not consider that its chief task should be to obtain a comprehensive knowledge of nature—of which we are ourselves a part—or of the present state of the civilized world in which we live; its main object is rather to acquire an accurate knowledge of the history of the ancient countries, and, above all, a knowledge of the Greek and Latin grammars. We grant that a thorough knowledge of classic antiquity is an exceedingly important and indispensable part of our higher education; however, our pleasant acquaintance with antiquity we owe in a much higher degree to painters and sculptors, to epic and dramatic poets, than to classical philologists or to dreaded grammarians. And to enjoy and understand these ancient poets, it is as little necessary for us to read them in the original text as it is for us to read the Bible in the original Hebrew. The enormous expense of time and labour demanded by this luxurious sport in classical grammars might be applied to infinitely better purpose, in the study of the wonderful domain of phenomena which have been opened up to us within the last half-century by the gigantic advances of natural science, more especially of geology, biology, and anthropology.

Unfortunately, however, the disparity between our daily increasing knowledge of the real world, and the limited standpoint of our so-called ideal education for the young, is becoming greater day by day. And it is, in fact, those persons who exercise most influence upon our practical education—the theologians and jurists—and likewise the privileged teachers, the philologists and historians, who know least about the most important phenomena of the actually existing world, and of the real history of nature. The structure and origin of our earth, as well as of our own human body—subjects which have become of the utmost interest owing to the astonishing progress of modern geology and anthropology— are unknown to the most of them. To speak of the human egg and its development, they consider either a ridiculous myth or a vulgar piece of immodesty. And yet this subject reveals to us a series of actually recognized facts, which cannot be surpassed in general interest or high importance by any other in the wide domain of human knowledge.

It is true these facts are not calculated to excite approval among persons who assume a complete distinction between man and the rest of nature, and who will not acknowledge the animal origin of the human race. That origin must be a very unpleasant truth to members of the ruling and privileged castes in those nations among which there exists an heredi- tary division of social classes, in consequence of false ideas about the laws of inheritance. It is well known that, even in our day, in many civilized countries the idea of hereditary grades of rank goes so far that, for example, the aristocracy imagine themselves to be of a nature totally different from that of ordinary citizens, and nobles who commit a dis- graceful offence are punished by being expelled from the caste of nobles, and thrust down among the pariahs of "vulgar citizens." What are these nobles to think of the blue blood in their privileged veins, when they learn that all human embryos, those of nobles as well as commoners, are scarcely distinguishable from the tailed embryos of dogs and other mammals during the first two months of development?

As the object of these pages is solely to further the general knowledge of natural truths, and to spread, in wider circles, a natural conception of the relations of man to the rest of nature, I shall be justified if I do not pay any regard to the widely spread prejudice in favour of an exceptional and privileged position for man in creation, and simply give here the embryological facts from which the reader will be able to draw conclusions affirming the groundlessness of those prejudices. I wish all the more to entreat my readers to reflect carefully upon these facts of ontogeny, as it is my firm conviction that a general knowledge of

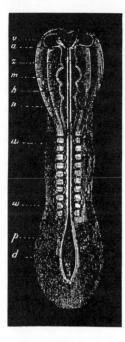

Figure 1 Embryo of a mammal or bird, in which the five brain-bladders have just commenced to develop. *v*, Fore brain; *z*, twixt brain; *m*, mid brain; *h*, hind brain; *n*, after brain; *p*, spinal marrow; *a*, eye-bladders; *w*, primitive vertebrae; *d*, spinal axis or notochord.

them can only promote the intellectual advance, and thereby the mental perfecting, of the human race.

Amidst all the infinitely rich and interesting material which lies before us in the ontogeny of vertebrate animals, that is, in the history of their individual development, I shall here confine myself to showing some of those facts which are of the greatest importance to the Theory of Descent in general, as well as in its special application to man. . . .

In all Craniota, that is, in all vertebrate animals possessing skull and brain, the brain, which is at first only the bladder-shaped dilatation of the anterior end of the spinal marrow, divides into five bladders lying one behind the other, four superficial, transverse in-nippings being formed. These *five brain-bladders*, out of which afterwards arise all the different parts of the intricately constructed brain, can be seen in their original condition in the embryo represented in Figure 1. It is just the same whether we examine the embryo of a dog, a fowl, a lizard, or any other higher vertebrate animal. For the embryos of the different skulled animals (at least the three higher classes of them, the reptiles, birds, and mammals) cannot be in any way distinguished at the stage represented in Figure 1. The whole form of the body is as yet exceedingly simple, being merely a thin, leaf-like disc. Face, legs, intestines, etc., are as yet completely wanting. But the five bladders are already quite distinct from one another.

The *first* bladder, the *fore brain*, is in so far the most important that it principally forms the larger hemispheres of the so-called larger brain (cerebrum), that part which is the seat of the higher mental activities. The more these activities are developed in the series of vertebrate animals, the more do the two lateral halves of the fore brain, or the larger hemispheres, grow at the expense of the other bladders, and overlap them in front and from above. In man, where they are most strongly developed, agreeing with his higher mental activity, they eventually almost entirely cover the other parts from above (compare Figures *A*, *B*, *E*, *F* and *C*,

D, G, H of Plate I). The *second* bladder, the *twist brain* (*z*), forms that portion of the brain which is called *the centre of sight*, and stands in the closest relation to the eyes (*a*), which grow right and left out of the fore brain in the shape of two bladders, and later lie at the bottom of the twixt brain. The *third* bladder, the *mid brain* (*m*), for the most part vanishes in the formation of the so-called *four bulbs*, a bossy portion of the brain, which is strongly developed in reptiles and birds (Figures *E, F,* Plate I), whereas in mammals it recedes much more (Figures *G, H,* Plate I). The *fourth* bladder, the *hind brain* (*h*), forms the so-called *little hemispheres*, together with the middle part of the *small brain* (cerebellum), a part of the brain as to the function of which the most contradictory conjectures are entertained, but which seems principally to regulate the co-ordination of movements. Lastly, the *fifth* bladder, the *after brain* (*n*), develops into that very important part of the central nervous system which is called the *prolonged narrow* (medulla oblongata). It is the central organ of the respiratory movements, and of other important functions, and an injury to it immediately causes death, whereas the large hemispheres of the fore brain (or the organ of the "soul," in a restricted sense) can be removed bit by bit, and even completely destroyed, without causing the death of the vertebrate animal—only its higher mental activities disappearing in consequence.

These five brain-bladders, in all vertebrate animals which possess a brain at all, are originally arranged in the same manner and develop gradually in the different groups so differently, that it is afterwards very difficult to recognize the corresponding parts in the fully developed brains. In the early stage of development which is represented in Figure 1, it seems as yet quite impossible to distinguish the embryos of the different mammals, birds, and reptiles from one another. But if we compare the much more developed embryos on Plate I with one another, we can clearly see an inequality in their development, and especially it will be perceived that the brain of the two mammals (*G* and *H*) already strongly differ from that of birds (*F*) and of reptiles (*E*). In the two latter the mid brain predominates, but in the former the fore brain. Even at this stage the brain of the bird (*F*) is scarcely distinguishable from that of the tortoise (*E*), and in like manner the brain of the dog (*G*) is as yet almost the same as that of man (*H*). If, on the other hand, we compare the brains of these four vertebrate animals in a fully developed condition, we find them so very different in all anatomical particulars, that we cannot doubt for a moment as to which animal each brain belongs.

I have here explained the original equality, the gradual commencement, and the ever-increasing separation or differentiation of the embryos in the different vertebrate animals, taking the brain as a special example, just because this organ of the soul's activity is of special interest. But I might as well have discussed in its stead the heart, or the liver, or the limbs, in short, any other part of the body, since the same wonder of creation is here ever repeated, namely, that all parts are originally the same in the different vertebrate animals, and that the variations by which the different classes, orders, families, genera, etc., differ and deviate from one another, are only gradually developed. . . .

There are certainly few parts of the body which are so differently constructed as the *limbs or extremities* of the vertebrate animals. Now, I wish the reader to compare, in Figures *A-H* on Plate I, the four extremities (*bv*) of the embryos with one another, and he will scarcely be able to perceive any important differences between the human arm (*H, bv*), the wing of a bird (*F, bv*), the slim fore leg of a dog (*G, bv*), and the plump fore leg of the tortoise (*E, bv*). In comparing the hinder extremities (*bh*) in these figures he will find it equally difficult to distinguish the leg of a man (*H, bh*), of a bird (*F, bh*), the hind leg of a dog (*G, bh*), and that of a tortoise (*F, bh*). The fore as well as the hinder extremities are as yet short, broad lumps, at the ends of which the foundations of the five toes are placed, connected as yet by a membrane. At a still earlier stage (Figures *A-D*) the five toes are not marked out at all, and it is quite impossible to distinguish even the fore and hinder extremities from one another. The latter, as well as the former, are nothing but simple roundish processes, which have grown out of the side of the trunk. At the very early stage represented in Figure 1 they are completely wanting, and the whole embryo is a simple trunk without a trace of limbs.

I wish especially to draw attention in Plate I, which represent embryos in early stages of development (Figures *A-D*)—and in which we are not able to recognize a trace of the full-grown animal—to an exceedingly important formation, which originally is common to all vertebrate animals, but which at a later period is transformed into the most different organs. Every one surely knows the *gill-arches* of fish, those arched bones which lie behind one another, to the number of three or four, on each side of the neck, and which support the gills, the respiratory organs of the fish (double rows of red leaves, which are popularly called "fishes' ears"). Now, these gill-arches originally exist exactly the same in man (*D*), in dogs (*C*), in fowls (*B*), and in tortoises (*A*), as well as in all other vertebrate animals. (In Figures *A-D* the three gill-arches of the right side of the neck are marked k_1, k_2, k_3.) Now, it is only in fishes that these remain in their original form, and develop into respiratory organs. In the other vertebrate animals they are partly employed in the formation of the face (especially the jaw apparatus), and partly in the formation of the organ of hearing.

Finally, when comparing the embryos on Plate I, we must not fail to give attention again to the *human tail* (*s*), an organ which, in the original condition, man shares with all other vertebrate animals. The discovery of tailed men was long anxiously expected by many monistic philosophers, in order to establish a closer relationship between man and the other mammals. And in like manner their dualistic opponents often maintained with pride that the complete want of a tail formed one of the most important bodily distinctions between men and animals, though they did not bear in mind the many tailless animals which really exist. Now, man in the first months of development possesses a real tail as well as his nearest kindred, the tailless apes (orang-outang, chimpanzee, gorilla), and vertebrate animals in general. But whereas, in most of them—for example, the dog (*C, G*)—in the course of development it always grows longer, in man (Figures *D, H*) and in tailless mammals, at a certain period of development, it degenerates and finally completely disappears. However, even in fully developed men, the remnant of the tail is seen in the three, four, or five tail vertebræ (vertebræ coccygeæ) as an aborted or rudimentary organ, which forms the hinder or lower end of the vertebral column, an infallible proof of our derivation from tailed ancestors.

Most persons even now refuse to acknowledge the most important deduction of the Theory of Descent, that is, the paleontological development of man from ape-like, and through them from still lower, mammals, and consider such a transformation of organic form as impossible. But, I ask, are the phenomena of the individual development of man, the fundamental features of which I have here given, in any way less wonderful? Is it not in the highest degree remarkable that all vertebrate animals of the most different classes—fishes, amphibious animals, reptiles, birds, and mammals—in the first periods of their embryonic development cannot be distinguished at all, and even much later, at a time when reptiles and birds are already distinctly different from mammals, that the dog and the man are almost identical? Verily, if we compare those two series of development with one another, and ask ourselves which of the two is the more wonderful, it must be confessed that *ontogeny*, or the short and quick history of development of the *individual*, is much more mysterious than *phylogeny*, or the long and slow history of development of the *tribe*. For one and the same grand change of form is accomplished by the latter in the course of many thousands of years, and by the former in the course of a few months. Evidently this most rapid and astonishing transformation of the individual in ontogenesis, which we can actually point out at any moment by direct observation, is in itself much more wonderful and astonishing than the corresponding, but much slower and gradual transformation which the long chain of ancestors of the same individual has gone through in phylogenesis.

The two series of organic development, the ontogenesis of the individual and the phylogenesis of the tribe to which it belongs, stand in the closest causal connection with each other. . . . As I have shown, *ontogenesis, or the development of the individual, is a short and quick repetition* (recapitulation) *of phylogenesis, or the development of the tribe to which it belongs, determined by the laws of inheritance and adaptation;* by tribe I mean the ancestors which form the chain of progenitors of the individual concerned.

The agreement between many of the germinal forms of the higher animals and the developed forms of kindred lower animals is so striking that they were observed even by the earlier naturalists. Oken, Treviranus, and others drew attention to them as early as the beginning of our century. Meckel, in 1821, spoke of a "resemblance between the development of the embryo and the animal tribe." In 1828 Bär critically discussed the question, how far within a type or tribe (for instance, the vertebrates) the germinal forms of the higher animals pass through the permanent forms of the lower. However, there could, of course, be no actual understanding of this wonderful resemblance as long as the theory of descent had not become recognized. When Darwin, in 1859, at last accomplished this, he also, in his fourteenth chapter of his chief work, briefly referred to the great importance of the embryonic evidence. Still Fritz Müller was the first to discuss the subject fully and clearly, which he did in connection with the crustacea in his admirable work "On Darwin." . . . This fundamental proposition is the most important general law of organic development, *the fundamental biogenetic law.*

In this intimate connection of ontogeny and phylogeny, I see one of the most important and irrefutable proofs of the Theory of Descent. No one can explain these phenomena unless he has recourse to the laws of Inheritance and Adaptation; by these alone are they explicable. . . . As so high and complicated an organism as that of man, or the organism of any other mammal, rises upwards from a simple cellular state, and progresses in its differentiation and perfecting, it passes through the same series of transformations which its animal progenitors have passed through, during immense spaces of time, inconceivable ages ago. . . . Certain very early and low stages in the development of man, and the other vertebrate animals in general, correspond completely in many points of structure with conditions which last for life in the lower fishes. The next phase presents us with a change of the fish-like being into a kind of amphibious animal. At a later period the mammal, with its special characteristics, develops out of the amphibian, and we can clearly see, in the successive stages of its later development, a series of steps of progressive transformation which evidently correspond with the differences of different mammalian orders and families. Now, it is precisely in the same succession that we also see the ancestors of man, and of the higher mammals, appear one after the other in the earth's history; first fishes, then amphibians, later the lower, and at last the higher mammals. Here, therefore, the embryonic development of the individual is completely parallel to the paleontological development of the whole tribe to which it belongs, and this exceedingly interesting and important phenomenon can be explained only by the interaction of the laws of Inheritance and Adaptation.

And, indeed, in order properly to understand and to apply the biogenetic fundamental law, it must be remembered that the hereditary repetition of the original chain of primary forms is but seldom (or, strictly speaking, never!) perfectly complete in the corresponding and parallel chain of embryonic forms. For the changing conditions of existence exercise their influence upon every single embryonic form as well as upon the fully developed organism. Besides, the law of abridged inheritance constantly endeavours to effect a simplification of the original process of development. On the other hand, however, the embryo may, by its adaptation to new conditions of life (e.g. by the development of protecting coverings), acquire new forms, which were wanting in the original figure of the primary form that had been transmitted to it by inheritance. Hence the figure of the embryo must necessarily (especially in its later stages of development) deviate more or less from the original figure of the corresponding primary form, and, indeed, the more so the more highly developed the organism is.

Accordingly, all the phenomena of the embryonic or individual development (Ontogenesis) may in reality fall into two different groups. The first group comprises the primeval development or the recapitulative development (Palingenesis), and exhibits still all those primeval conditions which have been transmitted by inheritance from the primary forms (thus, for instance, in the human embryo, the gill-arches, the chorda, the tail, etc.). The second group, on the other hand, contains the disturbed or falsified development (Cenogenesis), and obscures the original figure of the individual development by the introduction of new and foreign shapes, which did not exist in the earlier forms, and were acquired by the embryo only by adaptation to the peculiar conditions of the individual development (thus, for instance, in the human embryo, the egg-coverings, the yelk-sack, the placenta, etc.).

Every critical investigation and estimation of the individual development has, therefore, first of all to distinguish how many of the embryonic facts are *palingenetic documents* (pertaining to the recapitulative development), and how many, on the other hand, are *cenogenetic variations* of those documents (pertaining to the disturbed history). The more that the original *palingenesis* is retained in the embryonic development of every organism by *inheritance*, the more faithful will be the picture it gives us of the history of its original development; but, on the other hand, the more that cenogenesis has influenced the germinal form by adaptation, the more the primary image will be obliterated or altered.

The important parallelism of the paleontological and of the individual developmental series now directs our attention to a third developmental series, which stands in the closest relations to these two, and which likewise runs, on the whole, parallel to them. I mean that series of development of forms which constitutes the object of investigation in *comparative anatomy*, and which I will briefly call the *systematic developmental series of species*. By this we understand the chain of the different, but related and connected forms, which exist *side by side* at any one period of the earth's history; as, for example, at the present moment. While comparative anatomy compares the different forms of fully developed organisms with one another, it endeavours to discover the common prototypes which underlie, as it were, the manifold forms of kindred species, genera, classes, etc., and which are more or less concealed by their particular differentiation. It endeavours to make out the series of progressive steps which are indicated in the different degrees of perfection of the divergent branches of the tribe. In fact, to keep to the illustration already employed, comparative anatomy shows us how the individual organs and systems of organs in the tribe of vertebrate animals—in the different classes, families, and species of it—have unequally developed, differentiated, and perfected themselves. It shows us how far the succession of classes of vertebrate animals, from the Fishes upwards, through the Amphibia to the Mammals, and here again from the lower to the higher orders of Mammals, forms a progressive series or ladder. What light is thrown upon the subject by the knowledge of this progressive development of the organs, may be gathered from the works of the great comparative anatomists of all ages—in the works of Goethe, Meckel, Cuvier, Johannes Müller, Gegenbaur, and Huxley.

The developmental series of mature forms, which comparative anatomy points out in the different diverging and ascending steps of the organic system, and which we call the systematic developmental series, corresponds with one portion of the paleontological developmental series; it deals with the anatomical result of the latter in the present; and is, at the same time, parallel with the individual developmental series; and this, again, is parallel with the paleontological series.

The varied differentiation, and the unequal degree of perfecting which comparative anatomy points out in the developmental series of the system, is chiefly determined by the ever-increasing variety of conditions of existence to which the different groups adapt themselves in the struggle for life, and by the different degrees of rapidity and completeness with which this adaptation has been effected. Conservative groups which have retained their inherited peculiarities most tenaciously remain, in consequence, at the lowest and rudest stage of development. Those groups progressing most rapidly and variously, and which have adapted themselves to changed conditions of existence most readily, have attained the highest degree of perfection. The further the organic world developed in the course of the earth's history, the greater must the gap between the lower conservative and the higher progressive groups have become, as in fact may be seen too in the history of nations. In this way also is explained the historical fact, that the most perfect animal and vegetable groups have developed themselves in a comparatively short time to a considerable height, while the lowest or most conservative groups have remained stationary throughout all ages in their original simple stage, or have progressed, but very slowly and gradually.

The series of man's progenitors clearly shows this state of things. The sharks of the present day are still very like the primary fish, which are among the most ancient vertebrate progenitors of man, and the lowest amphibians of the present day (the gilled salamanders and salamanders) are very like the amphibians which first developed themselves out of fishes. So, too, the later ancestors of man, the Monotremata and Marsupials, the most ancient mammals, are at the same time the most imperfect animals of the class. which still exist. The laws of inheritance and adaptation known to us are completely sufficient to explain this exceedingly important and interesting phenomenon, which may be briefly designated as the *parallelism of individual, of paleontological, and of systematic development*, and of their respective progress and *differentiation*. No opponent of the Theory of Descent has been able to give an explanation of this extremely wonderful fact, whereas it is perfectly explained, according to the Theory of Descent, by the laws of Inheritance and Adaptation.

If we examine this parallelism of the three organic series of development more accurately, we have to add the following special distinctions.

Ontogeny, or the history of the individual development of every organism (embryology and metamorphology), presents us with a simple *unbranching* or graduated chain of forms; and so it is with that *portion of phylogeny* which comprises the paleontological history of development of the *direct ancestors* of every individual organism. But *the whole of phylogeny*—which meets us in the *natural system* of every organic tribe or phylum, and which is concerned with the investigation of the paleontological development *of all* the branches of this tribe—forms a *branching* or tree-shaped developmental series, a veritable pedigree. If we examine and compare the branches of this pedigree, and place them together according to the degree of their differentiation and perfection, we obtain the tree-shaped, branching, *systematic developmental series of comparative anatomy*. Strictly speaking, therefore, the latter is parallel only to a portion of *the whole of phylogeny*, and consequently only partially parallel to ontogeny; for ontogeny itself is parallel only to *a portion* of phylogeny.

Of late years it has been a much-disputed point which of the three great series of development is of most importance to transformism and for our knowledge of the primary relationships. This dispute is superfluous; for, as a rule, all three are of equal value; in individual cases, however, the phylogenetic investigator will have to examine every special case critically to ascertain whether he is to set greater value on the facts of paleontology, of ontogeny, or of comparative anatomy.

EDWARD DRINKER COPE (1840–1897)

PARALLELISM OR INEXACT PARALLELISM?

WHEN the early or transitional stage of a higher form is exactly the same as a permanent lower form, the parallelism is said to be "exact." . . .

When the transitional stage of the higher only resembles the lower form in some one or more features, but not in all, the parallelism is said to be "inexact." It is evident that "exact parallelism" can only exist between ancestor and descendant in the same restricted line, and can be therefore only demonstrated in the case of the nearest relatives, between which a perfect phylogeny is known. So soon as new subordinate characters are assumed, or a change in the order of appearance of charac-

SOURCE: E. D. Cope. *The Primary Factors of Organic Evolution* (Chicago: Open Court, 1896). Selections from "Parallelism," Chapter 3, pp. 200–210. Abridged. Footnotes deleted.

ters supervenes, the parallelism becomes "inexact," and such is the kind of parallelism usually observed. And it is more inexact the more widely removed in relationship are the forms compared. Thus the parallelism between the embryo man with five branchial slits, and the adult shark, is very inexact; but that between a true fish and a shark is much less inexact. That between a higher and a lower shark is still more exact, and so on. Exact parallelism in growth is called by Haeckel palingenesis or palingeny. The growth which has, through changes introduced subsequent to the origin of a line of descent, become inexact, or "falsified," is termed by the same author cenogenesis or cenogeny.

The superposition of characters which constitutes evolution, means that more numerous characters are possessed by the higher than the lower types. This involves a greater number of changes during the ontogenetic growth of each individual of the higher type. In other words, characters acquired during the phylogenetic history are continually assumed by the progressive form at earlier and earlier periods of life. This process has been metaphorically termed by Professor Alpheus Hyatt and myself "acceleration." All progressive organic evolution is by acceleration, as here described. Retrogressive evolution may be accomplished by a retardation in the rate of growth of the taxonomic characters, so that instead of adding, and accumulating them, those already possessed are gradually dropped; the adults repeating in a reversed order the progressive series, and approaching more and more the primitive embryonic stages. This process I have termed "retardation." Retardation is not however, always exact, even in retracing a true phylogenetic line, whence in such instances the process may not be correctly described as retardation. Professor Hyatt has applied to such types the term "senile," and gerontic; and to the resulting condition, the term "senility." . . .

An excellent illustration of inexact parallelism is to be found on comparison of man with the lower Vertebrata. In the structure of his extremities and dentition, he agrees with the type of Mammalia prevalent during the Eocene period (cfr. Phenacodus). Hence in these respects he resembles the immature stages of those mammals which have undergone special modifications of limbs and extremities, such as Ungulata in which cenogeny has not obliterated the early stages from the embryonic record. These forms are probably extinct. In the shape of his head man resembles the embryos of all Vertebrata, in the protuberant forehead, and vertical face and jaws. In this part of the structure most Vertebrata have grown farther from the embryonic type than has man, so that the human face may be truly said to be the result of a process of retardation. Nevertheless, in the structure of his nervous, circulatory, and for the most part, of his reproductive system, man stands at the summit of the Vertebrata. It is in those parts of his structure that are necessary to supremacy by force of body only, that man is retarded and embryonic.

OBJECTIONS TO THE DOCTRINE OF PARALLELISM

An objection to the theory of parallelism in its full sense has been recently put forward by Mr. C. Herbert Hurst. He says, "My object now is to show that in neither case can a record of the variation at any one stage of evolution be preserved in the ontogeny, much less can the ontogeny come to be a series of stages representing in proper chrono- logical order some of the stages of adult structure which have been passed through in the course of evolution." Again: "The early stages of the fish embryo are very like those of the bird embryo. These two do cor- respond to each other. The statement that the embryonic structure of a bird follows a course which is from beginning to end roughly parallel with, but somewhat divergent from, the course followed by a fish, is borne out by the actual facts. A bird does not develop into a fish and then into a reptile, and then into a bird. There is no fish-stage, no reptile- stage, in its ontogeny. The adult resembles an adult fish only very re- motely. Every earlier stage resembles the corresponding earlier stage of the fish more closely. There is a parallelism between the two ontogenies. *There is no parallelism between the ontogeny and the phylogeny of either a bird or any other animal whatever.* A seeming parallelism will fall through when closely examined." "The promise that this theory gave of serving as a guide to knowledge of past history without the labor involved in paleontological research, was indeed tempting: and where the royal road to learning has been shown by it, it is not surprising that some zoologists should have entered for the race along this road. To what goal that road has led may be learned by a comparison of the numerous theories as to the ancestry of the 'Chordata' which have been put forward by those who have adopted the theory without enquir- ing as to its validity."

I have made this quotation as showing the point of view from which the doctrine of parallelism when incorrectly stated may be assailed. There is truth in the author's accusation that embryologists who have not used their results with proper caution, have been frequently led to incorrect and even absurd results. The errors of this class of biologists are mainly due to their ignorance of species in the adult state, and their ignorance of systematic biology or taxonomy. They profess to regard this branch of the science as only suitable for beginners, and as comparatively unim- portant, as compared with their own; yet one might as well attempt the study of philology without a knowledge of alphabets, as to study phylogeny without the knowledge of natural taxonomy. The correct discrimination of species, genera, etc., imposes much greater burdens on the faculty of judgment, than does anything to be found in any science which includes observation and record only. But Mr. Hurst's statement is somewhat overdrawn, and he does not give embryologists the credit which is due to their theory of recapitulation. I think he will find the following, which I wrote in 1872 to be a correct statement of the facts, and a fair induction as to principles.

"The smaller the number of structural characters which separate two species when adult, the more nearly will the less complete of the series be identical with an incomplete stage of the higher species. As we compare species which are more and more different, the more necessarily must we confine the assertion of parallelism to single parts of the animals, and less to the whole animal. When we reach species as far removed as man and a shark, which are separated by the extent of the series of vertebrated animals, we can only say that the infant man is identical in its numerous origins of the arteries from the heart, and in the cartilaginous skeletal tissue, with the class of sharks, and in but few other respects. But the importance of this consideration must be seen from the fact that it is *on single characters of this kind that divisions of the zoölogist depend.* Hence we can say truly that one order is identical with an incomplete stage of another order, though the species of the one may never at the present time bear the same relation in their entirety to the species of the other. Still more frequently can we say that such a genus is the same in character as a stage passed by the next higher genus; but when we can say this of species, it is because their distinction is almost gone. It will then depend on the opinion of the naturalist as to whether the repressed characters are permanent or not. Parallelism is then reduced to this definition: that each separate character of every kind, which we find in. a species, represents a more or less complete stage of the fullest growth of which the character appears to be capable. In proportion as those characters in one species are contrasted with those of another by reason of their number, by so much must we confine our comparison to the characters alone, and the divisions they represent; but when the contrast is reduced by reason of the fewness of differing characters, so much the more truly can we say that the one species is really a suppressed or incomplete form of the other. The denial of this principle by the authorities cited has been in consequence of this relation having been assigned to orders and classes, when the statement should have been confined *to single characters*, and divisions characterized by them. There seems, however, to have been a want of exercise of the classifying quality or power of 'abstraction' of the mind on the part of the objectors."

HERBERT SPENCER (1820–1903)
PRINCIPLES FOR THE THEORY OF RECAPITULATION

ALREADY I have emphasized the truth that Nature is always more complex than we suppose—that there are complexities within complexities. Here we find illustrated this truth under another aspect. When seeking to formulate the arguments from Embryology, we are shown that the facts as presented in Nature are not to be expressed in the simple generalizations we at first make.

While we recognize this truth we must also recognize the truth that only by enunciation and acceptance of imperfect generalizations can we progress to perfect ones. The order of Evolution is conformed to by ideas as by other things. The advance is, and must be, from the indefinite to the definite. It is impossible to express the totality of any natural phenomenon in a single proposition. To the primary statement expressing that which is most dominant have to be added secondary statements qualifying it. We see this even in so simple a case as the flight of a projectile. The young artillery officer is first taught that a cannon-shot describes a curve treated as a parabola, though literally part of an extremely eccentric ellipse not distinguishable from a parabola. Presently he learns that atmospheric resistance, causing a continual decrease of velocity, entails a deviation from that theoretical path which is calculated on the supposition that the velocity is uniform; and this incorrectness he has to allow for. Then, further, there comes the lateral deviation due to wind, which may be appreciable if the wind is strong and the range great. To introduce him all at once to the correct conception thus finally reached would be impossible: it has to be reached through successive qualifications. And that which holds even in this simple case necessarily holds more conspicuously in complex cases.

"Arguments from Embryology" suggests a metaphor, which is, indeed, something more than a metaphor. There is an embryology of conceptions.

SOURCE: H. Spencer. *The Principles of Biology*, Revised and Enlarged edition, 2 vols. (New York: Appleton, 1898). Originally published 1864. Volume I. "The Arguments from Embryology." Chapter 5, pp. 450–467. Abridged. Footnotes deleted.

That this statement is not wholly a figure of speech, we shall see on considering that cerebral organization is a part of organization at large; and that the evolving nervous plexus which is the correlative of an evolving conception, must conform to the general law of change conformed to in the evolution of the whole nervous structure as well as in the evolution of the whole bodily structure. As the body has at first a rude form, very remotely suggesting that which is presently developed by the superposing of modifications on modifications; so the brain as a whole and its contained ideas together make up an inner world answering with extreme indefiniteness to that outer world to which it is brought by successive approximations into tolerable correspondence; and so any nervous plexus and its associated hypothesis, which refer to some external group of phenomena under investigation, have to reach their final developments by successive corrections.

This being the course of discovery must also be the course of exposition. In pursuance of this course we may therefore fitly contemplate that early *formula* of embryological development which we owe to von Baer.

Where the generalization of von Baer respecting the relations of embryos was set forth, there was given the warning, above repeated with greater distinctness, that it is only an adumbration.

In the words of his translator, he "found that in its earliest stage, every organism has the greatest number of characters in common with all other organisms in their earliest stages; that at a stage somewhat later, its structure is like the structures displayed at corresponding phases by a less extensive multitude of organisms; that at each subsequent stage, traits are acquired which successively distinguished the developing embryo from groups of embryos that it previously resembled—thus step by step diminishing the class of embryos which it still resembles; and that thus the class of similar forms is finally narrowed to the species of which it is a member."

Assuming for a moment that this generalization is true as it stands, or rather, assuming that the qualifications needed are not such as to destroy its correspondence with the average facts, we shall see that it has profound significance. For if we follow out in thought the implications—if we conceive the germs of all kinds of organisms simultaneously developing, and imagine that after taking their first step together, at the second step one half of the vast multitude diverges from the other half; if, at the next step, we mentally watch the parts of each great assemblage beginning to take two or more routes of development; if we represent to ourselves such bifurcations going on, stage after stage, in all the branches; we shall see that there must result an aggregate analogous, in its arrangement of parts, to a tree. If this vast genealogical tree be contemplated as a whole, made up of trunk, main branches, secondary branches, and so on as far as the terminal twigs; it will be perceived that all the various kinds of organisms represented by these terminal twigs, forming the periphery of the tree, will stand related to one another in small groups, which are united into groups of groups, and so on. The embryological tree, expressing the developmental relations of organisms, will be similar to the tree which symbolizes their classificatory relations. That subordination of classes, orders, genera, and species, to which naturalists have been gradually led, is just that subordination which results from the divergence and re-divergence of embryos, as they all unfold. On the hypothesis of evolution this parallelism has a meaning— indicates that primordial kinship of all organisms, and that progressive differentiation of them, which the hypothesis alleges. But on any other hypothesis the parallelism is meaningless; or rather, it raises a difficulty; since it implies either an effect without a cause or a design without a purpose.

This conception of a tree, symbolizing the relationships of types and a species derived from the same root, has a concomitant conception. The implication is that each organism, setting out from the simple nucleated cell, must in the course of its development follow the line of the trunk, some main branch, some sub-branch, some sub-sub-branch, etc., of this embryological tree; and so on till it reaches that ultimate twig representing the species of which it is a member. It must in a general way go through the particular line of forms which preceded it in all past times: there must be what has been aptly called a "recapitulation" of the successive ancestral structures. This, at least, is the conclusion necessitated by the generalization we are considering under its original crude form.

Von Baer lived in the days when the Development Hypothesis was mentioned only to be ridiculed, and he joined in the ridicule. What he conceived to be the meaning of these groupings of organisms and these relations among their embryological histories, is not obvious. The only alternative to the hypothesis of Evolution is the hypothesis of Special Creation; and as he did not accept the one it is inferable that he accepted the other. But if he did this he must in the first place have found no answer to the inquiry why organisms specially created should have the embryological kinships he described. And in the second place, after discovering that his alleged law was traversed by many and various nonconformities, he would have been without any explanation of these. Observe the positions which were open to him and the reasons which show them to be untenable.

If it be said that the conditions of the case necessitated the derivation of all organisms from simple germs, and therefore necessitated a morphological unity in their primitive states; there arises the obvious answer, that the morphological unity thus implied, is not the only morphological unity to be accounted for. Were this the only unity, the various kinds of organisms, setting out from a common primordial form, should all begin from the first to diverge individually, as so many radii from a centre; which they do not. If, otherwise, it be said that organisms were framed upon certain types, and that those of the same type continue developing together in the same direction, until it is time for them to begin putting on their specialities of structure; then the answer is, that when they do finally diverge they ought severally to develop in direct lines towards their final forms. No reason can be assigned why, having parted company, some should progress towards their final forms by irregular or circuitous routes. On the hypothesis of design such deviations are inexplicable.

The hypothesis of evolution, however, while it pre-supposes those kinships among embryos in their early forms which are found to exist, also leads us to expect nonconformities in their courses of development. If, as any rational theory of evolution implies, the progressive differentiations of types from one another during past times, have resulted from the direct and indirect effects of external conditions—if races of organisms have become different, either by immediate adaptations to unlike habits of life, or by the mediate adaptations resulting from preservation of the individuals most fitted for such habits of life, or by both; and if most embryonic changes are significant of changes that were undergone by ancestral races; then these irregularities must be anticipated. For the successive changes in modes of life pursued by successive ancestral races, can have had no regularity of sequence. In some cases they must have been more numerous than in others; in some cases they must have been greater in degree than in others; in some cases they must have been to simpler modes, in some cases to more complex modes, and in some cases to modes neither higher nor lower. Of two cognate races which diverged in the remote past, the one may have had descendants that have remained tolerably constant in their habits, while the other may have had descendants that have passed through widely-aberrant modes of life; and yet some of these last may have eventually taken to modes of life like those of the other races derived from the same stock. And if the metamorphoses of embryos indicate, in a general way, the changes of structure undergone by ancestors; then, the later embryologic changes of such two allied races will be somewhat different, though they may end in very similar forms. An illustration will make this clear. Mr. Darwin says: "Petrels are the most aërial and oceanic of birds, but in the quiet sounds of Tierra del Fuego, the *Puffinuria berardi*, in its general habits, in its astonishing power of diving, its manner of swimming, and of flying when unwillingly it takes flight, would be mistaken by any one for an auk or grebe; nevertheless, it is essentially a petrel, but with many parts of its organization profoundly modified." Now if we suppose these grebe-like habits to be continued through a long epoch, the petrel-form to be still more obscured, and the approximation to the grebe-form still closer; it is manifest that while the chicks of the grebe and the *Puffinuria* will, during their early stages of development, display that likeness involved by their common derivation from some early type of bird, the chick of the *Puffinuria* will eventually begin to show deviations, representative of the ancestral petrel-structure, and will afterwards begin to lose these distinctions and assume the grebe-structure.

Hence, remembering the perpetual intrusions of organisms on one another's modes of life, often widely different; and remembering that these intrusions have been going on from the beginning; we shall be prepared to find that the general law of embryonic parallelism is qualified by irregularities which are mostly small, in many cases considerable, and occasionally great. The hypothesis of evolution accounts for these: it does more—it implies the necessity of them.

The substitutions of organs and the suppressions of organs, are among those secondary embryological phenomena which harmonize with the belief in evolution but cannot be reconciled with any other belief. Some embryos, during early stages of development, possess organs that afterwards dwindle away, as there arise other organs to discharge the same functions. And in other embryos organs make their appearance, grow to certain points, have no functions to discharge, and disappear by absorption.

We have a remarkable instance of substitution in the temporary appliances for respiration, which some embryos exhibit. During the first phase of its development, the mammalian embryo possesses a system of blood-vessels distributed over what is called the *area vasculosa*—a system of vessels homologous with one which, among fishes, serves for aërating the blood until the permanent respiratory organs come into play. Now since this system of blood-vessels, not being in proximity to an oxygenated medium, cannot be serviceable to the mammalian embryo during development of the lungs, as it is serviceable in the embryo-fish during development of the gills, this needless formation of it is unaccountable as a result of design. But it is quite congruous with the supposition that the mammalian type arose out of lower vertebrate types. For in such case the mammalian embryo, passing through states representing in a general way those which its remote ancestors had in common with the lower

Vertebrata, develops this system of vessels in like manner with them. An instance more significant still is furnished by certain *Amphibia*. One of the facts early made familiar to the natural-history student is that the tadpole breathes by external branchiæ, and that these, needful during its aquatic life, dwindle away as fast as it develops the lungs fitting it for terrestrial life. But in one of the higher *Amphibia*, the viviparous Salamander, these transformations ordinarily undergone during the free life of the larva, are undergone by the embryo in the egg. The branchiæ are developed though there is no use for them: lungs being substituted as breathing appliances before the creature is born.

Even more striking than the substitutions of organs are the suppressions of organs. Mr. Darwin names some cases as "extremely curious; for instance, the presence of teeth in fœtal whales, which when grown up have not a tooth in their heads; . . . It has even been stated on good authority that rudiments of teeth can be detected in the beaks of certain embryonic birds." Irreconcilable with any teleological theory, these facts do not even harmonize with the theory of fixed types which are maintained by the development of all the typical parts, even where not wanted; seeing that the disappearance of these incipient organs during fœtal life spoils the typical resemblance. But while to other hypotheses these facts are stumbling-blocks, they yield strong support to the hypothesis of evolution.

Allied to these cases, are the cases of what has been called retrograde development. Many parasitic creatures and creatures which, after leading active lives for a time, become fixed, lose, in their adult states, the limbs and senses they had when young. It may be alleged, however, that these creatures could not secure the habitats needful for them, without possessing, during their larval stages, eyes and swimming appendages which eventually become useless; that though, by losing these, their organization retrogresses in one direction, it progresses in another direction; and that, therefore, they do not exhibit the needless development of a higher type on the way to a lower type. Nevertheless there are instances of a descent in organization, following an apparently-superfluous ascent. Mr. Darwin says that in some genera of cirripedes, "the larvæ become developed either into hermaphrodites having the ordinary structure, or into what I have called complemental males, and in the latter, the development has assuredly been retrograde; for the male is a mere sack, which lives for a short time, and is destitute of mouth, stomach, or other organ of importance, excepting for reproduction."

But now let us comtemplate more closely the energies at work in the unfolding embryo, or rather the energies which the facts appear to imply.

Whatever natures we ascribe to the hypothetical units proper to each kind of organism, we must conclude that from the beginning of embryonic development, they have a proclivity towards the structure of that organism. Because of their phylogenetic origin, they must tend towards the form of the primitive type; but the superposed modifications, conflicting with their initial tendency, must cause a swerving towards each successively higher type. To take an illustration:—If in the germ-plasm out of which will come a vertebrate animal there is a proclivity towards the primitive piscine form, there must, if the germ-plasm is derived from a mammal, be also from the outset a proclivity towards the mammalian form. While the initial type tends continually to establish itself the terminal type tends also to establish itself. The intermediate structures must be influenced by their conflict, as well as by the conflict of each with the proclivities towards the amphibian and reptilian types. This complication of tendencies is increased by the intervention of several other factors.

There is the factor of economy. An embryo in which the transformations have absorbed the smallest amount of energy and wasted the smallest amount of matter, will have an advantage over embryos the transformations of which have cost more in energy and matter: the young animal will set out with a greater surplus of vitality, and will be more likely than others to live and propagate. Again, in the embryos of its descendants, inheriting the tendency to economical transformation, those which evolve at the least cost will thrive more than the rest and be more likely to have posterity. Thus will result a continual shortening of the processes. We can see alike that this must take place and that it does take place. If the whole series of phylogenetic changes had to be repeated—if the embryo mammal had to become a complete fish, and then a complete amphibian, and then a complete reptile, there would be an immense amount of superfluous building up and pulling down, entailing great waste of time and of materials. Evidently these abridgments which economy entails, necessitate that unfolding embryos bear but rude resemblances to lower types ancestrally passed through—vaguely represent their dominant traits only.

From this principle of economy arise several derivative principles, which may be best dealt with separately.

In some cases the substitution of an abridged for an unabridged course of evolution causes the entire disappearance of certain intermediate forms. Structural arrangements once passed through during the unfolding are dropped out of the series.

In the evolution of these embryos with which there is not laid up a large amount of food-yolk there occurs at the outset a striking omission of this kind. When, by successive fissions, the fertilized cell has given rise to a cluster of cells constituting a hollow sphere, known as a *blastula*, the next change under its original form is the introversion of one side, so as to produce two layers in place of one. An idea of the change may be obtained by taking an india-rubber ball (having a hole through which the air may escape) and thrusting in one side until its anterior surface touches the interior surface of the other side. If the cup-shaped structure resulting be supposed to have its wide opening gradually narrowed, until it becomes the mouth of an internal chamber, it will represent what is known as a *gastrula*—a double layer of cells, of which the outer is called epiblast and the inner hypoblast (answering to ectoderm and endoderm) inclosing a cavity known as the *archenteron*, or primitive digestive sac. But now in place of this original mode of forming the *gastrula*, there occurs a mode known as delamination. Throughout its whole extent the single layer splits so as to become a double layer—one sphere of cells inclosing the other; and after this direct formation of the double layer there is a direct formation of an opening through it into the internal cavity. There is thus a shortening of the primitive process: a number of changes are left out.

Often a kindred passing over of stages at later periods of development may be observed. In certain of the *Mollusca*, as the *Patella chiton*, the egg gives origin to a free-swimming larva known as a trochosphere, from which presently comes the ordinary molluscous organization. In the highest division of the Molluscs, however, the Cephalopods, no trochosphere is formed. The nutritive matter laid up in the egg is used in building up the young animal without any indication of an ancestral larva.

Among principles derived from the principle of economy is the principle of pre-adaptation—a name which we may appropriately coin to indicate an adaptation made in advance of the time at which it could have arisen in the course of phylogenetic history.

How pre-adaptation may result from economy will be shown by an illustration which human methods of construction furnish. Let us assume that building houses of a certain type has become an established habit, and that, as a part of each house, there is a staircase of given size. And suppose that in consequence of changed conditions—say the walling in of the town, limiting the internal space and increasing ground-rents—it becomes the policy to build houses of many stories, let out in flats to different tenants. For the increased passing up and down, a staircase wider at its lower part will be required. If now the builder, when putting up the ground floor, follows the old dimensions, then after all the stories are built, the lower part of the staircase, if it is to yield equal facilities for passage, must be reconstructed. Instead of a staircase adapted to those few stories which the original type of house had, economy will dictate a pre-adaptation of the staircase to the additional stories.

On carrying this idea with us, we shall see that if from some type of organism there is evolved a type in which enlargement of a certain part is needed to meet increased functions, the greater size of this part will begin to show itself during early stages of unfolding. That unbuilding and rebuilding which would be needful were it laid down of its original size, will be made needless if from the beginning it is laid down of a larger size. Hence, in successive generations, the greater prosperity and multiplication of individuals in which this part is at the outset somewhat larger than usual, must eventually establish a marked excess in its development at an early stage. The facts agree with this inference.

Referring to the contrasts between embryos, Mr. Adam Sedgwick says that "a species is distinct and distinguishable from its allies from the very earliest stages." Whereas, according to the law of von Baer, "animals so closely allied as the fowl and duck would be indistinguishable in the early stages of development," "yet I can distinguish a fowl and a duck embryo on the second day by the inspection of a single transverse section through the trunk." This experience harmonizes with the statement of the late Prof. Agassiz, that in some cases traits characterizing the species appear at an earlier period than traits characterizing the genus.

Similar in their implications are the facts recently published by Dr. E. Mehnert, concerning the feet of pentadactyle vertebrates. A leading example is furnished by the foot in the struthious birds. Out of the original five digits the two which eventually become large while the others disappear, soon give sign of their future predominance: their early sizes being in excess of those required for the usual functional requirements in birds, and preparing the way for their special requirements in the struthious birds. Dr. Mehnert shows that a like lesson is given by the relative developments of legs and wings in these birds. Ordinarily in vertebrates the fore limbs grow more rapidly than the hind limbs; but in the ostrich, in which the hind limbs or legs have to become so large while the wings are but little wanted, the leg development goes in advance of the wing-development in early embryonic stages: there is a pre-adaptation.

Much more striking are examples furnished by creatures whose modes of existence require that they shall have enormous fertility—require that the generative system shall be very large. Ordinarily the organs devoted to maintenance of the race develop later than the organs devoted to maintenance of the individual. But this order is inverted in certain *Entozoa*. To these creatures, imbedded in nutritive matters, self-maintenance cost nothing, and the structures devoted to it are relatively of less importance than the structures devoted to race-maintenance, which, to make up for the small chance any one germ has of getting into a fit habitat, have to produce immense numbers of germs. Here the rudiments of the generative systems are the first to become visible—here, in virtue of the principle of pre-adaptation, a structure belonging to the terminal form asserts itself so early in the developmental process as almost to obliterate the structure of the initial form.

It may be that in some cases where the growth of certain organs goes in advance of the normal order, the element of time comes into play—the greater time required for construction. To elucidate this let us revert to our simile. Suppose that the staircase above instanced, or at any rate its lower part, is required to be of marble with balusters finely carved. If this piece of work is not promptly commenced and pushed on fast, it will not be completed when the rest of the house is ready: workmen and tools will still block it up at a time when it should be available. Similarly among the parts of an unfolding embryo, those in which there is a great deal of constructive work must early take such shape as will allow of this. Now of all the tissues, the nervous tissue is that which takes longest to repair when injured; and it seems a not improbable inference that it is a tissue which is slower in its histological development than others. If this be so, we may see why, in the embryos of the higher vertebrates, the central nervous system quickly grows large in comparison to the other systems—why by pre-adaptation the brain of a chick develops in advance of other organs so much more than the brain of a fish.

Yet another complication has to be noted. From the principle of economy, it seems inferable that decrease and disappearance of organs which were useful in ancestral types but have ceased to be useful, should take place uniformly but they do not. In the words of Mr. Adam Sedgwick, "some ancestral organs persist in the embryo in a functionless rudimentary (vestigial) condition and at the same time without any reference to adult structures, while other ancestral organs have disappeared without leaving a trace." This anomaly is rendered more striking when joined with the fact that some of the structures which remain conspicuous are relatively ancient, while some which have been obliterated are relatively modern—e.g., "gill slits [which date back to the fish-ancestor], have been retained in embryology, whereas other organs which have much more recently disappeared, e.g., teeth of birds, fore-limbs of snakes [dating back to the reptile ancestor], have been entirely lost." Mr. Sedgwick ascribes these anomalies to the difference between larval development and embryonic development, and expresses his general belief thus:

The conclusion here reached is that, whereas larval development must retain traces (it may be very faint) of ancestral stages of structure because they are built out of ancestral stages, embryonic development need not necessarily do so, and very often does not; that embryonic development in so far as it is a record at all, is a record of structural features of previous larval stages. Characters which disappear during free life disappear also in the embryo, but characters which though lost by the adult are retained in the larva may ultimately be absorbed into the embryonic phase and leave their traces in embryonic development.

To set forth the evidence justifying this view would encumber too much the general argument. Towards elucidation of such irregularities let me name two factors which should I think be taken into account.

Abridgment of embryonic stages cannot go on uniformly with all disused organs. Where an organ is of such size that progressive diminution of it will appreciably profit the young animal, by leaving it a larger surplus of unused material, we may expect progressive diminution to occur. Contrariwise, if the organ is relatively so small that each decrease will not, by sensibly increasing the reserve of nutriment, give the young animal an advantage over others, decrease must not be looked for: there may be a survival of it even though of very ancient origin.

Again, the reduction of a superfluous part can take place only on condition that the economy resulting from each descending variation of it, is of greater importance than are the effects of variations simultaneously occurring in other parts. If by increase or decrease of any other parts of the embryo, survival of the animal is furthered in a greater degree than by decrease of this superfluous part, then such decrease is unlikely; since it is illegitimate to count upon the repeated concurrence of favourable variations in two or more parts which are independent. So that if changes of an advantageous kind are going on elsewhere in the embryo a useless part may remain long undiminished.

Yet another cause operates, and perhaps cooperates. Embryonic survival of an organ which has become functionless, may readily happen if, during subsequent stages of development, parts of it are utilized as parts of other organs. In the words of Mr. J. T. Cunningham:

It seems to be a general fact that a structure which in metamorphosis disappears completely may easily be omitted altogether in embryonic development, while one which is modified into something else continues to pass more or less through its original larval condition.

One more factor of considerable importance should be taken into account. A disused organ which entails evil because construction of it involves needless cost, may entail further evil by being in the way. This, it seems to me, is the reason why the fore-limbs of snakes have disappeared from their embryos. When the long-bodied lizard out of which the ophidian type evolved, crept through stiff herbage, and moved its head from side to side to find openings, there resulted alternate bends of its body, which were the beginnings of lateral undulations; and we may easily see that in proportion as it thus progressed by insinuating itself through interstices, the fore-limbs, less and less used for walking, would be more and more in the way; and the lengthening of the body, increasing the undulatory motion and decreasing the use of the fore-limbs, would eventually make them absolute impediments. Hence besides the benefit in economy of construction gained by embryos in which the fore-limbs were in early stages a little less developed than usual, they would gain an advantage by having, when mature, smaller fore-limbs than usual, leading to greater facility of locomotion. There would be a double set of influences causing, through selection, a comparatively rapid decrease of these appendages. And we may I think see also, on contemplating the kind of movement, that the fore-limbs would be more in the way than the hind limbs, which would consequently dwindle with such smaller rapidity as to make continuance of the rudiments of them comprehensible.

So that while the embryonic law enunciated by von Baer is in harmony with the hypothesis of evolution, and is, indeed, a law which this hypothesis implies, the nonconformities to the law are also interpretable by this hypothesis.

Parallelism between the courses of development in species allied by remote ancestry, is liable to be variously modified in correspondence with the later ancestral forms passed through after divergence of such species. The substitution of a direct for an indirect process of formation, which we have reason to believe will show itself, must obscure the embryonic history. And the principle of economy which leads to this substitution produces effects that are very irregular and uncertain in consequence of the endlessly varied conditions. Thus several causes conspire to produce deviations from the general law.

PART FOUR

Toward a Science of
Human Development

ONLY a few years after the publication of *The Origin of Species*, the roster of notable sciences that mustered support for recapitulation theory had lengthened impressively and included biology, comparative anatomy, embryology, and zoology. The discovery of a definite number of tiny rodlike chromosomes in the nuclei of tissue cells occurred in 1883, but not until Mendel's papers were rediscovered in 1900 did investigators realize that the chromosome possessed hereditary properties. The men of science who constructed the first developmental principles, therefore, were self-assured and supremely self-confident in building towering theoretical scaffolds on pangenesis and Lamarckianism. With doctrines explaining fertilization, heredity, and variation affixed securely to the natural sciences, one major axis of evolutionary thought moved to extend the principles of recapitulation to individual physical development. Darwinian lieutenants Haeckel, Cope, and Spencer centered their attention mainly on palingenetic-cenogenetic confusion during embryological growth; every observed discrepancy in the phylogenetic-ontogenetic sequence was countered with an explanatory principle, for example, "abridgement," "inexact parallelism," "proclivity," and "economy."

Another prominent axis, comprised of equally dedicated and zealous persons, endeavored to elucidate the nature of man's psychical evolution and development. On this plane, fossil-shell deposits and anatomical comparisons among living animals, although highly useful for constructing a scale of physical evolution via recapitulation theory, were of little avail in explaining the evolution of man's self-consciousness, complex reasoning powers, and amazing cultural artifacts. Darwin had assumed in *The Origin of Species* that the theory of evolution would explain both organic and psychical evolution, but he left unanswered the critical issue of evolutionary relations among physical, mental, and emotional aspects of development. Because of the absence of any prior investigations of man's animal heritage, data on which Darwin might draw were completely lacking.

Moreover, Darwin was too preoccupied in deriving physical affinities, studying the effect of natural selection, and sustaining the hypothesis of evolution generally to single out his own species for particular attention.

Darwin need not have lost any sleep over his neglect of man in *The Origin of Species*, for no savant in the history of science ever kindled the unswerving fidelity of so brilliant a cohort. When Darwin sorely lacked direct support for species evolution, Fritz Müller rose to the occasion with a comparative study of the Crustacea. When it was time to face squarely the question of man's evolution from lower life-forms, Thomas H. Huxley stepped to the foreground. Huxley, more than any other single individual, cemented man in the scheme of evolution, and in so doing, provided the zoological framework for intensive speculation about psychical development in man.

During the quarter century that Darwin spent agonizingly preparing the manuscript for *The Origin of Species*, Huxley procured an education unmatched in his era for thoroughness and comprehensiveness. The son of an impecunious schoolmaster, Huxley initially tutored himself to gain entry to medical school. His first assignment, after he had been graduated and commissioned as assistant surgeon in the English fleet, placed him on a vessel exploring the channels north of Australia. The abundant tropical life-forms entranced Huxley, and his curiosity led him in his spare moments to embark on a series of amateur zoological investigations. The outstanding quality of his work merited his appointment as Professor of Biological Sciences in a government School of Mines in England. This appointment provided opportunity for paleontological, physiological, and comparative-anatomical research. Huxley's stature grew immensely both from public lectures and from textbooks, until eventually he was acclaimed England's leading biologist. Honors and awards were showered on him throughout the years of his distinguished professional career, and today his marble statue stands beside that of Darwin in the South Kensington Museum in London.[1]

Huxley, like Darwin, upheld species immutability at the outset of his remarkable career. But in the 1850s his investigations of the place of the human species in zoological classification convinced him that certain structural aspects of man, namely those associated with his brain, were shared by many existing lower animals. Knowing of Galileo's punishment and Lamarck's fate, Huxley ruefully admitted that he "embarked in no public discourse of these matters."[2] The appearance of *The Origin of*

[1] E. Nordenskiöld, *The History of Biology* (New York: Tudor, 1935), p. 489.
[2] T. H. Huxley, *Man's Place in Nature and Other Anthropological Essays* (New York: Appleton, 1896), p. viii.

Species, however, enormously emboldened him. Darwin's inferences, he found, were "not only in full harmony with the conclusions at which I had arrived, respecting the structural relations of apes and man, but [were] strongly supported by them."[3] Darwin might have shunned man in the *Origin,* but the dauntless Huxley would respond forthrightly to the vexing issue! For the central theme of six public lectures in 1860, scant months after Darwin's great achievement, he chose *The Relation of Man to the Lower Animals.* By 1863 he had published *Man's Place in Nature,* a full-length volume detailing the evolution of man from lower animals. In comparing skull and skeletal structures, Huxley had demonstrated that, homologously, man was more akin to the gorilla than was this imposing anthropoid to the lowly gibbon.

Huxley's masterful exposition on the evolution of man won the heartfelt gratitude of the beleaguered early evolutionary theorists at the same time that Haeckel was beginning to promote Darwinism on the European Continent. Both Haeckel and Huxley possessed an exhaustive knowledge of science and a pugnacity, alert and sensitive, and neither knowingly evaded a controversy. But Huxley exuded more clarity and lucidity. He could unravel the most involved questions, rendering them vulnerable to easily understandable answers. Where Haeckel was vituperative, Huxley tended to be supercilious. His imposing prestige and persuasiveness greatly augmented the impact of *Man's Place in Nature.* As the following excerpts from this once startling work reveal, Huxley forged incontrovertible links in the evolutionary chain from amoeba to man.

Thomas H. Huxley (1825–1895)
MAN'S PLACE IN NATURE

The question of questions for mankind—the problem which underlies all others, and is more deeply interesting than any other—is the ascertainment of the place which Man occupies in nature and of his relations to the universe of things. Whence our race has come; what are the limits of our power over nature, and of nature's power over us; to what goal we are tending; are the problems which present themselves anew

---

[3] *Ibid.,* p. ix.

Source: T. H. Huxley. *Man's Place in Nature and other Anthropological Essays* (New York: Appleton, 1896). Originally published 1863. Selections from "On the Relations of Man to the Lower Animals," Chapter 2, pp. 76–156. Abridged. Footnotes deleted.

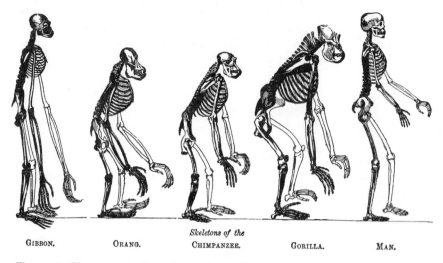

Skeletons of the

GIBBON.   ORANG.   CHIMPANZEE.   GORILLA.   MAN.

Figure 1   Photographically reduced from diagrams of the natural size (except that of the Gibbon, which was twice as large as nature), drawn by Mr. Waterhouse Hawkins from specimens in the Museum of the Royal College of Surgeons.

and with undiminished interest to every man born into the world. Most of us, shrinking from the difficulties and dangers which beset the seeker after original answers to these riddles, are contented to ignore them altogether, or to smother the investigating spirit under the feather-bed of respected and respectable tradition. But, in every age, one or two restless spirits, blessed with that constructive genius, which can only build on a secure foundation, or cursed with the spirit of mere scepticism, are unable to follow in the well-worn and comfortable track of their forefathers and contemporaries, and unmindful of thorns and stumbling-blocks, strike out into paths of their own. The sceptics end in the infidelity which asserts the problem to be insoluble, or in the atheism which denies the existence of any orderly progress and governance of things: the men of genius propound solutions which grow into systems of Theology or of Philosophy, or veiled in musical language which suggests more than it asserts, take the shape of the Poetry of an epoch.

Each such answer to the great question, invariably asserted by the followers of its propounder, if not by himself, to be complete and final, remains in high authority and esteem, it may be for one century, or it may be for twenty: but, as invariably, Time proves each reply to have been a mere approximation to the truth—tolerable chiefly on account of the ignorance of those by whom it was accepted, and wholly intolerable when tested by the larger knowledge of their successors.

In a well-worn metaphor, a parallel is drawn between the life of man and the metamorphosis of the caterpillar into the butterfly; but the comparison may be more just as well as more novel, if for its former term we take the mental progress of the race. History shows that the human mind, fed by constant accessions of knowledge, periodically grows too large for its theoretical coverings, and bursts them asunder to appear in new habiliments, as the feeding and growing grub, at intervals, casts its too narrow skin and assumes another, itself but temporary. Truly the imago state of Man seems to be terribly distant, but every moult is a step gained, and of such there have been many.

Since the revival of learning, whereby the Western races of Europe were enabled to enter upon that progress towards true knowledge, which was commenced by the philosophers of Greece, but was almost arrested in subsequent long ages of intellectual stagnation, or, at most, gyration, the human larva has been feeding vigorously, and moulting in proportion. A skin of some dimension was cast in the 16th century, and another towards the end of the 18th, while, within the last fifty years, the extraordinary growth of every department of physical science has spread among us mental food of so nutritious and stimulating a character that a new ecdysis seems imminent. But this is a process not unusually accompanied by many throes and some sickness and debility, or, it may be, by graver disturbances; so that every good citizen must feel bound to facilitate the process, and even if he have nothing but a scalpel to work withal, to ease the cracking integument to the best of his ability.

In this duty lies my excuse for the publication of these essays. For it will be admitted that some knowledge of man's position in the animate world is an indispensable preliminary to the proper understanding of his relations to the universe. . . .

The importance of such an inquiry is indeed intuitively manifest. Brought face to face with these blurred copies of himself, the least thoughtful of men is conscious of a certain shock, due perhaps, not so much to disgust at the aspect of what looks like an insulting caricature, as to the awakening of a sudden and profound mistrust of time-honoured theories and strongly-rooted prejudices regarding his own position in nature, and his relations to the under-world of life; while that which remains a dim suspicion for the unthinking, becomes a vast argument, fraught with the deepest consequences, for all who are acquainted with the recent progress of the anatomical and physiological sciences.

I now propose briefly to unfold that argument, and to set forth, in a form intelligible to those who possess no special acquaintance with anatomical science, the chief facts upon which all conclusions respecting the nature and the extent of the bonds which connect man with the brute world must be based: I shall then indicate the one immediate conclusion which, in my judgment, is justified by those facts, and I shall finally discuss the bearing of that conclusion upon the hypotheses which have been entertained respecting the Origin of Man.

The facts to which I would first direct the reader's attention, though ignored by many of the professed instructors of the public mind, are easy of demonstration and are universally agreed to by men of science; while their significance is so great, that whoso has duly pondered over them will, I think, find little to startle him in the other revelations of Biology. I refer to those facts which have been made known by the study of Development.

It is a truth of very wide, if not of universal, application, that every living creature commences its existence under a form different from and simpler than, that which it eventually attains. . . .

There is not much apparent resemblance between a barn-door Fowl and the Dog who protects the farm-yard. Nevertheless the student of development finds, not only that the chick commences its existence as an egg, primarily identical, in all essential respects, with that of the Dog, but that the yelk of this egg undergoes division—that the primitive groove arises, and that the contiguous parts of the germ are fashioned, by precisely similar methods, into a young chick, which, at one stage of its existence, is so like the nascent Dog, that ordinary inspection would hardly distinguish the two.

The history of the development of any other vertebrate animal, Lizard, Snake, Frog, or Fish, tell the same story. There is always, to begin with, an egg having the same essential structure as that of the Dog:—the yelk of that egg always undergoes division or *segmentation* as it is often called: the ultimate products of that segmentation constitute the building materials for the body of the young animal; and this is built up round a primitive groove, in the floor of which a notochord is developed. Furthermore, there is a period in which the young of all these animals resemble one another, not merely in outward form, but in all essentials of structure, so closely, that the differences between them are inconsiderable, while, in their subsequent course they diverge more and more widely from one another. And it is a general law, that, the more closely any animals resemble one another in adult structure, the longer and the more intimately do their embryos resemble one another; so that, for example, the embryos of a Snake and of a Lizard remain like one another longer than do those of a Snake and of a Bird; and the embryo of a Dog and of a Cat remain like one another for a far longer period than do those of a Dog and a Bird; or of a Dog and an Opossum; or even than those of a Dog and a Monkey.

Thus the study of development affords a clear test of closeness of structural affinity, and one turns with impatience to inquire what results are yielded by the study of the development of Man. Is he something apart? Does he originate in a totally different way from Dog, Bird, Frog, and Fish, thus justifying those who assert him to have no place in nature and no real affinity with the lower world of animal life? Or does he originate in a similar germ, pass through the same slow and gradually progressive modifications, depend on the same contrivances for protection and nutrition, and finally enter the world by the help of the same mechanism? The reply is not doubtful for a moment, and has not been doubtful any time these thirty years. Without question, the mode of origin and the early stages of the development of man are identical with those of the animals immediately below him in the scale:—without a doubt, in these respects, he is far nearer the Apes, than the Apes are to the Dog. . . .

A careful study of the resemblances and differences presented by animals has, in fact, led naturalists to arrange them into groups, or assemblages, all the members of each group presenting a certain amount of definable resemblance, and the number of points of similarity being smaller as the group is larger and *vice versa*. Thus, all creatures which agree only in presenting the few distinctive marks of animality form the *Kingdom* ANIMALIA. The numerous animals which agree only in possessing the special characters of Vertebrates form one *Sub-kingdom* of this Kingdom. Then the Sub-kingdom VERTEBRATA is subdivided into the five *Classes*, Fishes, Amphibians, Reptiles, Birds, and Mammals, and these into smaller groups called *Orders;* these into *Families* and *Genera;* while the last are finally broken up into the smallest assemblages, which are distinguished by the possession of constant, not-sexual, characters. These ultimate groups are Species.

Every year tends to bring about a greater uniformity of opinion throughout the zoological world as to the limits and characters of these groups, great and small. At present, for example, no one has the least doubt regarding the characters of the classes Mammalia, Aves, or Reptilia; nor does the question arise whether any thoroughly well-known animal should be placed in one class or the other. Again, there is a very general agreement respecting the characters and limits of the orders of Mammals, and as to the animals which are structurally necessitated to take a place in one or another order.

No one doubts, for example, that the Sloth and the Ant-eater, the Kangaroo and the Opossum, the Tiger and the Badger, the Tapir and the Rhinoceros, are respectively members of the same orders. These successive pairs of animals may, and some do, differ from one another immensely, in such matters as the proportions and structure of their limbs; the number of their dorsal and lumbar vertebræ; the adaptation of their frames to climbing, leaping, or running; the number and form of their teeth; and the characters of their skulls and of the contained brain. But, with all these differences, they are so closely connected in all the more important and fundamental characters of their organization, and so distinctly separated by these same characters from other animals, that zoologists find it necessary to group them together as members of one order. And if any new animal were discovered, and were found to present no greater difference from the Kangaroo or from the Opossum, for example, than these animals do from one another, the zoologist would not only be logically compelled to rank it in the same order with these, but he would not think of doing otherwise.

Bearing this obvious course of zoological reasoning in mind, let us endeavour for a moment to disconnect our thinking selves from the mask of humanity; let us imagine ourselves scientific Saturnians, if you will, fairly acquainted with such animals as now inhabit the Earth and employed in discussing the relations they bear to a new and singular "erect and featherless biped," which some enterprising traveller, overcoming the difficulties of space and gravitation, has brought from that distant planet for our inspection, well preserved, may be, in a cask of rum. We should all, at once, agree upon placing him among the mammalian vertebrates; and his lower jaw, his molars, and his brain, would leave no room for doubting the systematic position of the new genus among those mammals, whose young are nourished during gestation by means of a placenta, or what are called the "placental mammals."

Further, the most superficial study would at once convince us that, among the orders of placental mammals, neither the Whales, nor the hoofed creatures, nor the Sloths and Ant-eaters, nor the carnivorous Cats, Dogs, and Bears, still less the Rodent Rats and Rabbits, or the Insectivorous Moles and Hedgehogs, or the Bats, could claim our *Homo*, as one of themselves.

There would remain then, but one order for comparison, that of the Apes (using that word in its broadest sense), and the question for discussion would narrow itself to this—is Man so different from any of these Apes that he must form an order by himself? Or does he differ less from them than they differ from one another, and hence must take his place in the same order with them?

Being happily free from all real, or imaginary, personal interest in the results of the inquiry thus set afoot, we should proceed to weigh the arguments on one side and on the other, with as much judicial calmness as if the question related to a new Opossum. We should endeavour to ascertain, without seeking either to magnify or diminish them, all the characters by which our new Mammal differed from the Apes; and if we found that these were of less structural value than those which distinguish certain members of the Ape order from others universally admitted to be of the same order, we should undoubtedly place the newly discovered tellurian genus with them.

I now proceed to detail the facts which seem to me to leave us no choice but to adopt the last-mentioned course.

It is quite certain that the Ape which most nearly approaches man, in the totality of its organisation, is either the Chimpanzee or the Gorilla; and as it makes no practical difference, for the purposes of my present argument, which is selected for comparison, on the one hand, with Man, and on the other hand, with the rest of the Primates,* I shall select the latter (so far as its organisation is known)—as a brute now so celebrated in prose and verse, that all must have heard of him, and have formed some conception of his appearance. I shall take up as many of the most important points of difference between man and this remarkable creature, as the space at my disposal will allow me to discuss, and the necessities of the argument demand; and I shall inquire into the value and magnitude of these differences, when placed side by side with those which separate the Gorilla from other animals of the same order.

In the general proportions of the body and limbs there is a remarkable difference between the Gorilla and Man, which at once strikes the eye. The Gorilla's brain-case is smaller, its trunk larger, its lower limbs shorter, its upper limbs longer in proportion than those of Man.

I find that the vertebral column of a full-grown Gorilla, in the Museum of the Royal College of Surgeons, measures 27 inches along its anterior curvature, from the upper edge of the atlas, or first vertebra of the neck, to the lower extremity of the sacrum; that the arm, without the hand, is 31½ inches long; that the leg, without the foot, is 26½ inches long; that the hand is 9¾ inches long; the foot 11¼ inches long.

In other words, taking the length of the spinal column as 100, the arm equals 115, the leg 96, the hand 36, and the foot 41.

In the skeleton of a male Bosjesman, in the same collection, the proportions, by the same measurement, to the spinal column, taken as 100, are—the arm 78, the leg 110, the hand 26, and the foot 32. In a woman of the same race the arm is 83, and the leg 120, the hand and foot remaining the same. In a European skeleton I find the arm to be 80, the leg 117, the hand 26, the foot 35.

* We are not at present thoroughly acquainted with the brain of the Gorilla, and therefore, in discussing cerebral characters, I shall take that of the Chimpanzee as my highest term among the Apes.

Thus the leg is not so different as it looks at first sight, in its proportion to the spine in the Gorilla and in the Man—being very slightly shorter than the spine in the former, and between $\frac{1}{10}$ and $\frac{1}{5}$ longer than the spine in the latter. The foot is longer and the hand much longer in the Gorilla; but the great difference is caused by the arms, which are very much longer than the spine in the Gorilla, very much shorter than the spine in the Man.

The question now arises how are the other Apes related to the Gorilla in these respects—taking the length of the spine, measured in the same way, at 100. In an adult Chimpanzee, the arm is only 96, the leg 90, the hand 43, the foot 39—so that the hand and the leg depart more from the human proportion and the arm less, while the foot is about the same as in the Gorilla.

In the Orang, the arms are very much longer than in the Gorilla (122), while the legs are shorter (88); the foot is longer than the hand (52 and 48), and both are much longer in proportion to the spine.

In the other man-like Apes again, the Gibbons, these proportions are still further altered; the length of the arms being to that of the spinal column as 19 to 11; while the legs are also a third longer than the spinal column, so as to be longer than in Man, instead of shorter. The hand is half as long as the spinal column, and the foot, shorter than the hand, is about $\frac{5}{11}$ths of the length of the spinal column.

Thus *Hylobates* is as much longer in the arms than the Gorilla, as the Gorilla is longer in the arms than Man; while, on the other hand, it is as much longer in the legs than the Man, as the Man is longer in the legs than the Gorilla, so that it contains within itself the extremest deviations from the average length of both pairs of limbs.[*]

The Mandrill presents a middle condition, the arms and legs being nearly equal in length, and both being shorter than the spinal column; while hand and foot have nearly the same proportions to one another and to the spine, as in Man.

In the Spider monkey (*Ateles*) the leg is longer than the spine, and the arm than the leg; and, finally, in that remarkable Lemurine form, the Indri (*Lichanotus*), the leg is about as long as the spinal column, while the arm is not more than $\frac{11}{18}$ of its length; the hand having rather less and the foot rather more, than one third the length of the spinal column.

These examples might be greatly multiplied, but they suffice to show that, in whatever proportion of its limbs the Gorilla differs from Man,

[*] See the figures of the skeletons of four anthropoid apes and of man, drawn to scale, p. 136.

the other Apes depart still more widely from the Gorilla and that, consequently, such differences of proportion can have no ordinal value.

We may next consider the differences presented by the trunk, consisting of the vertebral column, or backbone, and the ribs and pelvis, or bony hipbasin, which are connected with it, in Man and in the Gorilla respectively.

In Man, in consequence partly of the disposition of the articular surfaces of the vertebræ, and largely of the elastic tension of some of the fibrous bands, or ligaments, which connect these vertebræ together, the spinal column, as a whole, has an elegant S-like curvature, being convex forwards in the neck, concave in the back, convex in the loins, or lumbar region, and concave again in the sacral region; an arrangement which gives much elasticity to the whole backbone, and diminishes the jar communicated to the spine, and through it to the head, by locomotion in the erect position.

Furthermore, under ordinary circumstances, Man has seven vertebræ in his neck, which are called *cervical;* twelve succeed these, bearing ribs and forming the upper part of the back, whence they are termed *dorsal;* five lie in the loins, bearing no distinct, or free, ribs, and are called *lumbar;* five, united together into a great bone, excavated in front, solidly wedged in between the hip bones, to form the back of the pelvis, and known by the name of the *sacrum,* succeed these; and finally, three or four little more or less movable bones, so small as to be insignificant, constitute the *coccyx* or rudimentary tail.

In the Gorilla, the vertebral column is similarly divided into cervical, dorsal, lumbar, sacral, and coccygeal vertebræ, and the total number of cervical and dorsal vertebræ, taken together, is the same as in Man; but the development of a pair of ribs to the first lumbar vertebra, which is an exceptional occurrence in Man, is the rule in the Gorilla; and hence, as lumbar are distinguished from dorsal vertebræ only by the presence or absence of free ribs, the seventeen "dorso-lumbar" vertebræ of the Gorilla are divided into thirteen dorsal and four lumbar, while in Man they are twelve dorsal and five lumbar.

Not only, however, does Man occasionally possess thirteen pair of ribs, but the Gorilla sometimes has fourteen pairs, while an Orang-Utan skeleton in the Museum of the Royal College of Surgeons has twelve dorsal and five lumbar vertebræ, as in Man. Cuvier notes the same number in a *Hylobates.* On the other hand, among the lower Apes, many possess twelve dorsal and six or seven lumbar vertebræ; the Douroucouli has fourteen dorsal and eight lumbar, and a Lemur (*Stenops tardigradus*) has fifteen dorsal and nine lumbar vertebræ.

The vertebral column of the Gorilla, as a whole, differs from that of Man in the less marked character of its curves, especially in the slighter convexity of the lumbar region. Nevertheless, the curves are present, and are quite obvious in young skeletons of the Gorilla and Chimpanzee which have been prepared without removal of the ligaments. In young Orangs similarly preserved on the other hand, the spinal column is either straight, or even concave forwards, throughout the lumbar region.

Whether we take these characters then, or such minor ones as those which are derivable from the proportional length of the spines of the cervical vertebræ, and the like, there is no doubt whatsoever as to the marked difference between Man and the Gorilla; but there is as little, that equally marked differences, of the very same order, obtain between the Gorilla and the lower Apes.

The Pelvis, or bony girdle of the hips, of Man is a strikingly human part of his organisation; the expanded haunch bones affording support for his viscera during his habitually erect posture, and giving space for the attachment of the great muscles which enable him to assume and to preserve that attitude. In these respects the pelvis of the Gorilla differs very considerably from his (Figure 2). But go no lower than the Gibbon, and see how vastly more he differs from the Gorilla than the latter does from Man, even in this structure. Look at the flat narrow haunch bones—the long and narrow passage—the coarse, outwardly curved, ischiatic prominences on which the Gibbon habitually rests, and which are coated by the so-called "callosities," dense patches of skin, wholly absent in the Gorilla, in the Chimpanzee, and in the Orang, as in Man!

In the lower Monkeys and in the Lemurs the difference becomes more striking still, the pelvis acquiring an altogether quadrupedal character.

But now let us turn to a nobler and more characteristic organ—that by which the human frame seems to be, and indeed is, so strongly distinguished from all others—I mean the skull. The differences between a Gorilla's skull and a Man's are truly immense (Figure 3). In the former, the face, formed largely by the massive jaw-bones, predominates over the brain-case, or cranium proper: in the latter, the proportions of the two are reversed. In the Man, the occipital foramen, through which passes the great nervous cord connecting the brain with the nerves of the body, is placed just behind the centre of the base of the skull, which thus becomes evenly balanced in the erect posture; in the Gorilla, it lies in the posterior third of that base. In the Man, the surface of the skull is comparatively smooth, and the supraciliary ridges or brow prominences usually project but little—while, in the Gorilla, vast crests are developed upon the skull, and the brow ridges overhang the cavernous orbits, like great penthouses.

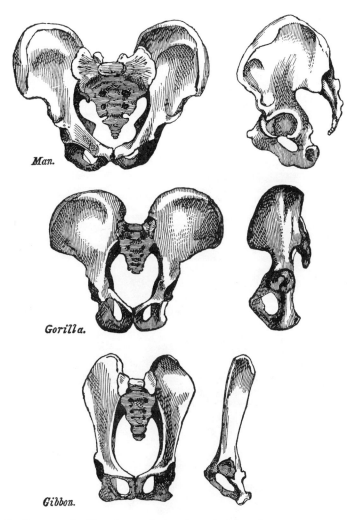

Man.

Gorilla.

Gibbon.

Figure 2 Front and side views of the bony pelvis of Man, the Gorilla, and Gibbon; reduced from drawings made from nature, of the same absolute length, by Mr. Waterhouse Hawkins.

Sections of the skulls, however, show that some of the apparent defects of the Gorilla's cranium arise, in fact, not so much from deficiency of brain-case as from excessive development of the parts of the face. The cranial cavity is not ill-shaped, and the forehead is not truly flattened or very retreating, its really well-formed curve being simply disguised by the mass of bone which is built up against it (Figure 3).

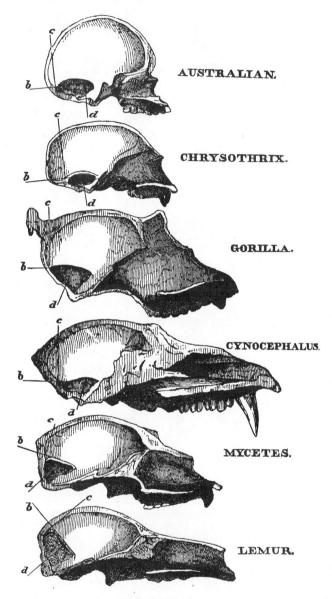

Figure 3   Sections of the skulls of Man and various Apes.

But the roofs of the orbits rise more obliquely into the cranial cavity, thus diminishing the space for the lower part of the anterior lobes of the brain, and the absolute capacity of the cranium is far less than that of Man. So far as I am aware, no human cranium belonging to an adult man has yet been observed with a less cubical capacity than 62 cubic inches, the smallest cranium observed in any race of men by Morton, measuring 63 cubic inches; while, on the other hand, the most capacious Gorilla skull yet measured has a content of not more than 34½ cubic inches. Let us assume, for simplicity's sake, that the lowest Man's skull has twice the capacity of that of the highest Gorilla.

No doubt, this is a very striking difference, but it loses much of its apparent systematic value, when viewed by the light of certain other equally indubitable facts respecting cranial capacities.

The first of these is, that the difference in the volume of the cranial cavity of different races of mankind is far greater, absolutely, than that between the lowest Man and the highest Ape, while, relatively, it is about the same. For the largest human skull measured by Morton contained 114 cubic inches, that is to say, had very nearly double the capacity of the smallest; while its absolute preponderance, of 52 cubic inches—is far greater than that by which the lowest adult male human cranium surpasses the largest of the Gorillas ($62 - 34\frac{1}{2} = 27\frac{1}{2}$). Secondly, the adult crania of Gorillas which have as yet been measured differ among themselves by nearly one-third, the maximum capacity being 34.5 cubic inches, the minimum 24 cubic inches; and, thirdly, after making all due allowance for difference of size, the cranial capacities of some of the lower Apes fall nearly as much, relatively, below those of the higher Apes as the latter fall below Man.

Thus, even in the important matter of cranial capacity, Men differ more widely from one another than they do from the Apes; while the lowest Apes differ as much, in proportion, from the highest, as the latter does from Man. The last proposition is still better illustrated by the study of the modifications which other parts of the cranium undergo in the Simian series.

It is the large proportional size of the facial bones and the great projection of the jaws which confers upon the Gorilla's skull its small facial angle and brutal character.

But if we consider the proportional size of the facial bones to the skull proper only, the little *Chrysothrix* (Figure 3) differs very widely from the Gorilla, and, in the same way, as Man does; while the Baboons (*Cynocephalus*, Figure 3) exaggerate the gross proportions of the muzzle of the great Anthropoid, so that its visage looks mild and human by comparison with theirs. The difference between the Gorilla and the

Baboon is even greater than it appears at first sight; for the great facial mass of the former is largely due to a downward development of the jaws; an essentially human character, superadded upon that almost purely forward, essentially brutal, development of the same parts which characterises the Baboon, and yet more remarkably distinguishes the Lemur.

Similarly, the occipital foramen of *Mycetes* (Figure 3), and still more of the Lemurs, is situated completely in the posterior face of the skull, or as much further back than that of the Gorilla, as that of the Gorilla is further back than that of Man; while, as if to render patent the futility of the attempt to base any broad classificatory distinction on such a character, the same group of Platyrhine, or American monkeys, to which the *Mycetes* belongs, contains the *Chrysothrix* whose occipital foramen is situated far more forward than in any other ape, and nearly approaches the position it holds in Man.

Again, the Orang's skull is as devoid of excessively developed supraciliary prominences as a Man's, though some varieties exhibit great crests elsewhere; and in some of the Cebine apes and in the *Chrysothrix*, the cranium is as smooth and rounded as that of Man himself.

What is true of these leading characteristics of the skull, holds good, as may be imagined, of all minor features; so that for every constant difference between the Gorilla's skull and the Man's, a similar constant difference of the same order (that is to say, consisting in excess or defect of the same quality) may be found between the Gorilla's skull and that of some other ape. So that, for the skull, no less than for the skeleton in general, the proposition holds good, that the differences between Man and the Gorilla are of smaller value than those between the Gorilla and some other Apes. . . .

Hardly any part of the bodily frame, then, could be found better calculated to illustrate the truth that the structural differences between Man and the highest Ape are of less value than those between the highest and the lower Apes, than the hand or the foot; and yet, perhaps, there is one organ the study of which enforces the same conclusion in a still more striking manner—and that is the Brain.

But before entering upon the precise question of the amount of difference between the Ape's brain and that of Man, it is necessary that we should clearly understand what constitutes a great, and what a small difference in cerebral structure; and we shall be best enabled to do this by a brief study of the chief modifications which the brain exhibits in the series of vertebrate animals.

The brain of a fish is very small, compared with the spinal cord into which it is continued, and with the nerves which come off from it: of the segments of which it is composed—the olfactory lobes, the cerebral hemispheres, and the succeeding divisions—no one predominates so much over the rest as to obscure or cover them; and the so-called optic lobes are, frequently, the largest masses of all. In Reptiles, the mass of the brain, relatively to the spinal cord, increases and the cerebral hemispheres begin to predominate over the other parts; while in Birds this predominance is still more marked. The brain of the lowest Mammals, such as the duck-billed Platypus and the Opossums and Kangaroos, exhibits a still more definite advance in the same direction. The cerebral hemispheres have now so much increased in size as, more or less, to hide the representatives of the optic lobes, which remain comparatively small, so that the brain of a Marsupial is extremely different from that of a Bird, Reptile, or Fish. A step higher in the scale, among the placental Mammals, the structure of the brain acquires a vast modification—not that it appears much altered externally, in a Rat or in a Rabbit, from what it is in a Marsupial—nor that the proportions of its parts are much changed, but an apparently new structure is found between the cerebral hemispheres, connecting them together, as what is called the "great commissure" or "corpus callosum." The subject requires careful re-investigation, but if the currently received statements are correct, the appearance of the "corpus callosum" in the placental mammals is the greatest and most sudden modification exhibited by the brain in the whole series of vertebrated animals—it is the greatest leap anywhere made by Nature in her brain work. For the two halves of the brain being once thus knit together, the progress of cerebral complexity is traceable through a complete series of steps from the lowest Rodent, or Insectivore, to Man; and that complexity consists, chiefly, in the disproportionate development of the cerebral hemispheres and of the cerebellum, but especially of the former, in respect to the other parts of the brain.

In the lower placental mammals, the cerebral hemispheres leave the proper upper and posterior face of the cerebellum completely visible, when the brain is viewed from above; but, in the higher forms, the hinder part of each hemisphere, separated only by the tentorium from the anterior face of the cerebellum, inclines backwards and downwards, and grows out, as the so-called "posterior lobe," so as at length to overlap and hide the cerebellum. In all Mammals, each cerebral hemisphere contains a cavity which is termed the "ventricle;" and as this ventricle is prolonged, on the one hand, forwards, and on the other downwards, into the substance of the hemisphere, it is said to have two horns or "cornua," an "anterior cornu," and a "descending cornu." When the posterior lobe is well developed, a third prolongation of the ventricular cavity extends into it, and is called the "posterior cornu."

In the lower and smaller forms of placental Mammals the surface of the cerebral hemispheres is either smooth or evenly rounded, or exhibits a very few grooves, which are technically termed "sulci," separating ridges or "convolutions" of the substance of the brain; and the smaller species of all orders tend to a similar smoothness of brain. But, in the higher orders, and especially the larger members of these orders, the grooves, or sulci, become extremely numerous, and the intermediate convolutions proportionately more complicated in their meanderings, until, in the Elephant, the Porpoise, the higher Apes, and Man, the cerebral surface appears a perfect labyrinth of tortuous foldings.

Where a posterior lobe exists and presents its customary cavity—the posterior cornu—it commonly happens that a particular sulcus appears upon the inner and under surface of the lobe, parallel with and beneath the floor of the cornu—which is, as it were, arched over the roof of the sulcus. It is as if the groove had been formed by indenting the floor of the posterior horn from without with a blunt instrument, so that the floor should rise as a convex eminence. Now this eminence is what has been termed the "Hippocampus minor;" the "Hippocampus major" being a larger eminence in the floor of the descending cornu. What may be the functional importance of either of these structures we know not.

As if to demonstrate, by a striking example, the impossibility of erecting any cerebral barrier between man and the apes, Nature has provided us, in the latter animals, with an almost complete series of gradations from brains little higher than that of a Rodent, to brains little lower than that of Man. And it is a remarkable circumstance, that though, so far as our present knowledge extends, there *is* one true structural break in the series of forms of Simian brains, this hiatus does not lie between Man and the man-like apes, but between the lower and the lowest Simians; or, in other words, between the old and new world apes and monkeys, and the Lemurs. Every Lemur which has yet been examined, in fact, has its cerebellum partially visible from above, and its posterior lobe, with the contained posterior cornu and hippocampus minor, more or less rudimentary. Every Marmoset, American monkey, old world monkey, Baboon, or Man-like ape, on the contrary, has its cerebellum entirely hidden, posteriorly, by the cerebral lobes, and possesses a large posterior cornu, with a well-developed hippocampus minor.

In many of these creatures, such as the Saimiri (*Chrysothrix*), the cerebral lobes overlap and extend much further behind the cerebellum, in proportion, than they do in man (Figure 3)—and it is quite certain that, in all, the cerebellum is completely covered behind, by well developed posterior lobes. The fact can be verified by every one who possesses the skull of any old or new world monkey. For, inasmuch as the brain in all mammals completely fills the cranial cavity, it is obvious that a cast of the interior of the skull will reproduce the general form of the brain, at any rate with such minute and, for the present purpose, utterly unimportant differences as may result from the absence of the developing membranes of the brain in the dry skull. But if such a cast be made in plaster, and compared with a similar cast of the interior of a human skull, it will be obvious that the cast of the cerebral chamber, representing the cerebrum of the ape, as completely covers over and overlaps the cast of the cerebellar chamber, representing the cerebellum, as it does in the man (Figure 4). A careless observer, forgetting that a soft structure like the brain loses its proper shape the moment it is taken out of the skull, may indeed mistake the uncovered condition of the cerebellum of an extracted and distorted brain for the natural relations of the parts; but his error must become patent even to himself if he try to replace the brain within the cranial chamber. To suppose that the cerebellum of an ape is naturally uncovered behind is a miscomprehension comparable only to that of one who should imagine that a mans' lungs always occupy but a small portion of the thoracic cavity, because they do so when the chest is opened, and their elasticity is no longer neutralized by the pressure of the air.

And the error is the less excusable, as it must become apparent to every one who examines a section of the skull of any ape above a Lemur, without taking the trouble to make a cast of it. For there is a very marked groove in every such skull, as in the human skull—which indicates the line of attachment of what is termed the *tentorium*—a sort of parchment-like shelf, or partition, which, in the recent state, is interposed between the cerebrum and cerebellum, and prevents the former from pressing upon the latter. (See Figure 3.)

This groove, therefore, indicates the line of separation between that part of the cranial cavity which contains the cerebrum, and that which contains the cerebellum; and as the brain exactly fills the cavity of the skull, it is obvious that the relations of these two parts of the cranial cavity at once informs us of the relations of their contents. Now in man, in all the old world, and in all the new world Simiæ, with one exception, when the face is directed forwards, this line of attachment of the tentorium, or impression for the lateral sinus, as it is technically called, is nearly horizontal, and the cerebral chamber invariably overlaps or projects behind the cerebellar chamber. In the Howler Monkey or *Mycetes* (see Figure 3) the line passes obliquely upwards and backwards, and the cerebral overlap is almost nil; while in the Lemurs, as in the lower mammals, the line is much more inclined in the same direction, and the cerebellar chamber projects considerably beyond the cerebral.

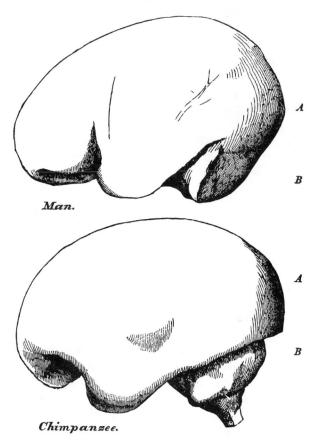

Man.

Chimpanzee.

Figure 4 Drawings of the internal casts of a Man's and of a Chimpanzee's skull, of the same absolute length, and placed in corresponding positions: (A) cerebrum; (B) cerebellum. The former drawing is taken from a cast in the Museum of the Royal College of Surgeons, the latter from the photograph of the cast of a Chimpanzee's skull, which illustrates the paper by Mr. Marshall, "On the Brain of the Chimpanzee," in the *Natural History Review* for July, 1861. The sharper definition of the lower edge of the cast of the cerebral chamber in the Chimpanzee arises from the circumstance that the tentorium remained in that skull and not in the Man's. The cast more accurately represents the brain in the Chimpanzee than in the Man; and the great backward projection of the posterior lobes of the cerebrum of the former, beyond the cerebellum, is conspicuous.

When the gravest errors respecting points so easily settled as this question respecting the posterior lobes, can be authoritatively propounded, it is no wonder that matters of observation, of no very complex character, but still requiring a certain amount of care, should have fared worse. Any one who cannot see the posterior lobe in an ape's brain is not likely to give a very valuable opinion respecting the posterior cornu or the hippocampus minor. If a man cannot see a church, it is preposterous to take his opinion about its altar-piece or painted window—so that I do not feel bound to enter upon any discussion of these points, but content myself with assuring the reader that the posterior cornu and the hippocampus minor, have now been seen—usually, at least as well developed as in man, and often better—not only in the Chimpanzee, the Orang, and the Gibbon, but in all the genera of the old world baboons and monkeys, and in most of the new world forms, including the Marmosets.

In fact, all the abundant and trustworthy evidence (consisting of the results of careful investigations directed to the determination of these very questions, by skilled anatomists) which we now possess, leads to the conviction that, so far from the posterior lobe, the posterior cornu, and the hippocampus minor, being structures peculiar to and characteristic of man, as they have been over and over again asserted to be, even after the publication of the clearest demonstration of the reverse, it is precisely these structures which are the most marked cerebral characters common to man with the apes. They are among the most distinctly Simian peculiarities which the human organism exhibits.

As to the convolutions, the brains of the apes exhibit every stage of progress, from the almost smooth brain of the Marmoset, to the Orang and the Chimpanzee, which fall but little below Man. And it is most remarkable that, as soon as all the principal sulci appear, the pattern according to which they are arranged is identical with that of the corresponding sulci of man. The surface of the brain of a monkey exhibits a sort of skeleton map of man's, and in the man-like apes the details become more and more filled in, until it is only in minor characters, such as the greater excavation of the anterior lobes, the constant presence of fissures usually absent in man, and the different disposition and proportions of some convolutions, that the Chimpanzee's or the Orang's brain can be structurally distinguished from Man's.

So far as cerebral structure goes, therefore, it is clear that Man differs less from the Chimpanzee or the Orang, than these do even from the Monkeys, and that the difference between the brains of the Chimpanzee and of Man is almost insignificant, when compared with that between the Chimpanzee brain and that of a Lemur.

It must not be overlooked, however, that there is a very striking difference in absolute mass and weight between the lowest human brain and that of the highest ape—a difference which is all the more remarkable when we recollect that a full-grown Gorilla is probably pretty nearly twice as heavy as a Bosjesman, or as many an European woman. It may be doubted whether a healthy human adult brain ever weighed less than thirty-one or two ounces, or that the heaviest Gorilla brain has exceeded twenty ounces.

This is a very noteworthy circumstance, and doubtless will one day help to furnish an explanation of the great gulf which intervenes between the lowest man and the highest ape in intellectual power;* but it has little systematic value, for the simple reason that, as may be concluded from what has been already said respecting cranial capacity, the differ-

---

* I say *help* to furnish: for I by no means believe that it was any original difference of cerebral quality, or quantity, which caused that divergence between the human and the pithecoid stirpes, which has ended in the present enormous gulf between them. It is no doubt perfectly true, in a certain sense, that all difference of function is a result of difference of structure; or, in other words, of difference in the combination of the primary molecular forces of living substance; and, starting from this undeniable axiom, objectors occasionally, and with much seeming plausibility, argue that the vast intellectual chasm between the Ape and Man implies a corresponding structural chasm in the organs of the intellectual functions; so that, it is said, the non-discovery of such vast differences proves, not that they are absent, but that Science is incompetent to detect them. A very little consideration, however, will, I think, show the fallacy of this reasoning. Its validity hangs upon the assumption, that intellectual power depends altogether on the brain—whereas the brain is only one condition out of many on which intellectual manifestations depend: the others being, chiefly, the organs of the senses and the motor apparatuses, especially those which are concerned in prehension and in the production of articulate speech.

A man born dumb, notwithstanding his great cerebral mass and his inheritance of strong intellectual instincts, would be capable of few higher intellectual manifestations than an Orang or a Chimpanzee, if he were confined to the society of dumb associates. And yet there might not be the slightest discernible difference between his brain and that of a highly intelligent and cultivated person. The dumbness might be the result of a defective structure of the mouth, or of the tongue, or a mere defective innervation of these parts; or it might result from congenital deafness, caused by some minute defect of the internal ear, which only a careful anatomist could discover.

The argument, that because there is an immense difference between a Man's intelligence and an Ape's, therefore, there must be an equally immense difference between their brains, appears to me to be about as well based as the reasoning by which one should endeavour to prove that, because there is a "great gulf" between a watch that keeps accurate time and another that will not go at all, there is therefore a great structural hiatus between the two watches. A hair in the balance-wheel, a little rust on a pinion, a bend in a tooth of the escapement, a something so slight that only the practised eye of the watchmaker can discover it, may be the source of all the difference.

And believing, as I do, with Cuvier, that the possession of articulate speech is the grand distinctive character of man (whether it be absolutely peculiar to him or not), I find it very easy to comprehend, that some equally inconspicuous structural difference may have been the primary cause of the immeasurable and practically infinite divergence of the Human from the Simian Stirps.

ence in weight of brain between the highest and the lowest men is far greater, both relatively and absolutely, than that between the lowest man and the highest ape. The latter, as has been seen, is represented by, say twelve, ounces of cerebral substance absolutely, or by 32:20 relatively; but as the largest recorded human brain weighed between 65 and 66 ounces, the former difference is represented by more than 33 ounces absolutely, or by 65:32 relatively. Regarded systematically, the cerebral differences of man and apes, are not of more than generic value; his Family distinction resting chiefly on his dentition, his pelvis, and his lower limbs.

Thus, whatever system of organs be studied, the comparison of their modifications in the ape series leads to one and the same result—that the structural differences which separate Man from the Gorilla and the Chimpanzee are not so great as those which separate the Gorilla from the lower apes.

But in enunciating this important truth I must guard myself against a form of misunderstanding, which is very prevalent. I find, in fact, that those who endeavour to teach what nature so clearly shows us in this matter, are liable to have their opinions misrepresented and their phraseology garbled, until they seem to say that the structural differences between man and even the highest apes are small and insignificant. Let me take this opportunity then of distinctly asserting, on the contrary, that they are great and significant; that every bone of a Gorilla bears marks by which it might be distinguished from the corresponding bone of a Man; and that, in the present creation, at any rate, no intermediate link bridges over the gap between *Homo* and *Troglodytes*.

It would be no less wrong than absurd to deny the existence of this chasm; but it is at least equally wrong and absurd to exaggerate its magnitude and, resting on the admitted fact of its existence, to refuse to inquire whether it is wide or narrow. Remember, if you will, that there is no existing link between Man and the Gorilla, but do not forget that there is a no less sharp line of demarcation, a no less complete absence of any transitional form between the Gorilla and the Orang, or the Orang and the Gibbon. I say, not less sharp, though it is somewhat narrower. The structural differences between Man and the Man-like apes certainly justify our regarding him as constituting a family apart from them; though, inasmuch as he differs less from them than they do from other families of the same order, there can be no justification for placing him in a distinct order.

And thus the sagacious foresight of the great lawgiver of systematic zoology, Linnæus, becomes justified, and a century of anatomical research brings us back to his conclusion, that man is a member of the same order (for which the Linnæan terms PRIMATES ought to be retained) as the Apes and Lemurs. This order is now divisible into seven families, of about equal systematic value: the first, the ANTHROPINI, contains Man alone; the second, the CATARHINI, embraces the old world apes; the third, the PLATYRHINI, all new world apes, except the Marmosets; the fourth, the ARCTOPITHECINI, contains the Marmosets; the fifth, the LEMURINI, the Lemurs—from which *Cheiromys* should probably be excluded to form a sixth distinct family, the CHEIROMYINI; while the seventh, the GALEOPITHECINI, contains only the flying Lemur *Galeopithecus*,—a strange form which almost touches on the Bats, as the *Cheiromys* puts on a Rodent clothing, and the Lemurs simulate Insectivora.

Perhaps no order of mammals presents us with so extraordinary a series of gradations as this—leading us insensibly from the crown and summit of the animal creation down to creatures, from which there is but a step, as it seems, to the lowest, smallest, and least intelligent of the placental Mammalia. It is as if nature herself had foreseen the arrogance of man, and with Roman severity had provided that his intellect, by its very triumphs, should call into prominence the slaves, admonishing the conqueror that he is but dust.

These are the chief facts, this the immediate conclusion from them to which I adverted in the commencement of this Essay. The facts, I believe, cannot be disputed; and if so, the conclusion appears to me to be inevitable.

But if Man be separated by no greater structural barrier from the brutes than they are from one another—then it seems to follow that if any process of physical causation can be discovered by which the genera and families of ordinary animals have been produced, that process of causation is amply sufficient to account for the origin of Man. In other words, if it could be shown that the Marmosets, for example, have arisen by gradual modification of the ordinary Platyrhini, or that both Marmosets and Platyrhini are modified ramifications of a primitive stock—then, there would be no rational ground for doubting that man might have originated, in the one case, by the gradual modification of a man-like ape; or, in the other case, as a ramification of the same primitive stock as those apes.

At the present moment, but one such process of physical causation has any evidence in its favour; or, in other words, there is but one hypothesis regarding the origin of species of animals in general which has any scientific existence—that propounded by Mr. Darwin. For Lamarck, sagacious as many of his views were, mingled them with so much that was crude and even absurd, as to neutralize the benefit which his originality might have effected, had he been a more sober and cautious thinker; and though I have heard of the announcement of a formula touching "the ordained continuous becoming of organic forms," it is obvious that it is the first duty of a hypothesis to be intelligible, and that a qua-quâ-versal proposition of this kind, which may be read backwards, or forwards, or sideways, with exactly the same amount of signification, does not really exist, though it may seem to do so.

At the present moment, therefore, the question of the relation of man to the lower animals resolves itself, in the end, into the larger question of the tenability, or untenability, of Mr. Darwin's views. But here we enter upon difficult ground, and it behoves us to define our exact position with the greatest care.

It cannot be doubted, I think, that Mr. Darwin has satisfactorily proved that what he terms selection, or selective modification, must occur, and does occur, in nature; and he has also proved to superfluity that such selection is competent to produce forms as distinct, structurally, as some genera even are. If the animated world presented us with none but structural differences, I should have no hesitation in saying that Mr. Darwin had demonstrated the existence of a true physical cause, amply competent to account for the origin of living species, and of man among the rest.

But, in addition to their structural distinctions, the species of animals and plants, or at least a great number of them, exhibit physiological characters—what are known as distinct species, structurally, being for the most part either altogether incompetent to breed one with another; or if they breed, the resulting mule, or hybrid, is unable to perpetuate its race with another hybrid of the same kind.

A true physical cause is, however, admitted to be such only on one condition—that it shall account for all the phenomena which come within the range of its operation. If it is inconsistent with any one phenomenon, it must be rejected; if it fails to explain any one phenomenon, it is so far weak, so far to be suspected; though it may have a perfect right to claim provisional acceptance.

Now, Mr. Darwin's hypothesis is not, so far as I am aware, inconsistent with any known biological fact; on the contrary, if admitted, the facts of Development, of Comparative Anatomy, of Geographical Distribution and of Paleontology, become connected together, and exhibit a meaning such as they never possessed before; and I, for one, am fully convinced, that if not precisely true, that hypothesis is as near an approximation to the truth as, for example, the Copernican hypothesis was to the true theory of the planetary motions.

But, for all this, our acceptance of the Darwinian hypothesis must be provisional so long as one link in the chain of evidence is wanting; and so long as all the animals and plants certainly produced by selective breeding from a common stock are fertile, and their progeny are fertile with one another, that link will be wanting. For, so long, selective breeding will not be proved to be competent to do all that is required of it to produce natural species.

I have put this conclusion as strongly as possible before the reader, because the last position in which I wish to find myself is that of an advocate for Mr. Darwin's, or any other views; if by an advocate is meant one whose business it is to smooth over real difficulties, and to persuade where he cannot convince.

In justice to Mr. Darwin, however, it must be admitted that the conditions of fertility and sterility are very ill understood, and that every day's advance in knowledge leads us to regard the hiatus in his evidence as of less and less importance, when set against the multitude of facts which harmonize with, or receive an explanation from, his doctrines.

I adopt Mr. Darwin's hypothesis, therefore, subject to the production of proof that physiological species may be produced by selective breeding; just as a physical philosopher may accept the undulatory theory of light, subject to the proof of the existence of the hypothetical ether; or as the chemist adopts the atomic theory, subject to the proof of the existence of atoms; and for exactly the same reasons, namely, that it has an immense amount of primâ facie probability: that it is the only means at present within reach of reducing the chaos of observed facts to order; and lastly, that it is the most powerful instrument of investigation which has been presented to naturalists since the invention of the natural system of classification, and the commencement of the systematic study of embryology.

But even leaving Mr. Darwin's views aside, the whole analogy of natural operations furnishes so complete and crushing an argument against the intervention of any but what are termed secondary causes, in the production of all the phenomena of the universe; that, in view of the intimate relations between Man and the rest of the living world, and between the forces exerted by the latter and all other forces, I can see no excuse for doubting that all are co-ordinated terms of Nature's great progression, from the formless to the formed—from the inorganic to the organic—from blind force to conscious intellect and will.

Comment

SEVERAL years after Huxley had demonstrated the evolution of both cerebral convolutions in the brain and increased coordination within the nervous system, Darwin, tirelessly documenting evidence for evolution wherever he happened to find it, turned his attention to evolutionary relations among the physical, mental, and emotional attributes in higher species. In the 1830s he had amassed a sheath of notes on which he planned to base a discussion of the nature of man. Not until 1871, however, three years after he had consummated his two-volume text on pangenesis, was he finally able to publish *The Descent of Man and Selection in Relation to Sex*. Although the title leads one to anticipate an elaborate exposition on the evolution of the human species, in actuality the book deals almost wholly with the origins of secondary sexual characteristics in lower animals. Darwin became intrigued with such outward physical features as the majestic horns of stags, the resplendent coloration of male butterflies, and the richly hued comb of cocks. The primary emphasis of the text is on showing how these characteristics might have arisen as a result of special sexual selection. The stronger and more attractive males, Darwin held, have been consistently victorious in competing for the favor of the females; hence they have transmitted their characteristics obtained by natural selection and by acquired characters to their progeny.

In both *Descent* and his later *The Expression of the Emotions in Man and Animals*, Darwin exhibited a magnificent genius for demonstrating fundamental relationships among different levels of animal and human behavior. He indulged in a fair measure of anthropomorphism, attributing all kinds of human ideas, values, and inclinations to members of the animal world. Although much of his evidence was comprised of the casual observations of breeders and naturalists, his countless anecdotes, woven into whole fabric, impressively suggested that animals imitate one another, maintain parental affections, and express sympathy, grief, anger, fear, astonishment, pride, disappointment, and disgust in much the same way as man does. Indeed, most twentieth-century comparative psychologists agree that lower animals parallel man in several manifestations of emotional behavior; Darwin, however, also hypothesized that the broad correspondence between the emotional life of man and that of animals suggested the probability of a similar resemblance in intellectual functions.

Darwin was absolutely convinced that fundamental differences between the intellectual functions operative in man and those in other mammals were nonexistent: "The mental faculties of man and the lower animals do not differ in kind, though immensely in degree."[4] Darwin assumed that discrepancies in rank on the phylogenetic scale determined differences in intellectual behavior. Moreover, from the viewpoint of recapitulation theory, the homo sapiens at given stages in his growth would parallel the maximum intellectual attainment of lower animals. The con-

[4] C. Darwin, *The Descent of Man and Selection in Relation to Sex*, Second Revised Edition (New York: Appleton, 1922), p. 147.

clusion was inescapable that lower animals must have the same kind of intelligence as the higher ones, but in less abundant measure. Accordingly, in *Descent*, Darwin viewed the mind as representing a culmination in the organic series and, thus, as subject to the same developmental laws as the physical body:

If no organic being excepting man had possessed any mental power, or if his powers had been of a wholly different nature from those of the lower animals, then we should never have been able to convince ourselves that our high faculties had been gradually developed. But it can be shown that there is no fundamental difference of this kind. We must admit that there is a much wider interval in mental power between one of the lowest fishes, as a lamprey or lancelet, and one of the higher apes, than between an ape and a man; yet this interval is filled up by numberless gradations.

Nor is the difference slight in moral disposition between a barbarian, such as the man described by the old navigator Byron, who dashed his child on the rocks for dropping a basket of sea-urchins, and a Howard or Clarkson; and in intellect, between a savage who uses hardly any abstract terms, and a Newton or Shakespeare. Differences of this kind between the highest men of the highest races and the lowest savages are connected by the finest gradations.[5]

So strongly entrenched were the basic dogma of *Descent of Man* and *Expression of Emotions* that the possibility of distinctions in kind between intellectual functions of animals and man was unthinkable to early evolutionary theorists. Most were enthusiastically committed to Lamarckianism and recapitulation, and a few were virtually inebriated by the proposition that animals and children display similar emotions and thoughts. Recapitulation theory dictated that mental continuity *must* exist and that man must head the parade of evolutionary progress; hence, in their naïve anthropomorphizing, a wild assortment of motives, attitudes, customs, and cognitions were attributed to pristine infrahumans.

No one among the resolute romanticists articulated so rapturously and fancifully upon the evolutionary functions of man's physical, emotional, and intellectual powers as did Henry Drummond: "No one who has felt the force of the recapitulation argument for the evolution of bodily function, even making all allowances for the differences of the things compared, will deny the weight of the corresponding argument for the evolution of mind."[6] Drummond was only a child of eight when *The Origin of Species* was published, and barely twenty when *Descent* appeared. Haeckel and Spencer had inextricably fused spiritualistic and

[5] *Ibid.*, pp. 65–66.
[6] H. Drummond, *The Ascent of Man*, Ninth Edition (New York: James Pott, 1899), p. 135.

naturalistic factors in ontogenetic growth with the theory of recapitulation, and to the youthful Drummond the disputes between the metaphysicians and the evolutionists seemed to have spent their force. The recapitulation theory showed how individuals grew and pointed to the divine end that was to be the culmination of their growth.

Drummond, from the vantage of his post as Professor of Natural Sciences at the University of Glascow, within the span of a few prolific years promulgated a series of publications calculated to inspire further even the most ardent evolutionist, for example, *Natural Law in the Spiritual World* (1888), *The Changed Life* (1891), *The Greatest Thing in the World* (1893), and *The Ascent of Man* (1894). These works, when viewed in the cool repose of historical retrospect, probably shed more illumination on the excesses to which uncurbed enthusiasm led a few evolutionary theorists than on the future of man. The following passages from *The Ascent of Man* illustrate the kind of ecstatic expressions that were characteristic of those engendered by the theory of recapitulation. One probably could not now defend Drummond's account as approaching even a quasi-naturalistic discussion of personality development, but to many individuals in 1900 it unquestionably represented a good start.

HENRY DRUMMOND (1851–1897)
THE ASCENT OF MAN

THE ASCENT OF THE BODY

THE earliest home of Primitive Man was a cave in the rocks—the simplest and most unevolved form of human habitation. One day, perhaps driven by the want within his hunting-grounds of the natural cave, he made himself a hut—an artificial cave. This simple dwelling-place was a one-roomed hut or tent of skin and boughs, and so completely does it satisfy the rude man's needs that down to the present hour no ordinary savage improves upon the idea. But as the hut surrounds itself with other huts and grows into a village, a new departure must take place. The village must have its chief, and the chief, in virtue of his larger life, requires

SOURCE: H. Drummond. *The Ascent of Man*, Ninth Edition (New York: James Pott, 1899). Originally published 1894. Selections from "The Ascent of the Body," Chapter 1, pp. 59–69, and "The Arrest of the Body," Chapter 3, pp. 99–109. Abridged. Footnotes deleted.

a more spacious home. Each village, therefore, adds to its one-roomed hut, a hut with two rooms. From the two-roomed hut we pass, among certain tribes, to three- and four-roomed huts, and finally to the many-chambered lodge of the Head-Chief or King.

This passage from the simple cave to the many-chambered lodge is an Evolution, and a similar development may be traced in the domestic architecture of all civilized societies. The laborer's cottage of modern England and the shieling of the Highland crofter are the survivals of the one-roomed hut of Primitive Man, scarcely changed in any essential with the lapse of years. In the squire's mansion also, and the nobleman's castle, we have the representatives, but now in an immensely developed form, of the many-roomed home of the chief. The steps by which the cottage became the castle are the same as those by which the cave in the rocks became the lodge of the chief. Both processes wear the hall-mark of all true development—they arise in response to growing necessities, and they are carried out by the most simple and natural steps.

In this evolution of a human habitation we have an almost perfect type of the evolution of that more august habitation, the complex tenement of clay in which Man's mysterious being has its home. The Body of Man is a structure of a million, or a million million cells. And the history of the unborn babe is, in the first instance, a history of additions, of room being added to room, of organ to organ, of faculty to faculty. The general process, also, by which this takes place is almost as clear to modern science as in the case of material buildings. A special class of observers has carefully watched these secret and amazing metamorphoses, and so wonderful has been their success with mind and microscope that they can almost claim to have seen Man's Body made. The Science of Embryology undertakes to trace the development of Man from a stage in which he lived in a one-roomed house—a physiological cell. Whatever the multitude of rooms, the millions and millions of cells, in which to-day each adult carries on the varied work of life, it is certain that when he first began to be he was the simple tenant of a single cell. Observe, it is not some animal-ancestor or some human progenitor of Man that lived in this single cell—that may or may not have been—but the individual Man, the present occupant himself. We are dealing now not with phylogeny—the history of the race—but with ontogeny—the problem of Man's Ascent from his own earlier self. And the point at the moment is not that the race ascends; it is that each individual man has once, in his own life-time, occupied a single cell, and starting from that humble cradle, has passed through stage after stage of differentiation, increase, and development, until the myriad-roomed adult-form was attained. Whence that first cradle came is at present no matter. . . .

Between the early cell and the infant's formed body, the ordinary observer sees the uneventful passage of a few brief months. But the evolutionist sees concentrated into these few months the labor and the progress of incalculable ages. Here before him is the whole stretch of time since life first dawned upon the earth; and as he watches the nascent organism climbing to its maturity he witnesses a spectacle which for strangeness and majesty stands alone in the field of biological research. What he sees is not the mere shaping or sculpturing of a Man. The human form does not begin as a human form. It begins as an animal; and at first, and for a long time to come there is nothing wearing the remotest semblance of humanity. What meets the eye is a vast procession of lower forms of life, a succession of strange inhuman creatures emerging from a crowd of still stranger and still more inhuman creatures; and it is only after a prolonged and unrecognizable series of metamorphoses that they culminate in some faint likeness to the image of him who is one of the newest yet the oldest of created things. Hitherto we have been taught to look among the fossiliferous formations of Geology for the buried lives of the earth's past. But Embryology has startled the world by declaring that the ancient life of the earth is not dead. It is risen. It exists to-day in the embryos of still-living things, and some of the most archaic types find again a resurrection and a life in the frame of man himself.

It is an amazing and almost incredible story. The proposition is not only that Man begins his earthly existence in the guise of a lower animal-embryo, but that in the successive transformations of the human embryo there is reproduced before our eyes a visible, actual, physical representation of part of the life-history of the world. Human Embryology is a condensed account, a recapitulation or epitome of some of the main chapters in the Natural History of the world. The same processes of development which once took thousands of years for their consummation are here condensed, foreshortened, concentrated into the space of weeks. Each platform reached by the human embryo in its upward course represents the embryo of some lower animal which in some mysterious way has played a part in the pedigree of the human race, which may itself have disappeared long since from the earth, but is now and forever built into the inmost being of Man. These lower animals, each at its successive stage, have stopped short in their development; Man has gone on. At each fresh advance his embryo is found again abreast of some other animal-embryo a little higher in organization than that just passed. Continuing his ascent that also is overtaken, the now very complex embryo making up to one animal-embryo after another until it has distanced all in its series and stands alone. As the modern stem-winding watch contains the old clepsydra and all the most useful features in all the timekeepers that were ever made; as the Walter printing-press contains the rude hand-machine of Gutenberg, and all the best in all the machines that followed it; as the modern locomotive of to-day contains the engine of Watt, the locomotive of Hedley, and most of the improvements of succeeding years, so Man contains the embryonic bodies of earlier and humbler and clumsier forms of life. Yet in making the Walter press in a modern workshop, the artificer does not begin by building again the press of Gutenberg, nor in constructing the locomotive does the engineer first make a Watt's machine and then incorporate the Hedley, and then the Stephenson, and so on through all the improving types of engines that have led up to this. But the astonishing thing is that, in making a Man, Nature does introduce the framework of these earlier types, displaying each crude pattern by itself before incorporating it in the finished work. The human embryo, to change the figure, is a subtle phantasmagoria, a living theatre in which a weird transformation scene is being enacted, and in which countless strange and uncouth characters take part. Some of these characters are well-known to science, some are strangers. As the embryo unfolds, one by one these animal actors come upon the stage, file past in phantom-like procession, throw off their drapery, and dissolve away into something else. Yet, as they vanish, each leaves behind a vital portion of itself, some original and characteristic memorial, something itself has made or won, that perhaps it alone could make or win—a bone, a muscle, a ganglion, or a tooth—to be the inheritance of the race. And it is only after nearly all have played their part and dedicated their gift, that a human form, mysteriously compounded of all that has gone before, begins to be discerned in their midst.

The duration of this process, the profound antiquity of the last survivor, the tremendous height he has scaled, are inconceivable by the faculties of Man. But measure the very lowest of the successive platforms passed in the ascent, and see how very great a thing it is even to rise at all. The single cell, the first definite stage which the human embryo attains, is still the adult form of countless millions both of animals and plants. Just as in modern England the millionaire's mansion—the evolved form— is surrounded by laborers' cottages—the simple form—so in Nature, living side by side with the many-celled higher animals, is an immense democracy of unicellular artizans. These simple cells are perfect living things. The earth, the water, and the air teem with them everywhere. They move, they eat, they reproduce their like. But one thing they do not do—they do not rise. These organisms have, as it were, stopped short in the ascent of life. And long as evolution has worked upon the earth, the vast numerical majority of plants and animals are still at this low stage of being. So minute are some of these forms that if their one-roomed huts were arranged in a row it would take twelve thousand to form a street a single inch in length. In their watery cities—for most of them are Lake-Dwellers—a population of eight hundred thousand million could be accommodated within a cubic inch. Yet, as there was a period in human history when none but cave-dwellers lived in Europe, so was there a time when the highest forms of life upon the globe were these microscopic things. See, therefore, the meaning of Evolution from the want of it. In a single hour or second the human embryo attains the platform which represents the whole life-achievement of myriads of generations of created things, and the next day or hour is immeasurable centuries beyond them. . . .

THE ARREST OF THE BODY

"On the Earth there will never be a higher Creature than Man."* It is a daring prophecy, but every probability of Science attests the likelihood of its fulfilment. The goal looked forward to from the beginning of time has been attained. Nature has succeeded in making a Man; she can go no further; Organic Evolution has done its work.

This is not a conceit of Science, nor a reminiscence of the pre-Copernican idea that the centre of the universe is the world, and the centre of the world Man. It is the sober scientific probability that with the body of Man the final fruit of the tree of Organic Evolution has appeared; that the highest possibilities open to flesh and bone and nerve and muscle have now been realized; that in whatever direction, and with whatever materials, Evolution still may work, it will never produce any material thing more perfect in design or workmanship; that in Man, in short, about this time in history, we are confronted with a stupendous crisis in Nature,—the Arrest of the Animal. The Man, the Animal Man, the Man of Organic Evolution, it is at least certain, will not go on. It is another Man who will go on, a Man within this Man; and that he may go on the first Man must stop. Let us try for a moment to learn what it is to stop. Nothing could teach Man better what is meant by his going on.

One of the most perfect pieces of mechanism in the human body is the Hand. How long it has taken to develop may be dimly seen by a glance at the long array of less accurate instruments of prehension which shade away with ever decreasing delicacy and perfectness as we descend the scale of animal life. At the bottom of that scale is the Amœba.

* Fiske, *Destiny of Man*, p. 26. What follows owes much to this suggestive *brochure*.

It is a speck of protoplasmic jelly, headless, footless, and armless. When it wishes to seize the microscopic particle of food on which it lives a portion of its body lengthens out, and, moving towards the object, flows over it, engulfs it, and melts back again into the body. This is its Hand. At any place, and at any moment, it creates a Hand. Each Hand is extemporized as it is needed; when not needed it is not. Pass a little higher up the scale and observe the Sea-Anemone. The Hand is no longer extemporized as occasion requires, but lengthened portions of the body are set apart and kept permanently in shape for the purpose of seizing food. Here, in the capital of twining tentacles which crowns the quivering pillar of the body, we get the rude approximation to the most useful portion of the human Hand—the separated fingers. It is a vast improvement on the earlier Hand, but the jointless digits are still imperfect; it is simply the Amœbe Hand cut into permanent strips.

Passing over a multitude of intermediate forms, watch, in the next place, the Hand of an African Monkey. Note the great increase in usefulness due to the muscular arm upon which the Hand is now extended, and the extraordinary capacity for varied motion afforded by the threefold system of jointing at shoulder, elbow, and wrist. The Hand itself is almost the human Hand; there are palm and nail and articulated fingers. But observe how one circumstance hinders the possessor from taking full advantage of these great improvements—this Hand has no thumb, or if it has, it is but a rudiment. To estimate the importance of this apparently insignificant organ, try for a moment without using the thumb to hold a book, or write a letter, or do any single piece of manual work. A thumb is not merely an additional finger, but a finger so arranged as to be *opposable to the other fingers*, and thus possesses a practical efficacy greater than all the fingers put together. It is this which gives the organ the power to seize, to hold, to manipulate, to do higher work; this simple mechanical device in short endows the Hand of intelligence with all its capacity and skill. Now there are animals, like the Colobi, which have no thumb at all; there are others, like the Marmoset, which possess the thumb, but in which it is not opposable; and there are others, the Chimpanzee for instance, in which the Hand is in all essentials identical with Man's. In the human form the thumb is a little longer, and the whole member more delicate and shapely, but even for the use of her highest product, Nature has not been able to make anything much more perfect than the hand of this anthropoid ape.

Is the Hand then finished? Can Nature take out no new patent in this direction? Is the fact that no novelty is introduced in the case of Man a proof that the ultimate Hand has appeared? By no means. And yet it is probable for other reasons that the ultimate Hand has appeared; that there will never be a more perfectly handed animal than Man. And why? Because the causes which up to this point have furthered the evolution of the Hand have begun to cease to act. In the perfecting of the bodily organs, as of all other mechanical devices, necessity is the mother of invention. As the Hand was given more and more to do, it became more and more adapted to its work. Up to a point, it responded directly to each new duty that was laid upon it. But only up to a point. There came a time when the necessities became too numerous and too varied for adaptation to keep pace with them. And the fatal day came, the fatal day for the Hand, when he who bore it made a new discovery. It was the discovery of Tools. Henceforth what the Hand used to do, and was slowly becoming adapted to do better, was to be done by external appliances. So that if anything new arose to be done, or to be better done, it was not a better Hand that was now made but a better tool. Tools are external Hands. Levers are the extensions of the bones of the arm. Hammers are callous substitutes for the fist. Knives do the work of nails. The vice and the pincers replace the fingers. The day that Cave-man first split the marrow bone of a bear by thrusting a stick into it, and striking it home with a stone—that day the doom of the Hand was sealed.

But has not Man to make his tools, and will not that induce the development of the Hand to an as yet unknown perfection? No. Because tools are not made with the Hand. They are made with the Brain. For a time, certainly, Man had to make his tools, and for a time this work recompensed him physically, and the arm became elastic and the fingers dexterous and strong. But soon he made tools to make these tools. In place of shaping things with the Hand, he invented the turning-lathe; to save his fingers he requisitioned the loom; instead of working his muscles he gave out the contract to electricity and steam. Man, therefore, from this time forward will cease to develop materially these organs of his body. If he develops them outside his body, filling the world everywhere with artificial Hands, supplying the workshops with fingers more intricate and deft than Organic Evolution could make in a millennium, and loosing energies upon them infinitely more gigantic than his muscles could generate in a lifetime, it is enough. Evolution after all is a slow process. Its great labor is to work up to a point where Invention shall be possible, and where, by the powers of the human mind, and by the mechanical utilization of the energies of the universe, the results of ages of development may be anticipated. Further changes, therefore, within the body itself are made unnecessary. Evolution has taken a new departure. For the Arrest of the Hand is not the cessation of Evolution but its immense acceleration, and the redirection of its energies into higher channels.

Take up the functions of the animal body one by one, and it will be seen how the same arresting finger is laid upon them all. To select an additional illustration, consider the power of Sight. Without pausing to trace the steps by which the Eye has reached its marvellous perfection, or to estimate the ages spent in polishing its lenses and adjusting the diaphragms and screws, ask the simple question whether, under the conditions of modern civilization, anything now is being added to its quickening efficiency, or range. Is it not rather the testimony of experience that if anything its power has begun to wane? Europe even now affords the spectacle of at least one nation so short-sighted that it might almost be called a myopic race. The same causes, in fact, that led to the Arrest of the Hand are steadily working to stop the development of the Eye. Man, when he sees with difficulty, does not now improve his Eye; he puts on a *pince-nez*. Spectacles—external eyes—have superseded the work of Evolution. When his sight is perfect up to a point, and he desires to examine objects so minute as to lie beyond the limit of that point, he will not wait for Evolution to catch up upon his demand and supply him, or his children's children, with a more perfect instrument. He will invest in a microscope. Or when he wishes to extend his gaze to the moon and stars, he does not hope to reach to-morrow the distances which to-day transcend him. He invents the telescope. Organic Evolution has not even a chance. In every direction the external eye has replaced the internal, and it is even difficult to suggest where any further development of this part of the animal can now come in. There are still, and in spite of all instruments, regions in which the unaided organs of Man may continue to find a field for the fullest exercise, but the area is slowly narrowing, and in every direction the appliances of Science tempt the body to accept those supplements of the Arts, which, being accepted, involve the discontinuance of development for all the parts concerned. Even where a mechanical appliance, while adding range to a bodily sense, has seemed to open a door for further improvement, some correlated discovery in a distant field of science, as by some remorseless fate, has suddenly taken away the opportunity and offered to the body only an additional inducement for neglect. Thus it might be thought that the continuous use of the telescope, in the attempt to discover more and more indistinct and distant heavenly bodies, might tend to increase the efficiency of the Eye. But that expectation has vanished already before a further fruit of Man's inventive power. By an automatic photographic apparatus fixed to the telescope, an Eye is now created vastly more delicate and in many respects more efficient than the keenest eye of Man. In at least five important particulars the Photographic Eye is the superior of the Eye of Organic Evolution. It can see where the human Eye, even with the best aids of optical instruments, sees nothing at all; it can distinguish certain objects with far greater clearness and definition; owing to the rapidity of its action it can instantly detect changes which are too sudden for the human eye to follow; it can look steadily for hours without growing tired; and it can record what it sees with infallible accuracy upon a plate which time will not efface. How long would it take Organic Evolution to arrive at an Eye of such amazing quality and power? And with such a piece of mechanism available, who, rather than employ it even to the neglect of his organs of vision, would be content to await the possible attainment of an equal perfection by his descendants some million years hence? Is there not here a conspicuous testimony to the improbability of a further Evolution of the sense of Sight in civilized communities—in other words, another proof of the Arrest of the Animal? What defiance of Evolution, indeed, what affront to Nature, is this? Man prepares a complicated telescope to supplement the Eye created by Evolution, and no sooner is it perfected than it occurs to him to create another instrument to aid the Eye in what little work is left for it to do. That is to say, he first makes a mechanical supplement to his Eye, then constructs a mechanical Eye, which is better than his own, to see through it, and ends by discarding, for many purposes, the Eye of Organic Evolution altogether.

As regards the other functions of civilized Man, the animal in almost every direction has reached its maximum. Civilization—and the civilized state, be it remembered, is the ultimate goal of every race and nation—is always attended by deterioration of some of the senses. Every man pays a definite price or forfeit for his taming. The sense of smell, compared with its development among the lower animals, is in civilized Man already all but gone. Compared even with a savage, it is an ascertained fact that the civilized Man in this respect is vastly inferior. So far as hearing is concerned, the main stimulus—fear of surprise by enemies—has ceased to operate, and the muscles for the erection of the ears have fallen into disuse. The ear itself in contrast with that of the savage is slow and dull, while compared with the quick sense of the lower animals, the organ is almost deaf. The skin, from the continuous use of clothes, has forfeited its protective power. Owing to the use of viands cooked, the muscles of the jaw are rapidly losing strength. The teeth, partly for a similar reason, are undergoing marked degeneration. The third molar, for instance, among some nations is already showing symptoms of suppression, and that this threatens ultimate extinction may be reasoned from the fact that the anthropoid apes have fewer teeth than the lower monkeys, and these fewer than the preceding generation of insectivorous mammals.

In an age of vehicles and locomotives the lower limbs find their occupation almost gone. For mere muscle, that on which his whole life once depended, Man has almost now no use. Agility, nimbleness, strength, once a stern necessity, are either a luxury or a pastime. Their outlet is the cricket-field or the tennis-court. To keep them up at all artificial means—dumb-bells, parallel-bars, clubs—have actually to be devised. Vigor of limb is not to be found in common life, we look for it in the Gymnasium; agility is relegated to the Hippodrome. Once all men were athletes; now you have to pay to see them. More or less with all the animal powers it is the same. To some extent at least some phonograph may yet speak for us, some telephone hear for us, the typewriter write for us, chemistry digest for us, and incubation nurture us. So everywhere the Man as Animal is in danger of losing ground. He has expanded until the world is his body. The former body, the hundred and fifty pounds or so of organized tissue he carries about with him, is little more than a mark of identity. It is not *he* who is there, he cannot be there, or anywhere, for he is everywhere. The material part of him is reduced to a symbol; it is but a link with the wider framework of the Arts, a belt between machinery and machinery. His body no longer generates, but only utilizes energy; alone he is but a tool, a medium, a turncock of the physical forces.

Now with what feelings do we regard all this? Is not the crowning proof of the thesis under review that we watch this evidence accumulating against the body with no emotion and hear the doom of our clay pronounced without a regret? It is nothing to aspiring Man to watch the lower animals still perfecting their mechanism and putting all his physical powers and senses to the shame. It is nothing to him to be distanced in nimbleness by the deer: has he not his bullet? Or in strength by the horse: has he not bit and bridle? Or in vision by the eagle: his field-glass out-sees it. How easily we talk of the body as a thing without us, as an impersonal *it*. And how naturally when all is over, do we advertise its irrelevancy to *ourselves* by consigning its borrowed atoms to the anonymous dust. The fact is, in one aspect, the body, to Intelligence, is all but an absurdity. One is almost ashamed to have one. The idea of having to feed it, and exercise it, and humor it, and put it away in the dark to sleep, to carry it about with one everywhere, and not only it but its wardrobe—other material things to make this material thing warm or keep it cool—the whole situation is a comedy. But judge what it would be if this exacting organism went on evolving, multiplied its members, added to its intricacy, waxed instead of waned? So complicated is it already that one shrinks from contemplating a future race having to keep in repair an apparatus more involved and delicate. The practical advantage is enormous of having all improvements henceforth external, of having insensate organs made of iron and steel rather than of wasting muscle and palpitating nerve. For these can be kept at no physiological cost, they cannot impede the other machinery, and when that finally comes to the last break-down there will be the fewer wheels to stop.

So great indeed is the advantage of increasing mechanical supplements to the physical frame rather than exercising the physical frame itself, that this will become nothing short of a temptation; and not the least anxious task of future civilization will be to prevent degeneration beyond a legitimate point, and keep up the body to its highest working level. For the first thing to be learned from these facts is not that the Body is nothing and must now decay, but that it is most of all and more than ever worthy to be preserved. The moment our care of its slackens, the Body asserts itself. It comes out from under arrest—which is the one thing to be avoided. Its true place by the ordained appointment of Nature is where it can be ignored; if through disease, neglect or injury it returns to consciousness, the effect of Evolution is undone. Sickness is degeneration; pain the signal to resume the evolution. On the one hand, one must "reckon the Body dead;" on the other, one must think of it in order not to think of it.

Comment

WHILE Drummond was making grand pronouncements, another recapitulation theorist, George John Romanes, struggled to complete a thorough description of the steps in mental evolution. Romanes deserves to be honored as a pioneer among cognitive theorists. Just as Spencer committed himself to arguing the case for physical recapitulation, Romanes consecrated himself to tracing the entire history of mental evolution, "from its first beginning in protoplasmic life up to its culmination in the brain of civilized man."[7] Convinced of the existence of a scale of genetic progression, Romanes set out to provide a standard against which all intellectual and emotional acts might be evaluated. *Animal Intelligence*, which appeared in 1882, was widely acclaimed for its compilation of keen anecdotes about animal behavior. Romanes, however, regarded the text as only a prelude to *Mental Evolution in Animals* (1883) and *Mental Evolution in Man* (1887). In the volume on animal intelligence, Romanes produced a diagram that purported to show graphically the pattern of mental genesis. The diagram served as a basis for both of the ensuing books and, to Romanes, indicated "in how striking quantitative, as well as quali-

[7] G. J. Romanes, *Mental Evolution in Animals* (New York: Appleton, 1884), p. 63.

tative, a manner the development of an individual human mind follows the order of mental evolution in the animal kingdom."[8]

In the following selections from *Mental Evolution in Animals* and *Mental Evolution in Man*, the one explaining the diagram and the other comparing the communicative development of Romanes' daughter with that of a bird, a dog, and so on, Romanes reveals a strong belief in the palingenetic development of intellectual functions. As the earliest developmental theorist on cognitive processes, Romanes lacked descriptive schema. He relied primitively on the philosophic arguments of nineteenth-century associationism. All animals and man, this viewpoint held, possessed the simplest mental resources for rudimentary perceiving and recalling of sensory impressions; certain higher animals and man acquired additional capacities for making compound associations and for extracting limited meaning from events; man alone, however, enjoyed the distinction of possessing the abilities necessary for abstract, symbolic reasoning and remembering. From such simple, mentalistic progressions it seemed plausible to assume that cenogenetic influences, inexact parallelism and economy, and so on, had not disarrayed psychical as they had physical recapitulation. In expressing his firm belief that children closely parallel animals in their thought to the point where human intelligence surpasses the highest evolutionary accomplishments of lower species, Romanes appended another article to the rapidly growing credenda soon to be assimilated into genetic psychology.

GEORGE JOHN ROMANES (1848–1894)
MENTAL EVOLUTION IN ANIMALS AND MAN

EXPLANATION OF THE DIAGRAM

IN order to give definition to the somewhat laborious investigation on which we are thus about to embark, I have thought it a good plan to draw a diagram or map of the probable development of Mind from its first beginnings in protoplasmic life up to its culmination in the brain

[8] G. J. Romanes, *Mental Evolution in Man* (New York: Appleton, 1889), p. 5.
SOURCE: G. J. Romanes. *Mental Evolution in Animals* (New York: Appleton, 1884). Diagram of "The Probable Development of Mind" and selections from "Explanation of the Diagram," Chapter 5, pp. 63–69. G. J. Romanes. *Mental Evolution in Man* (New York: Appleton, 1889). "Transition in the Individual," Chapter 11, pp. 213–235. Abridged. Footnotes deleted.

of civilized man. The diagram embodies the results of my analysis throughout, and will therefore be repeatedly alluded to in the course of that analysis—*i.e.*, throughout the present and also my future work. I may therefore begin by explaining the plan of this diagram.

The diagram, as I have just said, is intended to represent in one view the whole course of mental evolution, supposing, in accordance with our original hypothesis, such evolution to have taken place. Being a condensed epitome of the results of my analysis, it is in all its parts carefully drawn to a scale, the ascending grades or levels of which are everywhere determined by the evidence which I shall have to adduce. The diagram is therefore not so much the product of my individual imagination, as it is a summary of all the facts which science has been able so far to furnish upon the subject; and although it is no doubt true that the progress of science may affect the diagram to the extent of altering some of its details, I feel confident that the general structure of our knowledge concerning the evolution of mind is now sufficiently coherent to render it highly improbable that this diagrammatic representation of it will, in the future, be altered in any of its main features by any advances that science may be destined to make.

From the groundwork of Excitability, or the distinguishing peculiarity of living matter, I represent the structure of mind as arising by a double root—Conductility and Discrimination. To what has already been said on these topics it is needless to add more. We have seen that the distinguishing property of nerve-fibre is that of transmitting stimuli by a propagation of molecular disturbance irrespective of the passage of a contraction wave, and this property, laying as it does the basis for all subsequent co-ordination of protoplasmic (muscular) movements, as well as of the physical aspect of all mental operations, deserves to be marked off in our map as a distinct and important principle of development; it is the principle which renders possible the executive faculty of appropriately responding to stimuli. Not less deserving of similar treatment is the cognate principle of Discrimination, which, as we have seen, is destined to become the most important of the functions subsequently distinctive of nerve-cells and ganglia. But we have also seen that both Conductility and Discrimination first appear as manifested by the cellular tissues of plants, if not even in some forms of apparently undifferentiated protoplasm. It is, however, only when these two principles are united within the limits of the same structural elements that we first obtain optical evidence of that differentiation of tissue which the histologist recognizes as nervous; therefore I have represented the function of nerve-tissue in its widest sense, Neurility, as formed by a confluence of these two root-principles. Neurility then passes into Reflex Action and Volition, which I have represented as occupying the axis or stem of the psychological tree. On each side of this tree I have represented the outgrowth of branches, and for the sake of distinctness I have confined the branches which stand for the faculties of Intellect on one side, while placing those which represent the Emotions upon the other. The level to which any branch attains represents the degree of elaboration which the faculty named thereon presents; so that, for instance, when the branch Sensation, taking origin from Neurility, proceeds to a certain level of development, it gives off the commencement of Perception, and then continues in its own line of development to a somewhat higher level. Similarly, Imagination arises out of Perception, and so with all the other branches. Thus, the fifty levels which are drawn across the diagram are intended to represent degrees of elaboration; they are not intended to represent intervals of time. Such being the case, the various products of mental evolution are placed in parallel columns upon these various levels, so as to exhibit the comparative degrees of elaboration, or evolution, which they severally present. One of these columns is devoted to the psychological scale of intellectual faculties, and another to the psychological scale of the emotional. But for the danger of rendering the diagram confused, these faculties might have been represented as secondary branches of the psychological tree; in a model this might well be done, but in a diagram it would not be practical, and therefore I have restricted the branching structure to represent only the most generic or fundamental of the psychological faculties, and relegated those of more specific or secondary value to the parallel columns on either side of the branching structure. In these two columns I have throughout written the name of the faculty at what I conceive to be the earliest stage, or lowest level of its elaboration; i.e., where it first gives evidence of its existence. In another parallel column I have given the grades of mental evolution which I take to be characteristic of sundry groups in the animal kingdom, and in yet another column I have represented the grades of mental evolution which I take to be characteristic of different ages in the life of an infant. . . .

To avoid misapprehension I may add that in thus rendering a diagrammatic representation of the probable course of mental evolution with the comparisons of psychological development exhibited in the parallel columns, I do not suppose that the representation is more than a rough or general outline of the facts; and, indeed, I have only resorted to the expedient of thus representing the latter for the sake of convenience in my subsequent discussion. Rough as this outline of historical psychology may be, it will serve its purpose if it tends to facilitate the exposition of evidence, and afterwards serves as a dictionary of reference to the more important of the facts which I hope this evidence will be able to substantiate.

Such being the general use to which I intend to put the diagram, I may here most fitly make this general remark in regard to it. In the case alike of the stem, branches, and the two parallel columns on either side—*i.e.*, all the parts of the diagram which serve to denote psychological faculties—we must remember that they are diagrammatic rather than truly representative. For in nature it is as a matter of fact impossible to determine any hard and fast lines between the completed development of one faculty and the first origin of the next succeeding faculty. The passage from one faculty to another is throughout of that gradual kind which is characteristic of evolution in general, and which, while never preventing an eventual distinction of species, always renders it impossible to draw a line and say—Here species A ends and species B begins. Moreover, I cannot too emphatically impress my conviction that any psychological classification of faculties, however serviceable it may be for purposes of analysis and discussion, must necessarily be artificial. It would, in my opinion, be a most erroneous view to take of Mind to regard it as really made up of a certain number of distinct faculties—as erroneous, for example, as it would be to regard the body as made up of the faculties of nutrition, excitability, generation, and so on. All such distinctions are useful only for the purposes of analysis; they are abstractions of our own making for our own convenience, and not naturally distinct parts of the structure which we are examining.

But although it is desirable to keep these caveats in our memory, I do not think that either the artificial nature of psychological classification or the fact that we have to do with a gradual process of evolution, constitutes any serious vitiation of the mode of representation which I have adopted. For, on the one hand, some classification of faculties we must have for the purposes of our inquiry; and, on the other hand, I have as much as possible allowed for the unavoidable defect in the representation which arises from evolution being gradual, by making the branches of the arborescent structure wide at their bases, and by allowing each of them, after giving off the next succeeding branch, to continue on its own course of development; so that both the parent and daughter faculty are represented as occupying for a more or less considerable distance the same levels of development—in each case my estimate of the comparative elaboration which the completed faculty betokens being represented by the vertical height of its apex. Besides, as already stated, faculties named in the two parallel columns are written upon those levels where I have either *à priori* reasons or actual evidence to conclude that they first definitely appear in the growing structure of Mind; in this way the difficult question of assigning the lower limit of evolution at which any particular faculty begins to dawn is as much as possible avoided.

It is almost needless to add that in preparing this diagram I have resorted to speculation in as small a measure as the nature of the subject permits. Nevertheless it is obvious that the nature of the subject is such that, in order to complete the diagram in some of its parts, I have been obliged to resort to speculation pretty largely. I think, however, that as the exposition proceeds, it will be seen that, if the fundamental hypothesis of mental evolution having taken place is granted, my reasoning as to the probable history of the process does not anywhere involve speculation of an extravagant or dangerous kind. In matters of detail—such, for instance, as the comparative elevation of the different branches in the psychological tree—my estimates may, probably enough, be more or less erroneous; but the main facts as to the sequence of the faculties in the order of their comparative degrees of elaboration are mere corollaries from our fundamental hypothesis; and, as we shall see, these facts, as I have presented them, are sustained or corroborated by many others drawn from observations on the psychology of animals and children. Again, in the columns devoted to the emotions and faculties of intellect, the results of actual observation predominate over those yielded by speculation; while in the remaining columns the results tabulated are for the most part due to observation.

Therefore I submit that if the hypothesis of mental evolution be granted, and if all the matters of observable fact which the diagram serves to express are eliminated, comparatively little in the way of deductive reasoning is left; and of this little most follows as necessary consequence from the original hypothesis of mental evolution having taken place. Of course any one who does not already accept the theory of evolution in its entirety, may object that I am thus escaping from the charge of speculation only by assuming the truth of that which grants me all that I require. To this I answer that as far as the evidence of Mental Evolution, considered as a fact, is open to the charge of being speculative, I must leave the objector to lodge his objection against Mr. Darwin's *Origin of Species* and *Descent of Man*. I shall be abundantly satisfied with my own work if, taking the process of Mental Evolution as conceded, I can make it clear that the main outlines of its history may be determined without any considerable amount of speculation, as distinguished from deduction following by way of necessary consequence from the original hypothesis.

THE TRANSITION IN THE INDIVIDUAL

We are now, I think, in possession of sufficient material to begin our answer to the question with which we set out—namely, Is it conceivable that the human mind can have arisen by way of a natural genesis from the minds of the higher quadrumana? I maintain that the material now before us is sufficient to show, not only that this is conceivable, but inevitable.

First of all we must remember that we share in common with the lower animals not only perceptual, but also what I have termed receptual life. Thus far, no difference of kind can be even so much as suggested. The difference then, be it one of kind or of degree, concerns only those superadded elements of psychology which are peculiar to man, and which, following other psychologists, I have termed conceptual. I say advisedly the *elements*, because it is by no one disputed that all differences of conceptual life are differences of degree, or that from the ideation of a savage to that of a Shakespeare there is unquestionably a continuous ascent. The only question, then, that obtains is as to the relation between the highest recept of a brute and the lowest concept of a man.

Now, in considering this question we must first remember to what an extraordinarily high level of adaptive ideation the purely receptual life of brutes is able to carry them. If we contrast the ideation of my cebus, which honestly investigated the mechanical principle of a screw, and then applied his specially acquired knowledge to screws in general—if we contrast this ideation with that of palæolithic man, who for untold thousands of years made no advance upon the chipping of flints, we cannot say that, when gauged by the practical test of efficiency or adaptation, the one appears to be very much in advance of the other. Or, if we remember that these same men never hit upon the simple expedient of attaching a chipped flint to a handle, so as to make a hatchet out of a chisel, it cannot be said that in the matter of mechanical discovery early conceptual life displayed any great advance upon the high receptual life of my cebus. Nevertheless, I have allowed—nay insisted—that no matter how elaborate the structure of receptual knowledge may be, or how wonderful the adaptive action it may prompt, a "practical inference" or "receptual judgment" is always separated from a conceptual inference or true judgment by the immense distinction that it is not itself an object of knowledge. No doubt it is a marvellous fact that by means of receptual knowledge alone a monkey should be able to divine the mechanical principle of *a screw*, and afterwards apply his discovery to all cases of *screws*. But even here there is nothing to show that the monkey ever *thought* about the principle *as* a principle; indeed, we may rest well assured that he cannot possibly have done so, seeing that he was not in possession of the intellectual instruments—and, therefore, of the *antecedent conditions*—requisite for the purpose. All that the monkey did was to perceive receptually certain analogies: but he did not *conceive* them, or constitute them objects of thought *as* analogies. He was, therefore, unable to *predicate* the discovery he had made, or to set before his own mind as knowledge the knowledge which he had gained.

Or, to take another illustration, the bird which saw three men go into a building, and inferred that one must still have remained when only two came out, conducted the inference receptually: the only data she had were those supplied by differential sense-perceptions. But although these data were sufficient for the purpose of conducting what Mr. Mivart calls a "practical inference," and so of enabling her to know that a man still remained behind, they were clearly not enough to enable her to know the numerical relations *as* relations, or in any way to predicate to herself, $3 - 2 = 1$. In order to do this, the bird would have required to quit the region of receptual knowledge, and rise to that of conceptual: she would have required in some form or another to have substituted symbols for ideas. It makes no difference, so far as this distinction is concerned, when we learn that in dealing with certain savages "each sheep must be paid for separately: thus, suppose two sticks of tobacco to be the rate of exchange for one sheep, it would sorely puzzle a Dammara to take two sheep and give him two sticks." All that such facts show is that in some respects the higher receptual life of brutes attains almost as high a level of ideation as the lower conceptual life of man; and although this fact no doubt greatly lessens the difficulty which my opponents allege as attaching to the supposition that the two were genetically continuous, it does not in itself dispose of the psychological distinction between a recept and a concept.

This distinction, as we have now so often seen, consists in a recept being an idea which is not itself an object of knowledge, whereas a concept, in virtue of having been named by a self-conscious agent, is an idea which stands before the mind of that agent *as* an idea, or as a state of mind which admits of being introspectively contemplated as such. But although we have in this distinction what I agree with my opponents in regarding as the greatest single distinction that is to be met with in psychology, I altogether object to their mode of analyzing it. For what they do is to take the concept in its most highly developed form, and then contrast this with the recept of an animal. Nay, as we have seen, they even go beyond a concept, and allege that "the simplest element of thought" is a judgment as bodied forth in a proposition—*i.e.* *two* concepts *plus* the predication of a relationship between them! Truly, we might as well allege that the simplest element of matter is H_2SO_4, or the simplest element of sound a bar of the C Minor Symphony. Obviously, therefore, or as a mere matter of the most rudimentary psychological analysis, if we say that the simplest element of thought is a judgment, we must extend the meaning of this word from the mental act concerned in full predication, to the mental act concerned in the simplest conception.

And not only so. Not only have my opponents committed the slovenly error of regarding a predicative judgment as "the simplest element of thought;" they have also omitted to consider that even a concept requires to be analyzed with respect to its antecedents, before this the really simplest element of thought can be pointed to as proving a psychological distinction of kind in the only known intelligence which presents it. Now, the result of my analysis of the concept has been to show that it is preceded by what I have termed pre-concepts, which admit of being combined into what I have termed nascent, rudimentary, or pre-conceptual judgments. In other words, we have seen that the receptual life of man reaches a higher level of development than the receptual life of brutes, even before it passes into that truly conceptual phase which is distinguished by the presence of self-conscious reflection. In order, therefore, to mark off this higher receptual life of a human being from the lower receptual life of a brute, I have used the terms just mentioned.

So much, then, for these several stages of ideation, which I have now reiterated *ad nauseam.* Turning next to my analysis of their several modes of expression, or of their translation into their severally equivalent systems of signs, we have seen that many of the lower animals are able to communicate their recepts by means of gestures significant of objects, qualities, actions, desires, etc.; and that in the only case where they are able to articulate, they so communicate their recepts by means of words. Therefore, in a sense, these animals may be said to be using names; but, in order not to confuse this kind of naming with that which is distinctive of conceptual thought, I have adopted the scholastic terminology, and called the former kind of naming an act of denotating, as distinguished from an act of denominating. Furthermore, seeing that denotative language is able, as above observed, to signify qualities and actions as well as objects, it follows that in the higher receptual (*i.e.* pre-conceptual) stages of ideation, denotative language is able to construct what I have termed pre-conceptual propositions. These differ from true or conceptual propositions in the absence of true self-consciousness on the part of the speaker, who therefore, while communicating receptual knowledge, or stating truths, cannot yet know his own knowledge, or state the truths as true. But it does not appear that a pre-conceptual proposition differs from a conceptual one in any other respect, while it does appear that the one passes gradually into the other with the rise of self-consciousness in every growing child. Now, if all these things are so, we are entitled to affirm that analysis has displayed an uninterrupted transition between the denotation of a brute and the predication of a man. For the mere fact that it is the former phase alone which occurs in the brute, while in the man, *after having run a parallel course of development,* this phase passes into the other—the mere fact that this is so cannot be quoted as evidence that a similar transition never took place in the psychological history of our species, unless it could be shown that when the transition takes place in the psychological history of the individual, it does so in such a sudden and remarkable manner as of itself to indicate that the intellect of the individual has there and then undergone a change of kind.

Such being an outline sketch of my argument, I will now proceed to fill in the details, taking in historical order the various stages of ideation which I have named—*i.e.* the receptual, the pre-conceptual, and the conceptual.

Seeing that this is, as I apprehend, the central core of the question, I will here furnish some additional instances of receptual and pre-conceptual ideation as expressed by denotative and connotative signs on the part of a child which I carefully observed for the purpose.

At eighteen months old my daughter, who was late in beginning to speak, was fond of looking at picture-books, and as already stated in a previous chapter, derived much pleasure from naming animals therein represented—saying *Ba* for a sheep, *Moo* for a cow, uttering a grunt for a pig, and throwing her head up and down with a bray for a horse or an ass. These several sounds and gestures she had been taught by the nurse as noun-substantives, and she correctly applied them in every case, whether the picture-book happened to be one with which she was familiar or one which she had never seen before; and she would similarly name all kinds of animals depicted on the wall-paper, chair-covers, etc., in strange houses, or, in short, whenever she met with representations of objects the nursery names of which she knew. Thus there is no doubt that, long before she could form a sentence, or in any proper sense be said to speak, this child was able to denote objects by voice and gesture. At this time, also, she correctly used a limited number of denotative words significant of actions—*i.e.* active verbs.

Somewhat later by a few weeks she showed spontaneously the faculty of expressing an adjective. Her younger brother she had called "Ilda," and soon afterwards she extended the name to all young children. Later still, while looking over her picture-books, whenever she came upon a representation of a sheep with lambs, she would point to the sheep and say *Mama-Ba, while to the lambs she would say Ilda-Ba*. Similarly with ducks and ducklings, hens and chickens, and indeed with all the animals to which she had given names. Here it is evident that *Ilda* served to convey the generic idea of *Young*, and so, from having been originally used as a proper or denotative name, was now employed as an adjective or connotative name. But although it expressed a quality, the quality was one of so sensible a kind that the adjective amounted to virtually the same thing as substantive, so far as any faculty of abstraction was concerned: it was equivalent to the word *Baby*, when by connotative extension this comes to be used as an adjective in the apposition *Baby-Ba* for a lamb, etc.

Almost contemporaneously with the acquisition of adjectives, this child began to learn the use of a few passive verbs, and words significant of certain states of feeling; she also added to her vocabulary a few prepositions indicating space relations, such as *Up, Down*, etc.

While these advances were being made, a general progress of the sign-making faculty was also, and even more conspicuously, shown in another direction. For speech, in the sense of formal predication, not having yet begun, the development in question took place in the region of gesture. She was then (two years) able to express a great many simple ideas by the combined use of gesture-signs, vocal-tones, and a large connotative extension of her words. The gesture-signs, however, were still of the simplest or most receptual order, such as pulling one by the dress to open a door, pointing to a tumbler to signify her desire for a drink, etc. That is to say, the indicative stage of language largely coincided with, or overlapped, the earliest phases of the denotative and receptually connotative. I have already said that this indicative stage of language constituted the earliest appearance of the sign-making faculty which I observed in my own children, at a time when the only desire expressed seemed to be that of being taken to the object indicated; and, so far as I can ascertain, this is universally true of all children. But the point now is, that when the logic recepts had become more full, the desires expressed by pointing became of a more and more varied kind, until, at the age of two and a half (*i.e.* after significant articulation or true word-making had well set in), the indicative phase of language developed into regular pantomime, as the following instance will show. Coming into the house after having bathed in the sea for the first time, she ran to me to narrate her novel experience. This she did by first pointing to the shore, then pretending to take off her clothes, to walk into the sea, and to dip: next, passing her hands up the body to her head, she signified that the water had reached as high as her hair, which she showed me was still wet. The whole story was told without the use of a single articulate sound.

Now, in the case of these illustrations (and many more of the same kind might be added if needful), we find the same general fact exemplified—namely, that the earliest phase of language in the young child is that which I have called the indicative—*i.e.* tones and gestures significant of feelings, objects, qualities, and actions. This indicative phase of language, or sign-making, lasts much longer in some children than in others (particularly in those who are late in beginning to speak); and the longer it lasts the more expressive does it become of advancing ideation. But in all cases two things have to be observed in connection with it. The first is that, in its earliest stages, and onwards through a considerable part of its history, it is precisely identical with the corresponding phases of indicative sign-making in the lower animals. Thus, for instance, Professor Preyer observed that at sixteen months his own child—who at that age could not speak a word—used to make a gesture significant of petitioning with its hands ("Bittbewegung"), as indicative of desire for something to be done. This, of course, I choose as an instance of indicative sign-making at a comparatively high level of development; but it is precisely paralleled by an intelligent dog which "begs" before a water-jug to signify his desire for a drink, or before any other object in connection with which he desires something to be done. And so it is with children who pull one's dress towards a closed door through which they wish to pass, significantly cry for what they want to possess, or to have done for them, etc.: children are here doing exactly what cats and dogs will do under similar circumstances. And although many of the gesture-signs of children at this age (*i.e.* up to about eighteen months) are not precisely paralleled by those of the lower animals, it is easy to see that where there is any difference it is due to different circumstances of bodily shape, social conditions, etc.: it is not due to any difference of ideation. That the kind of ideation which is expressed by the indicative gestures of young children is the same as that which prompts the analogous gestures of brutes, is further shown by the fact that, even before any articulate words are uttered, the infant (like the animal) will display an understanding of many articulate words when uttered in its presence, and (also like the animal) will respond to such words by appropriate gestures. For instance, again to quote Preyer, he found that his hitherto speechless infant was able correctly to point to certain colours which he named; and although, as far as I am aware, no one has ever tried to teach an animal to do this, we know that trained dogs will display an even better understanding of words by means of appropriate gestures.*

* I took my daughter when she was seven years of age to witness the understanding of the ape "Sally." On coming away, I remarked to her that the animal seemed to be "quite as sensible as Jack"—*i.e.* her infant brother of eighteen months. She considered for a while, and then replied, "Well, I think she is sensibler." And I believe the child was right.

The other point which has to be noticed in connection with these early stages of indicative sign-making in the young child is that, sooner or later, they begin to overlap the earliest stage of articulate sign-making, or verbal denotation. In other words, denotative sign-making never begins to occur until indicative sign-making has advanced considerably; and when denotative sign-making does begin, it advances parallel with indicative: that is to say, both kinds of sign-making then proceed to develop simultaneously. But when the vocabulary of denotation has been sufficiently enriched to enable the child to dispense with the less efficient material furnished by indication, indicative signs gradually become starved out by denotative, and words replace gestures.

So far, then, as the earliest or indicative phase of language is concerned, no difference even of degree can be alleged between the infant and the animal. Neither can any such difference be alleged with respect to the earliest exhibitions of the next phases of language, namely, the denotative and receptually connotative. For we have seen that the only animals which happen to be capable of imitating articulate sounds will use these sounds with a truly denotative significance. Moreover, as we have also seen, within moderate limits they will even extend such denotative significance to other objects seen to belong to the same class or kind—thus raising the originally denotative sign to an incipiently connotative value. And although these receptually connotative powers of a parrot are soon surpassed by those of a young child, we have further seen that this is merely owing to the rapid advance in the *degree* of receptual life which takes place in the latter—or, in other words, that if a parrot resembled a dog in being able to see the resemblance between objects and their pictures, and also in being so much more able to understand the meanings of words, then, without doubt, their connotative extension of names would proceed further than it does; and hence in this matter the parallel between a parrot and child would proceed further than it does. The only reason, therefore, why a child thus gradually surpasses a parrot in the matter of connotation, is because the receptual life of a child gradually rises to that of a dog—as I have already proved by showing that the indicative or gesture-signs used by a child after it has thus surpassed the parrot, are psychologically identical with those which are used by a dog. Moreover, where denotation is late in beginning and slow in developing—as in the case of my own daughter—these indicative signs admit, as we have seen, of becoming much more highly perfected, so that under these circumstances a child of two years will perform a little pantomime for the purpose of relating its experiences. Now, this fact enables me to dispense with the imaginary comparison of a dog that is able to talk, or of a parrot as intelligent as a dog; for the fact furnishes me with the converse case of a child *not* able to talk at the usual age. No one can suggest that the intelligence of such a child at two years old differs in kind from that of another child of the same age, who, on account of having been earlier in acquiring the use of words, can afford to become less proficient in the use of gestures.* The case of a child late in talking may therefore be taken as a psychological index of the development of human ideation of the receptual order, which by accident admits of closer comparison with that of the higher mammalia than is possible in the case of a child who begins to talk at the usual age. But, as regards the former case, we have already seen that the gestures begin by being much less expressive than those of a dog, then gradually improve until they become psychologically identical, and, lastly, continue in the same gradual manner along the same line of advance. Therefore, if in this case no difference of kind can be alleged *until* the speaking age is reached, neither can it be alleged *after* the speaking age is reached in the case where this happens to be earlier. Or, in the words previously used, if a dog like a parrot were able to use verbal signs, or if a parrot were equal in intelligence to a dog, the connotative powers of a child would continue parallel with those of a brute through a somewhat longer reach of psychological development than we now find to be the case.

Remembering, then, that brutes so low in the psychological scale as talking birds reach the level of denoting objects, qualities, etc.; remembering that some of these birds will extend their denotative names to objects and qualities conspicuously belonging to the same class; remembering, further, that all children before they begin to speak have greatly distanced the talking birds in respect of indicative language or gesture-signs, while some children (or those late in beginning to speak) will raise this form of language to the level of pantomime, thus proving that the receptual ideation of infants just before they begin to speak is invariably above that of talking birds, and often far above that of any other animal;—remembering all these things, I say it would indeed be a most unaccountable fact if children, soon after they do begin to speak, did *not* display a great advance upon the talking birds in their use of denotative signs, and also in their extension of such signs into connotative words. As we

---

* Or, if any opponent were to suggest this, he would be committing argumentative surrender. For the citadel of his argument is, as we know, the faculty of conception, or the distinctively human power of objectifying ideas. Now, it is on all hands admitted that this power is impossible in the absence of self-consciousness. Will it, then, be suggested that my daughter had attained to self-consciousness and the introspective contemplation of her own ideas before she had attained to the faculty of speech, and therefore to the very *condition* to the naming of her ideas? If so, it would follow that there may be concepts without names, and thus the whole fortress of my opponents would crumble away.

have seen, it must be conceded by all prudent adversaries that, before he is able to use any of these signs, an infant is moving in the receptual sphere of ideation, and that this sphere is already (between one and two years) far above that of the parrot. Yet, like the parrot, one of the first uses that he makes of these signs is in the denotation of individual objects, etc. Next, like the more intelligent parrots, he extends the meaning of his denotative names to objects most obviously resembling those which were first designated. And from that point onwards he rapidly advances in his powers of connotative classification. But can it be seriously maintained, in view of all the above considerations, that this rapid advance in the powers of connotative classification betokens any difference of kind between the ideation of the child and that of the bird? If it is conceded (as it must be unless my opponents commit argumentative suicide), that before he could speak at all the infant was confined to the receptual sphere of ideation, and that within this sphere his ideation was already superior to the ideation of a bird—this is merely to concede that analogies *must* strike the child which are somewhat too remote to strike the bird. Therefore, while the bird will only extend its denotative name from one kind of dog to another, the child, after having done this, will go on to apply the name to an image, and, lastly, to the picture of a dog. Surely no one will be fatuous enough to maintain that here, at the commencement of articulate sign-making, there is any evidence of generic distinction between the human mind and the mind of even so poor a representative of animal psychology as we meet with in a parrot. But, if no such distinction is to be asserted here, neither can it be asserted anywhere else, until we arrive at the stage of human ideation where the mind is able to contemplate that ideation as such. So far, therefore, as the stages which we are now considering are concerned (*i.e.* the denotative and receptually connotative), I submit that my case is made out. And yet these are really the most important stages to be clear about; for, on account of their having been ignored by nearly all writers who argue that there is a difference of kind between man and brute the most important—because the initial—stages of transition have been lost sight of, and the fully developed powers of human thought contrasted with their low beginnings in the brute creation, without any attention having been paid to the probable history of their development. Hitherto, so far as I can find, no psychologist has presented clearly the simple question whether the faculty of naming is always and necessarily co-extensive with that of *thinking the names*; and, therefore, the two faculties have been assumed to be one and the same. Yet, as I have shown in an earlier chapter, even in the highest forms of human ideation we habitually use names without waiting to think of them as names—which proves that even in the highest regions of ideation the two faculties are not *necessarily* coincident. And here I have further shown that, whether we look to the brute or to the human being, we alike find that the one faculty is in its inception *wholly independent* of the other—that there are connotative names before there are any denominative thoughts, and that these connotative names, when they first occur in brute or child, betoken no further aptitude of ideation than is betokened by those stages in the language of gesture which they everywhere overlap. The named recepts of a parrot cannot be held by my opponents to be true concepts, any more than the indicative gestures of an infant can be held by them to differ in kind from those of a dog.

I submit, then, that neither as regards the indicative, the denotative, nor the connotative stages of sign-making is it argumentatively possible to allege any difference of kind between animal and human intelligence—apart, I mean, from any evidence of self-consciousness in the latter, or so long as the intelligence of either is moving in what I have called the receptual sphere. Let us, then, next consider what I have called the pre-conceptual stage of ideation, or that higher receptual life of a child which, while surpassing the receptual life of any brute, has not yet attained to the conceptual life of a man.

From what I have already said it must, I should suppose, be now conceded that, at the place where the receptual life of a child first begins to surpass the receptual life of any other mammal, no psychological difference of kind can be affirmed. Let us, therefore, consent to tap this pre-conceptual life at a considerably higher level, and analyze the quality of ideation which flows therefrom: let us consider the case of a child about two years old, who is able to frame such a rudimentary, communicative, or pre-conceptual proposition as *Dit ki* (Sister is crying). At this age, as already shown, there is no consciousness of self as a thinking agent, and, therefore, no power of stating a truth as true. *Dit* is the denotative name of one recept, *ki* the denotative name of another: the object and the action which these two recepts severally represent happen to occur together before the child's observation: the child therefore denotes them both simultaneously—*i.e. brings them into apposition.* This it does by merely following the associations previously established between the recept of a familiar object with its denotative name *dit*, and the recept of a frequent action with its denotative name *ki*. The apposition in consciousness of these two recepts, with their corresponding denotations, is thus effected *for* the child by what may be termed *the logic of events:* it is not effected *by* the child in the way of any intentional or self-conscious grouping of its ideas, such as we have seen to constitute the distinguishing feature of the logic of concepts.

Such being the state of the facts, I put to my opponents the following dilemma. Either you here have judgment, or else you have not. If you hold that this is judgment, you must also hold that animals judge, because I have proved already that (according to your own doctrine as well as mine) the only point wherein it can be alleged that the faculty of judgment differs in animals and in man consists in the presence or absence of self-consciousness. If, on the other hand, you answer that here you have not judgment, inasmuch as you have not self-consciousness, I will ask you at what stage in the subsequent development of the child's intelligence you would consider judgment to arise? If to this you answer that judgment first arises when self-consciousness arises, I will ask you to note that, as already proved, the growth of self-consciousness is itself a gradual process; so that, according to your present limitation of the term judgment, it becomes impossible to say when this faculty does arise. In point of fact, it grows by stages, *pari passu* with the growth of self-consciousness. But, if so, where the faculty of stating a truth perceived passes into the higher faculty of perceiving the truth as true, there must be a continuous series of gradations connecting the one faculty with the other. Up to the point where this series of gradation begins, we have seen that the mind of an animal and the mind of a man are parallel, or not distinguishable from each other by any one principle of psychology. Will you, then, maintain that up to this time the two orders of psychical existence are identical in kind, but that during its ascent through this final series of gradations the human mind in some way becomes distinct in kind, not merely from the mind of animals, *but also from its own previous self?* If so, I must at this point part company with you in argument, because at this point your argument ends in a contradiction. If A and B are affirmed to be similar in origin or kind, and if B is affirmed to grow into C—or to differ from both A and B only in degree—it becomes a contradiction further to affirm that C differs from A in kind. Therefore I submit that, so far as the pre-conceptual stage of ideation is concerned, it is still argumentatively impossible for my opponents to show that there is any psychological difference of kind between man and brute.

As regards this stage of ideation, then, I claim to have shown that, just as there is a pre-conceptual kind of naming, wherein originally denotative words are progressively extended through considerable degrees of connotative meaning; so there is a pre-conceptual kind of predication, wherein denotative and connotative terms are brought together without any conceptual cognizance of the relation thus virtually alleged between them. For I have proved in the last chapter that it is not until its third year that a child acquires true or conceptual self-consciousness, and therefore attains the condition to true or conceptual predication. Yet long before that time, as I have also proved, the child forms what I have called rudimentary, or pre-conceptual, and, therefore, *unthinking* propositions. Such propositions, then, are statements of truth made for the practical purposes of communication; but they are not statements of truth as true, and therefore not, strictly speaking, propositions at all. They are translations of the logic of recepts; but not of the logic of concepts. For neither the truth so stated, nor the idea thus translated, can ever have been placed before the mind as itself an object of thought. In order to have been thus placed, the mind must have been able to dissociate this its product from the rest of its structure—or, as Mr. Mivart says, to make the things affirmed "exist *beside* the judgment, not *in* it." And, in order to do this, the mind must have attained to self-consciousness. But, as just remarked, such is not yet the case with a child of the age in question; and hence we are bound to conclude that before there is judgment or predication in the sense understood by psychologists (conceptual), there is judgment and predication of a lower order (pre-conceptual), wherein truths are stated for the sake of communicating simple ideas, while the propositions which convey them are not themselves objects of thought. And, be it carefully observed, predication of this rudimentary or pre-conceptual kind is accomplished by the mere apposition of denotative signs, in accordance with the general principles of association. *A* being the denotative name of an object, *a*, and *B* the denotative name of a quality or action *b*, when *a b* occur together in nature, the relation between them is pre-conceptually affirmed by the mere act of bringing into apposition the corresponding denotations *A B*—an act which is rendered inevitable by the elementary laws of psychological association.*

The matter, then, has been reduced to the last of the three stages of ideation which have been marked out for discussion—namely, the conceptual. Now, whether or not there is any difference of kind between

---

* In this connection it is interesting to observe the absence of the copula. Notwithstanding the strongly imitative tendencies of a child's mind, and notwithstanding that our English children hear the copula expressed in almost every statement that is made to them, their own propositions, while still in the pre-conceptual phase, dispense with it. In thus trusting to apposition alone, without expressing any sign of relation, the young child is conveying in spoken language an immediate translation of the mental acts concerned in predication. As previously noticed, we meet with precisely the same fact in the natural language of gesture, even after this has been wrought up into the elaborate conceptual systems of the Indians and deaf-mutes. The same has to be said of all the more primitive forms of spoken language which are still extant among savages. So that here again we meet with additional proof, were any required, of the folly of regarding the copula as an essential ingredient of a proposition.

the ideation which is capable and the ideation which is not capable of itself becoming an object of thought, is a question which can only be answered by studying the relations that obtain between the two in the case of the growing child. But, as we have seen, when we do study these relations, we find that they are clearly those of a gradual or continuous passage of the one ideation into the other—a passage, indeed, so gradual and continuous that it is impossible, even by means of the closest scrutiny, to decide within wide limits where the one begins and the other ends. Therefore I need not here recur to this point. Having already shown that the very condition to the occurrence of conceptual ideation (namely, self-consciousness) if of gradual development in the growing child, it is needless to show at any greater length that the development of conceptual out of pre-conceptual ideation is of a similarly gradual occurrence. This fact, indeed, is in itself sufficient to dispose of the allegation of my opponents—namely, that there is evidence of receptual ideation differing from conceptual in origin or kind. Only if it could be shown—either that the receptual ideation of an infant differs in kind from that of an animal, or that the pre-conceptual ideation of a child so differs from the preceding receptual ideation of the same child, or lastly, that this pre-conceptual ideation so differs from the succeeding conceptual ideation—only if one or other of the alternatives could be proved would my opponents be able to justify their allegation. And, as a mere matter of logic, to prove either of the last two alternatives would involve a complete reconstruction of their argument. For at present their argument goes upon the assumption that throughout all the phases of its development a human mind is one in kind—that it is nowhere fundamentally changed from one order of existence to another. But in case any subtle opponent should suggest that, although I have proved the first of the above three alternatives untenable—and, therefore, that there is no difference even of degree between the mind of an infant and that of an animal—I have nevertheless ignored the possibility that in the subsequent development of every human being a special miracle may be wrought, which regenerates that mind, gives it a new origin, and so changes it as to kind—in case any one should suggest this, I here entertain the two last alternatives as logically possible. But, even so, as we have now so fully seen, study of the child's intelligence while passing through its several phases of development yields no shadow of evidence in favor of any of these alternatives; while, on the contrary, it most clearly reveals the fact that transition from each of the levels of ideation to the next above it is of so gradual and continuous a character that it is practically impossible to draw any real lines of demarcation between them. This, then, I say is in itself enough to dispose of the allegation of my opponents, seeing that it shows the allegation to be, not only gratuitous, but opposed to the whole body of evidence which is furnished by a study of the facts. Nevertheless, still restricting ourselves to grounds of psychology alone, there remains two general and important considerations of an independent or supplementary kind, which tend strongly to support my side of the argument. These two considerations, therefore, I will next adduce.

The first consideration is, that although the advance to self-consciousness from lower grades of mental development is no doubt a very great and important matter, it is not so great and important in comparison with what this development is afterwards destined to become, as to make us feel that it constitutes any distinction *sui generis*—or even, perhaps, the principal distinction—between the man and the brute. For while, on the one hand, we have now fully seen that, given the protoplasm of judgment and of predication as these occur in the young child (or as they may be supposed to have occurred in our semi-human ancestors), and self-consciousness must needs arise; on the other hand, there is evidence to show that when self-consciousness does arise, and even when it is fairly well developed, the powers of the human mind are still in an almost infantile condition. Thus, for instance, I have observed in my own children that, while before their third birthday they employed appropriately and always correctly the terms "I," "my," "self," "myself," at that age their powers of reasoning were so poorly developed as scarcely to be in advance of those which are exhibited by an intelligent animal. To give only one instance of this. My little girl when four and a half years old—or nearly two years after she had correctly used the terms indicative of true self-consciousness—wished to know what room was beneath the drawing-room of a house in which she had lived from the time of her birth. When she asked me to inform her, I told her to try to think out the problem for herself. She first suggested the bath-room, which was not only above the drawing-room, but also at the opposite side of the house; next she suggested the dining-room, which, although below the drawing-room, was also at the other side of the house; and so on, the child clearly having no power to think out so simple a problem as the one which she had spontaneously desired to solve. From which (as from many other instances on my notes in this connection) I conclude that the genesis of self-consciousness marks a comparatively low level in the evolution of the human mind—as we might expect that it should, if its genesis depends on the not unintelligible conditions which I have endeavored to explain. But, if so, does it not follow that great as the importance of self-consciousness afterwards proves to be as a condition to the higher development of ideation, in itself, or in its first beginning, it does not betoken any very perceptible improvement upon those powers of pre-conceptual ideation which it immediately follows? In other words, there is thus shown to be even less reason to regard the advent of self-consciousness as marking a psychological difference of kind, than there would be so to regard the advent of those higher powers of conceptual ideation which subsequently—though as gradually—supervene between early childhood and youth. Yet no one has hitherto ventured to suggest that the intelligence of a child and the intelligence of a youth display a difference of kind.

Or, otherwise stated, the psychological interval between my cebus and my child (when the former successfully investigated the mechanical principle of the screw by means of his highly developed receptual faculties, while the latter unsuccessfully attempted to solve a most simple topographical problem by means of her lowly developed conceptual faculties), was assuredly much less than that which afterwards separated the intelligence of my child from this level of its own previous self. Therefore, on merely psychological grounds, I conclude that there would be better—or *less bad*—reasons for alleging that there is an observable difference of kind between the lowest and the highest levels of conceptual ideation, than there is to allege that any such difference obtains between the lowest level of conceptual ideation and the highest level of receptual.

"The greatest of all distinctions in biology," when it first arises, is thus seen to lie in its *potentiality* rather than in its *origin*. Self-consciousness is, indeed, the condition to an immeasurable change in the mind which presents it; but, in order to become so, it must be itself conditioned: it must itself undergo a long and gradual development under the guiding principles of a natural evolution.

And now, lastly, the second supplementary consideration which I have to adduce is, that even in the case of a fully developed self-conscious intelligence, both receptual and preconceptual ideation continue to play an important part. That is to say, even in the full-summed powers of the human intellect, the three descriptions of ideation which I have distinguished are so constantly and so intimately blended together, that analysis of the adult mind corroborates the fact already yielded by analysis of the infantile mind, namely, that the distinctions (which I have been obliged to draw in order to examine the allegations of my opponents) are all essentially or intrinsically artificial. My position is that Mind is everywhere continuous, and if for purposes of analysis or classification we require to draw lines of demarcation between the lower and the higher faculties thereof, I contend that we should only do so as an evolutionist classifies his animal or vegetable species: higher or lower do not betoken differences of *origin*, but differences of *development*.

And just as the naturalist finds a general corroboration of this view in the fact that structural and functional characters are carried upwards from lower to higher forms of life, thus knitting them all together in the bonds of organic evolution; so may the psychologist find that even the highest forms of human intelligence unmistakably share the more essential characters met with in the lower, thus bearing testimony to their own lineage in a continuous system of mental evolution.

Comment

THE developmental history of higher animals, like that of many lower vertebrate and invertebrate groups, is characterized by the intervention of an extended period between embryogeny and the acquisition of mature adult structure and functions. The necessities of independent existence compel the larvae of many insects and the embryos of lower organisms to provide themselves with food and shelter during maturation. The growth period of higher organisms is marked by parental care and protection and by freedom from the rigors of obtaining food and shelter. Anaximander had recognized the helplessness of man during his infancy and youth, but the notion appears to have been wholly ignored until proponents of the theory of evolution routed the special-creationists. Then John Fiske, famed Harvard historian and philosopher and leading American proponent of Spencerian principles, revived the hoary idea in seeking to apply the theory of evolution to the social development of mankind.

Fiske was especially impressed by man's psychical progress during periods of evolution. The Hominidae had demonstrated an ever increasing mastery over materials and forces in nature and had brought them increasingly into his services through discoveries made possible by developing intellectual prowess. In the Lamarckian natural sciences Fiske found, as his biographer put it,

. . . a mass of scientific evidence, the truth of which could not be gainsaid, which was clear indication that the life of civilized man, as shown by his origin and his progressive development towards spiritual and ethical ideals, was the highest manifestation of the Divine Creator's power and purpose in this universe of things.[9]

Solidly convinced of the "facts" of man's cosmic destiny, Fiske searched the revelations of Spencer, Huxley, and Darwin for clues. His quest was not unrewarded. Evidence pointed to the probability that organic

[9] J. S. Clark, The Life and Letters of John Fiske, 2 vols. (Boston: Houghton Mifflin, 1917), Vol. I, pp. 315–316.

evolution advanced to a higher plane when, in the struggle for existence, psychical powers became more serviceable than physical functions. Fiske further recognized that gains in cerebral ingenuity were accompanied by corresponding prolongations of infancy. He saw that the span between birth and maturity had lengthened in man to one third of his life; moreover, the accompanying increase in self-consciousness had led to less self-regard and more mutual self-concern and thus, among primitive men, to the emergence of the family. Following these advances, social organization and systems of moral conduct arose. Surveying the vast accomplishments of evolution, Fiske believed his theory on the prolonging of infancy predicted that psychical forces would slowly but inevitably rid man of an egotistical animal nature and would replace his bestiality with psychical characters dominated by spiritual and ethical principles.

Fiske's theory on the origin of infancy and family relations was first offered in the October 1873 issue of the *North American Review* in an article entitled "The Progress from Brute to Man." Fiske felt elated! He thought he had published an extraordinarily important theory that explained why the human species growth period was longer than that of most other species. In 1884 he elaborated on his theory in a small volume entitled *The Destiny of Man in the Light of His Origin*. As the years receded, however, Fiske's disappointment grew. His monumental theory endured unheralded! Writing in the Preface to *A Century of Science*, twenty-five years after first promulgating the theory, Fiske lamented its anonymity:

In point of fact, not the faintest suggestion of this infancy theory can be found in all the writings of Darwin, Huxley, and Romanes. In Spencer's "Sociology," it is briefly mentioned with approval as an important contribution originating with me; and in Drummond's "Ascent of Man," which is really built upon it, credit is cordially given me. Indeed, down to the present time, I have been left almost in exclusive possession of that area of speculation. . . . There are many who assent to what I have put forth, but few who seem inclined to enter that difficult field on the marchland between biology, psychology, and sociology.[10]

Fiske also forfeited his claim to homage in the twentieth century on two counts. First, he subverted with teleological suppositions his understanding of natural consequences in evolution. Second, his theory of infancy was deficient in that it failed to hold for man's primate forerunners and for other higher animals, whose relatively long infancy period apparently had not led proportionately to significant advances in their social organization. Still, his lucid explanation of the way in which molecular

[10] J. Fiske, *A Century of Science*, Boston: Houghton Mifflin, 1900, pp. v–vi.

disturbances among cerebral cells and fibers, convolutions on the cerebral surface, and acquisition of learning capacity interrelated with the length of the infancy period resonates well with contemporary neuropsychological theories. At the close of the century, however, the latter issues were only secondarily important to Fiske. As the first of the selections reveals, Fiske was indeed infatuated with the evolutionary implications of the infancy theory. The second selection, nonetheless, offers an extended description of his provocative interpretation of human plasticity, and suggests that he may be due greater regard as the harbinger of an important psychological theory than he has been accorded.

John Fiske (1842–1901)

THE DESTINY OF MAN VIEWED IN THE LIGHT OF HIS ORIGIN

When Darwin's *Descent of Man* was published in 1871, it was of course a book characterized by all his immense learning, his wonderful fairness of spirit and fertility of suggestion. Still, one could not but feel that it did not solve the question of the origin of man. There was one great contrast between that book and his *Origin of Species*. In the earlier treatise he undertook to point out a *vera causa* of the origin of species, and he did it. In his *Descent of Man* he brought together a great many minor generalizations which facilitated the understanding of man's origin. But he did not come at all near to solving the central problem, nor did he anywhere show clearly why natural selection might not have gone on forever producing one set of beings after another distinguishable chiefly by physical differences. But Darwin's co-discoverer, Alfred Russel Wallace, at an early stage in his researches, struck out a most brilliant and pregnant suggestion. In that one respect Wallace went further than ever Darwin did. It was a point of which, indeed, Darwin admitted the importance. It was a point of which nobody could fail to understand the importance, that in the course of the evolution of a very highly organized animal, if there came a point at which it was of more advantage to that animal to have variations in his intelligence seized upon and im-

Source: J. Fiske. *A Century of Science* (New York: Houghton Mifflin, 1899). Selections from "The Part Played by Infancy in the Evolution of Man," Chapter 4, pp. 103–106. J. Fiske, *The Destiny of Man Viewed in the Light of His Origin* (Boston: Houghton Mifflin, 1884). "The Origin of Infancy," Chapter 4, pp. 35–41, "The Dawning of Consciousness," Chapter 5, pp. 42–50, and "Lengthening of Infancy and Concomitant Increase of Brain-Surface," Chapter 6, pp. 51–57.

proved by natural selection than to have physical changes seized upon, then natural selection would begin working almost exclusively upon that creature's intelligence, and he would develop in intelligence to a great extent, while his physical organism would change but slightly. Now, that of course applied to the case of man, who is changed physically but very slightly from the apes, while he has traversed intellectually such a stupendous chasm.

As soon as this statement was made by Wallace, it seemed to me to open up an entirely new world of speculation. There was this enormous antiquity of man, during the greater part of which he did not know enough to make history. We see man existing here on the earth, no one can say how long, but surely many hundreds of thousands of years, yet only during just the last little fringe of four or five thousand years has he arrived at the point where he makes history. Before that, something was going on, a great many things were going on, while his ancestors were slowly growing up to that point of intelligence where it began to make itself felt in the recording of events. This agrees with Wallace's suggestion of a long period of psychical change, accompanied by slight physical change.

Well, in the spring of 1871, when Darwin's *Descent of Man* came out, just about the same time I happened to be reading Wallace's account of his experiences in the Malay Archipelago, and how at one time he caught a female orang-outang with a new-born baby, and the mother died, and Wallace brought up the baby orang-outang by hand; and this baby orang-outang had a kind of infancy which was a great deal longer than that of a cow or a sheep, but it was nothing compared to human infancy in length. This little orang-outang could not get up and march around, as mammals of less intelligence do, when he was first born, or within three or four days; but after three or four weeks or so he would get up, and begin taking hold of something and pushing it around, just as children push a chair; and he went through a period of staring at his hands, as human babies do, and altogether was a good deal slower in getting to the point where he could take care of himself. And while I was reading of that I thought, Dear me! if there is any one thing in which the human race is signally distinguished from other mammals, it is in the enormous duration of their infancy; but it is a point that I do not recollect ever seeing any naturalist so much as allude to.

THE ORIGIN OF INFANCY

But before we can fully understand the exalted position which the Darwinian theory assigns to man, another point demands consideration.

The natural selection of psychical peculiarities does not alone account for the origin of Man, or explain his most signal difference from all other animals. That difference is unquestionably a difference in kind, but in saying this one must guard against misunderstanding. Not only in the world of organic life, but throughout the known universe, the doctrine of evolution regards differences in kind as due to the gradual accumulation of differences in degree. To cite a very simple case, what differences of kind can be more striking than the differences between a nebula, a sun, a planet like the earth, and a planet like our moon! Yet these things are simply examples of cosmical matter at four different stages of cooling. The physical differences between steam, water, and ice afford a more familiar example. In the organic world the perpetual modification of structures that has been effected through natural selection exhibits countless instances of differences in kind which have risen from the accumulation of differences in degree. No one would hesitate to call a horse's hoof different in kind from a cat's paw; and yet the horse's lower leg and hoof are undoubtedly developed from a five-toed paw. The most signal differences in kind are wont to arise when organs origi-nally developed for a certain purpose come to be applied to a very differ-ent purpose, as that change of the fish's air-bladder into a lung which accompanied the first development of land vertebrates. But still greater becomes the revolution when a certain process goes on until it sets going a number of other processes, unlocking series after series of causal agen-cies until a vast and complicated result is reached, such as could by no possibility have been foreseen. The creation of Man was one of these vast and complicated results due to the unlocking of various series of causal agencies; and it was the beginning of a deeper and mightier differ-ence in kind than any that slowly-evolving Nature had yet witnessed.

I have indicated, as the moment at which the creation of mankind began, the moment when psychical variations became of so much more use to our ancestors than physical variations that they were seized and enhanced by natural selection, to the comparative neglect of the latter. Increase of intellectual capacity, in connection with the developing brain of a single race of creatures, now became the chief work of natural selection in originating Man; and this, I say, was the opening of a new chapter, the last and most wonderful chapter, in the history of creation. But the increasing intelligence and enlarged experience of half-human man now set in motion a new series of changes which greatly complicated the matter. In order to understand these changes, we must consider for a moment one very important characteristic of developing intelligence.

The simplest actions in which the nervous system is concerned are what we call reflex actions. All the visceral actions which keep us alive from moment to moment, the movements of the heart and lungs, the contractions of arteries, the secretions of glands, the digestive operations of the stomach and liver, belong to the class of reflex actions. Throughout the animal world these acts are repeated, with little or no variation, from birth until death, and the tendency to perform them is completely organized in the nervous system before birth. Every animal breathes and digests as well at the beginning of his life as he ever does. Contact with air and food is all that is needed, and there is nothing to be learned. These actions, though they are performed by the nervous system, we do not class as psychical, because they are nearly or quite unattended by consciousness. The psychical life of the lowest animals consists of a few simple acts directed toward the securing of food and the avoidance of danger, and these acts we are in the habit of classing as instinctive. They are so simple, so few, and so often repeated, that the tendency to perform them is completely organized in the nervous system before birth. The animal takes care of himself as soon as he begins to live. He has nothing to learn, and his career is a simple repetition of the careers of countless ancestors. With him heredity is everything, and his individual experience is next to nothing.

As we ascend the animal scale till we come to the higher birds and mammals, we find a very interesting and remarkable change beginning. The general increase of intelligence involves an increasing variety and complication of experiences. The acts which the animal performs in the course of its life become far more numerous, far more various, and far more complex. They are therefore severally repeated with less frequency in the lifetime of each individual. Consequently the tendency to perform them is not completely organized in the nervous system of the offspring before birth. The short period of ante-natal existence does not afford time enough for the organization of so many and such complex habitudes and capacities. The process which in the lower animals is completed before birth is in the higher animals left to be completed after birth. When the creature begins its life it is not completely organized. Instead of the power of doing all the things which its parents did, it starts with the power of doing only some few of them; for the rest it has only latent capacities which need to be brought out by its individual experience after birth. In other words, it begins its separate life not as a matured creature, but as an infant which needs for a time to be watched and helped.

THE DAWNING OF CONSCIOUSNESS

Here we arrive at one of the most wonderful moments in the history of creation—the moment of the first faint dawning of consciousness, the foreshadowing of the true life of the soul. Whence came the soul we no more know than we know whence came the universe. The primal origin of consciousness is hidden in the depths of the bygone eternity. That it cannot possibly be the product of any cunning arrangement of material particles is demonstrated beyond peradventure by what we now know of the correlation of physical forces. The Platonic view of the soul, as a spiritual substance, an effluence from Godhood, which under certain conditions becomes incarnated in perishable forms of matter, is doubtless the view most consonant with the present state of our knowledge. Yet while we know not the primal origin of the soul, we have learned something with regard to the conditions under which it has become incarnated in material forms. Modern psychology has something to say about the dawning of conscious life in the animal world. Reflex action is unaccompanied by consciousness. The nervous actions which regulate the movements of the viscera go on without our knowledge; we learn of their existence only by study, as we learn of facts in outward nature. If you tickle the foot of a person asleep, and the foot is withdrawn by simple reflex action, the sleeper is unconscious alike of the irritation and of the movement, even as the decapitated frog is unconscious when a drop of nitric acid falls on his back and he lifts up a leg and rubs the place. In like manner the reflex movements which make up the life of the lowest animals are doubtless quite unconscious, even when in their general character they simulate conscious actions, as they often do. In the case of such creatures, the famous hypothesis of Descartes, that animals are automata, is doubtless mainly correct. In the case of instincts also, where the instinctive actions are completely organized before birth, and are repeated without variation during the whole lifetime of the individual, there is probably little if any consciousness. It is an essential prerequisite of consciousness that there should be a period of delay or tension between the receipt of an impression and the determination of the consequent movement. Diminish this period of delay and you diminish the vividness of consciousness. A familiar example will make this clear. When you are learning to play a new piece of music on the piano, especially if you do not read music rapidly, you are intensely conscious of each group of notes on the page, and of each group of keys that you strike, and of the relations of the one to the other. But when you have learned the piece by heart, you think nothing of either notes or keys, but play automatically while your attention is concentrated upon the artistic character of the music. If somebody thoughtlessly interrupts you with a question about Egyptian politics, you go on playing while you answer him politely. That is, where you had at first to make a conscious act of volition for each movement, the whole group of movements has now become automatic, and volition is only concerned in setting the process going. As the delay involved in the perception and the movement disappears, so does the consciousness of the perception and the movement tend to disappear. Consciousness implies perpetual discrimination, or the recognition of likenesses and differences, and this is impossible unless impressions persist long enough to be compared with one another. The physical organs in connection with whose activity consciousness is manifested are the upper and outer parts of the brain—the cerebrum and cerebellum. These organs never receive impressions directly from the outside world, but only from lower nerve-centres, such as the spinal cord, the medulla, the optic lobes, and other special centres of sensation. The impressions received by the cerebrum and cerebellum are waves of molecular disturbance sent up along centripetal nerves from the lower centres, and presently drafted off along centrifugal nerves back to the lower centres, thus causing the myriad movements which make up our active life. Now there is no consciousness except when molecular disturbance is generated in the cerebrum and cerebellum faster than it can be drafted off to the lower centres. It is the surplus of molecular disturbance remaining in the cerebrum and cerebellum, and reflected back and forth among the cells and fibres of which these highest centres are composed, that affords the physical condition for the manifestation of consciousness. Memory, emotion, reason, and volition begin with this retention of a surplus of molecular motion in the highest centres. As we survey the vertebrate sub-kingdom of animals, we find that as this surplus increases, the surface of the highest centres increases in area. In the lowest vertebrate animal, the amphioxus, the cerebrum and cerebellum do not exist at all. In fishes we begin to find them, but they are much smaller than the optic lobes. In such a highly organized fish as the halibut, which weighs about as much as an average-sized man, the cerebrum is smaller than a melon-seed. Continuing to grow by adding concentric layers at the surface, the cerebrum and cerebellum become much larger in birds and lower mammals, gradually covering up the optic lobes. As we pass to higher mammalian forms, the growth of the cerebrum becomes most conspicuous, until it extends backwards so far as to cover up the cerebellum, whose functions are limited to the conscious adjustment of muscular movements. In the higher apes the cerebrum begins to extend itself forwards, and this goes on in the human race. The cranial capacity of the European exceeds that of the Australian by forty cubic inches, or nearly four times as much as that by which the Australian exceeds the gorilla and the expansion is almost entirely in the upper and anterior portions. But the increase of the cerebral surface is shown not only in the general size of the organ, but to a still greater extent in the irregular creasing and furrowing of the surface. This creasing and furrowing begins to occur in the higher mammals, and in civilized man it is carried to an astonishing extent. The amount of intelligence is correlated with the number, the depth, and the irregularity of the furrows. A cat's brain has a few symmetrical creases. In an ape the creases are deepened into slight furrows, and they run irregularly, somewhat like the lines in the palm of your hand. With age and experience the furrows grow deeper and more sinuous, and new ones appear; and in man these phenomena come to have great significance. The cerebral surface of a human infant is like that of an ape. In an adult savage, or in a European peasant, the furrowing is somewhat marked and complicated. In the brain of a great scholar, the furrows are very deep and crooked, and hundreds of creases appear which are not found at all in the brains of ordinary men. In other words, the cerebral surface of such a man, the seat of conscious mental life, has become enormously enlarged in area; and we must further observe that it goes on enlarging in some cases into extreme old age.

Putting all these facts together, it becomes plain that in the lowest animals, whose lives consist of sundry reflex actions monotonously repeated from generation to generation, there can be nothing, or next to nothing, of what we know as consciousness. It is only when the life becomes more complicated and various, so that reflex action can no longer determine all its movements and the higher nerve-centres begin to be evolved, that the dawning of consciousness is reached. But with the growth of the higher centres the capacities of action become so various and indeterminate that definite direction is not given to them until after birth. The creature begins life as an infant, with its partially developed cerebrum representing capabilities which it is left for its individual experience to bring forth and modify.

LENGTHENING OF INFANCY, AND CONCOMITANT INCREASE OF BRAIN-SURFACE

The first appearance of infancy in the animal world thus heralded the new era which was to be crowned by the development of Man. With the beginnings of infancy there came the first dawning of a conscious life similar in nature to the conscious life of human beings, and there came, moreover, on the part of parents, the beginning of feelings and actions not purely self-regarding. But still more, the period of infancy was a period of plasticity. The career of each individual being no longer wholly predetermined by the careers of its ancestors, it began to become teachable. Individuality of character also became possible at the same time, and for the same reason. All birds and mammals which take care of their young are teachable, though in very various degrees, and all in like manner show individual peculiarities of disposition, though in most cases these are slight and inconspicuous. In dogs, horses, and apes there is marked teachableness, and there are also marked differences in individual character.

But in the non-human animal world all these phenomena are but slightly developed. They are but the dim adumbrations of what was by and by to bloom forth in the human race. They can scarcely be said to have served as a prophecy of the revolution that was to come. One generation of dumb beasts is after all very like another, and from studying the careers of the mastodon, the hipparion, the sabre-toothed lion, or even the dryopithecus, an observer in the Miocene age could never have foreseen the possibility of a creature endowed with such a boundless capacity of progress as the modern Man. Nevertheless, however dimly suggestive was this group of phenomena, it contained the germ of all that is preëminent in humanity. In the direct line of our ancestry it only needed that the period of infancy should be sufficiently prolonged, in order that a creature should at length appear, endowed with the teachableness, the individuality, and the capacity for progress which are the peculiar prerogatives of fully-developed Man. In this direct line the manlike apes of Africa and the Indian Archipelago have advanced far beyond the mammalian world in general. Along with a cerebral surface, and an accompanying intelligence, far greater than that of other mammals, these tailless apes begin life as helpless babies, and are unable to walk, to feed themselves, or to grasp objects with precision until they are two or three months old. These apes have thus advanced a little way upon the peculiar road which our half-human forefathers began to travel as soon as psychical variations came to be of more use to the species than variations in bodily structure. The gulf by which the lowest known man is separated from the highest known ape consists in the great increase of his cerebral surface, with the accompanying intelligence, and in the very long duration of his infancy. These two things have gone hand in hand. The increase of cerebral surface, due to the working of natural selection in this direction alone, has entailed a vast increase in the amount of cerebral organization that must be left to be completed after birth, and thus has prolonged the period of infancy. And conversely the prolonging of the plastic period of infancy, entailing a vast increase in teachableness and versatility, has contributed to the further enlargement of the cerebral surface. The mutual reaction of these two groups of facts must have gone on for an enormous length of time since man began thus diverging from his simian brethren. It is not likely that less than a million years have elapsed since the first page of this new chapter in the history of creation was opened: it is probable that the time has been much longer. In comparison with such a period, the whole recorded duration of human history shrinks into nothingness. The pyramids of Egypt seem like things of yesterday when we think of the Cave-Men of western Europe in the glacial period, who scratched pictures of mammoths on pieces of reindeer-antler with a bit of pointed flint. Yet during an entire geologic aeon before these Cave-Men appeared on the scene, "a being erect upon two legs," if we may quote from Serjeant Buzfuz, "and wearing the outward semblance of a man and not of a monster," wandered hither and thither over the face of the earth, setting his mark upon it as no other creature yet·had done, leaving behind him innumerable tell-tale remnants of his fierce and squalid existence, yet too scantily endowed with wit to make any written disclosure of his thoughts and deeds. If the physiological annals of that long and weary time could now be unrolled before us, the principal fact which we should discern, dominating all other facts in interest and significance, would be that mutual reaction between increase of cerebral surface and lengthening of babyhood which I have here described.

Thus through the simple continuance and interaction of processes that began far back in the world of warm-blooded animals, we get at last a creature essentially different from all others. Through the complication of effects the heaping up of minute differences in degree has ended in bringing forth a difference in kind. In the human organism physical variation has well-nigh stopped, or is confined to insignificant features, save in the grey surface of the cerebrum. The work of cerebral organization is chiefly completed after birth, as we see by contrasting the smooth ape-like brain-surface of the new-born child with the deeply-furrowed and myriad-seamed surface of the adult civilized brain. The plastic period of adolescence, lengthened in civilized man until it has come to cover more than one third of his lifetime, is thus the guaranty of his boundless progressiveness. Inherited tendencies and aptitudes still form the foundations of character; but individual experience has come to count as an enormous factor in modifying the career of mankind from generation to generation. It is not too much to say that the difference between man and all other living creatures, in respect to teachableness, progressiveness, and individuality of character, surpasses all other differences of kind that are known to exist in the universe.

PART FIVE

Genetic Psychology at Clark University

AFTER he had made a fortune in selling mining tools and implements to gold seekers in California, Jonas Gilman Clark, aspiring to be the founder and benefactor of a great university, returned in the 1880s to his native Worcester, Massachusetts. He enticed G. Stanley Hall, who was awed by Clark's affluence and ebullience, to leave his post as professor of psychology and director of one of the earliest psychological laboratories at Johns Hopkins University and to become the first president of Clark University.

Hall graduated from Williams College in 1867 and considered the ministry as a career seriously enough to enter Union Theological Seminary. His insatiable curiosity, however, soon led him to Germany for study. He returned to teach English and psychology at Antioch College from 1872 to 1876 and then went to Harvard to complete his formal education, where under William James he earned the first Ph.D. in psychology to be awarded in America. The cloistered years at American and European universities enabled Hall to become conversant in theology, philosophy, anthropology, biology, physiology, anatomy, psychology, and neurology. Moreover, his immense capacity for absorbing and integrating information surpassed that of most of the noted scholars with whom he studied. Esteemed a genius by many of his colleagues, G. Stanley Hall fielded the concepts from disciplines of great diversity with a facility and ease unequaled by any other American scholar.

Classes at Clark began auspiciously in the autumn of 1889. The natural sciences, spurred by the theory of evolution, had seasoned and matured. The social sciences, although still in their infancy, were beginning to distinguish themselves when the charismatic Hall charged upon the scene, magnetically drawing into synthesis random ideas from every conceivable source. He was bursting with ideas for innovations in higher education, which were gleaned from a revisit to European universities. Moreover, he was justly proud of the excellent faculty that he had recruited. Edmund C. Sanford, for example, manned the new psychology laboratory, Franz Boaz held forth in anthropology, and William H. Burham headed the pedagogy department. Sanford, a first-rate experimental psychologist, remained aloof from the controversy that emanated from the theory of recapitulation at Clark. Similarly, Boaz averted the effulgence of that controversy and eventually distinguished himself as one of the forerunners of contemporary anthropology. Burham, in contrast, became one of Hall's chief spokesmen for genetic psychology and after his ostensibly luminous career at Clark, glided into obscurity.

Shortly after the university had opened, however, Jonas Clark began to sense that his vision for a great university had been impaired and barricaded himself from Hall and the university trustees. More damagingly, he ceased appropriating funds and until his death in 1900, when the university inherited the bulk of his estate, fended off the disconsolate Hall with paralyzing duplicities. During these formative years at Clark, Hall could indulge in very little scholarly activity, but his tribulations proved to be in part a benefaction. He established himself as a buffer between Clark and his faculty, structured for them an atmosphere of freedom and independence, attracted a coterie of brilliant graduate students, and in spite of Clark's cantankerousness, created a graduate institution of estimable standing. Hall managed to resume teaching in 1893 and significantly, in one of his first acts as President-Professor, introduced the first course ever offered as a systematic exposition of genetic psychology.

G. Stanley Hall discerned the course, fittingly designated "Psychogenesis," as having been highly successful: "No course I have ever given sent so many of my students to the library or, I think, contributed quite so much to give them a general and wholesome conception of man's place in nature."[1] Hall lectured on "the stages by which the soul has evolved . . . theories of the origin of life as well as of mind . . . a crude outline of the findings of paleontology . . . the evolution of the inferior and then of the anthropoid apes . . . the rise of modern anthropology . . . the earliest human arts."[2] Aspects of the subject probably were being covered routinely in the biology, zoology, and anthropology departments, but Hall's unexcelled background in psychology and his implacable teleological and Neo-Lamarckian viewpoint added ardor and importunity to the genetic psychology program.

---

[1] G. S. Hall, *Life and Confessions of a Psychologist* (New York: Appleton, 1924), p. 365.
[2] *Ibid.*, pp. 363–364.

The fervor with which Hall ignited his lectures is readily understood from certain passages in his reminiscences. Here Hall revealed his Aristotelian underpinnings, confessed his indebtedness to earlier recapitulation theorists, and importantly, admitted his unscientific ambition to prove rather than substantiate the theory of recapitulation.

To conceive the Divine as a system of ganglia of reason which underlay and shaped all things seemed to me the consummation of philosophic endeavor. . . . Matter was sleeping mind. Mind was matter awakened, and vegetable and animal life and mind showed the stages of this awakening. Thus there was a kind of mystic, poetic stage of prelusion by which Darwin, Huxley, Spencer, Haeckel, and even Tyndall were, it seemed to me, prepared for in my philosophic history, and when these latter loomed large upon my horizon they were devoured with the utmost avidity. . . . To conceive the whole world, material and spiritual, as an organic unity, to eliminate all breaks and supernaturalism, and to realize that everything within and without was hoary with age, so that in most experiences we were dealing only with the topmost twigs of vast but deeply buried trees, gave me a totally new aspect of life. Inconsistencies troubled me little but I was everywhere in avid quest of illustrations of developmental stages to span all chasms, and I conceived all creative processes as still active, all about me, and above all felt that there was nothing really dead but that there was everywhere life abounding, filling all possibilities everywhere, which gave and still gives the deepest intellectual satisfaction that I have ever known. I was bat-eyed to difficulties and impatient at objections, and had a blind spot in my mind for every break in the developmental order and implicit faith that if there anywhere seemed to be gaps it was only because we lacked adequate knowledge.[3]

In 1883, after earning his Ph.D., Hall lingered in the Boston area. During this period he published the first American study of psychological development of children. The report consisted of analyses of a normative investigation that he had begun in 1880 to determine what knowledge the average Boston child of five or six might be expected to possess upon entering a public school. At the beginning of the school year Hall asked four kindergarten teachers to question the young boys and girls about animals, plants, celestial objects, their own bodies, numbers, stories, games, things they had done and had seen, religion, and so on. The ensuing publication, *The Content of Children's Minds*, and Henry P. Bowditch's 1879 study of the physical measurements of Boston schoolchildren mark the beginning of the child study movement in the United States. Nothing was known of individual development and its relation

[3] *Ibid.*, pp. 358–359. Reprinted by permission of Appleton-Century Co., affiliate of Meredith Press.

to school practices before Bowditch and Hall initiated their studies. Hall's investigation, linked as it was to evolution and recapitulation, exerted a sweeping influence and was promptly translated into several languages.

The decade intervening between Hall's publication of *The Content of Children's Minds* and his resumption of teaching witnessed Hall lecturing extensively throughout the United States. Hall sidestepped administrative burdens long enough to encourage teachers in at least seven states to establish associations for child study. In 1891 he founded, at his own expense, the *Pedagogical Seminary*, which was intended to be a journalistic outlet for papers on child and adolescent development. Within ten years, Hall had installed himself as the titular leader of a new field in child study and had made Clark University its hub. As a happy coincidence, the best of the nation's young Ph.D. prospects for programs in child study aggregated at Clark, such as Arnold Gesell and Frederick E. Bolton from school administrative posts in Wisconsin, and Lewis M. Terman, Henry H. Goddard, and Ellsworth G. Lancaster from teaching positions in Indiana, Maine, and Kansas, respectively.

The Content of Children's Minds produced the impetus for both the methods and the ideas of early genetic psychology. Hall's students relied heavily on the questionnaire method that he had pioneered. Extending Hall's approach, they set out, on the one hand, to assess what knowledge children at various ages might be expected to possess and to understand, and on the other, to discover which aspects of behavior were a result of learning and adaptation and which were recapitulatory, original, and atavistic. Questionnaire responses were elicited on almost every conceivable topic. Many queries concerned water, moons, trees, clouds, dogs, dolls, and puzzles. Information was compiled on situations that might provoke in children the qualities of fear, anger, love, pity, teasing, bullying, collecting, laughter, curiosity, rivalry, and jealousy. The data of early genetic psychology are of little use to contemporary child development specialists, partly because of the obsolescence of the recapitulatory framework, but even more importantly because of the methodological deficiencies inherent in the studies. Consider, for example, Hall's account of how teachers were asked to collect data:

In the paper on fears, for example, she gave a preliminary talk on the general subject and our lack of knowledge of it, how common and injurious fears were in childhood, and then instituted some general conversation on special fears—wind, snakes, lightning, cloud-forms, etc. Some would then confess their own childish experiences and this often was an open sesame. In this way it was sought to stimulate interest and awaken memory, and then each who desired to do so was invited to write out a rather full but very honest record of his own personal experiences with fear, following the rubrics of the questionnaire. Subjects of a different nature and those which required not memory but observation received, of course, different introductory treatment. The necessity of being definite and absolutely honest was always stressed. The questionnaire was often mimeographed or written on the board. Age, sex, and race were always to be specified as definitely as possible for each experience. No one was required to sign his or her paper although often by general consent the results were read in class so that each might benefit by the experience of all the others.[4]

G. Stanley Hall ruefully admitted that responses generated by this method raised perplexing questions.[5] He disclaimed their yielding definitive, conclusive answers to developmental questions, and he was fully aware both that the samples varied immensely in their representativeness of children in general and that only vaguely structured opinions were elicited. For all his genius and his acute awareness of scientific procedures, Hall still fondled the subjects' replies as if they were sacred. His compilers faithfully penned every precious clue to phylogenetic history and evolutionary destiny on the data sheets. Given the nature of the material, clues were plentiful, and in the hectic 1890s, dozens of papers bearing upon childhood and adolescence were published by the genetic psychologists at Clark. Finally, in 1904, only eleven years after initiating the course in "Psychogenesis," Hall had amassed enough data to publish *Adolescence*, a two-volume, 1373-page narration of improbable breadth and scope.

The following selections—two brief excerpts from the works of a colleague and a student of Hall's and an extended presentation from Chapter 10 of *Adolescence*—convey something of the enthusiasm and focus of the Clark group. The table and short comment from Alexander F. Chamberlain's *The Child* show the extent to which the recapitulation theorists relied on the theory that higher species experienced a prolonged growing period. It is noteworthy that Chamberlain, at that time a young instructor in anthropology at Clark, stressed Hall's emphasis of the theory while ignoring the likelihood that Hall had learned of it from Fiske. Ellsworth G. Lancaster proved to be one of the more productive of the orthodox recapitulation theorists. The passages reprinted here have been extracted from the conclusion of one of his prodigious analyses of questionnaire materials. They incorporate one of the clearest statements in genetic psychology as to the importance of adolescence in the recapitulatory scheme, and suggest why as an area of study adolescence seemed more consequential than childhood. The selection from Hall's magnum opus,

---

[4] Hall, *op. cit.*, p. 390. Reprinted by permission of Appleton-Century Co., affiliate of Meredith Press.
[5] *Ibid.*, p. 390.

disclosing his perspective on the future of genetic psychology, his views on adolescent instability, and his conviction that adolescence is "the only point of departure for the superanthropoid that man is to become," speaks eloquently for itself.

ALEXANDER FRANCIS CHAMBERLAIN (1865–1914)

THE PROLONGATION OF THE GROWING PERIOD IN MAN

The whole period of growth in man, adolescence (if we interpret the term literally), seems to form a considerably larger portion of his life than the corresponding epoch in the existence of other mammals. The fact that "the ratio of length of adolescence to length of life in the shortest-lived mammals is proportionately very much less than it is in longer-lived mammals," is noted by Dr. W. Ainslie Hollis and Mr. E. D. Bell. Dr. Hollis fixes the completed growth of man "by the union of the sternal epiphysis of the clavicle to its shaft at 25," although there are "great individual differences in the osseous union of the epiphyses," and "all the epiphyses were observed by Otto to be separate in the skeleton of a man aged 27 years, who, had he lived, might truthfully have posed as a youth when he was on the verge of 40." It is apparent, therefore, that 25 years as the time for the "completed growth" of man, and 75 years for his "length of life," are only approximate figures, since the former is perhaps too low, and the latter leaves out of consideration "exceptionally long lives." Mr. Bell, who accepts the time of union of the epiphyses with the skeleton as the "best measure of the period of maturity," considers that the period of maturity is "about from one and a half times to twice the period of puberty: one and two-thirds and twice seem common proportions. Man, for example, arrives at puberty at about 15, and is mature at 25; the lion and tiger arrive at puberty at 3 years, and are mature at 6."

The table, compiled from those of Dr. Hollis and Mr. Bell, shows the progressing lengthening of adolescence with mammalian longevity.

SOURCE: A. F. Chamberlain. *The Child: A Study in the Evolution of Man* (New York: Charles Scribner's Sons, 1900). Selection from "The Meaning of the Helplessness of Infancy," Chapter 1, pp. 7–9. Abridged. Footnotes deleted.

COMPARATIVE ADOLESCENCE AND LONGEVITY

Animal	Authority	Length of Adolescence	Length of Life (Years)
Dormouse	Hollis	3 Months	4–5
Guinea-pig	Flourens; Hollis	7 Months	6–7
Lop Rabbit (Buck)	R. O. Edwards	9 Months	8
Lop Rabbit (Doe)	R. O. Edwards	8 Months	8
Cat	Mivart	1 Year	12
Cat	Jennings	2 Years	15
Goat	Pegler	1 Year and 3 months	12
Fox	Mivart	1 Year and 6 months	13–14
English Cattle	Hollis	2 Years	18
Large Dogs	Dalziel	2 Years	15–20
English thoroughbred Horses	Hollis	4 Years and 6 months	30
Hog	Long; Hollis	5 Years	30
Hippopotamus	Chambers's Encyclopædia	5 Years	30
Lion	Mivart	6 Years	30–40
English Horse (Hunter)	Blaine; Hollis	6 Years and 3 months	35
Arab Horse	Hollis	8 Years	40
Camel	Flourens	8 Years	40
Man	Buffon	25 Years	90–100
Man (Englishman)	Hollis	25 Years	75
Elephant	Darwin	30 Years	100
Elephant	Holder, etc.	35 Years	120

Human adolescence would appear to be from one-third to one-fourth of life according to Hollis and Buffon. The centenarian's term of life makes it but one-fourth, as compared with the one-fifth of the Arab horse, the two-fifteenths of the thoroughbred horse, the one-ninth of English cattle, the one-eighth of the lop rabbit, the one-twelfth of the guinea-pig, and the one-sixteenth of the mouse. If the expectation of life at 25 years of age be considered, some 40 years remain to man after such maturity, adolescence and length of life being in the proportion of $1:2\frac{3}{5}$. In many respects this lengthening of the period of growth or adolescence in man is one of the most remarkable phenomena of his existence—intra-uterine life, infancy, childhood, youth, seem all to have increased in duration, for the shaping of the human being, and the complicated environment accompanying modern civilisation tends to lengthen more and more the period of immaturity. In a sense, then, the child is really the "father of the man," for the modern man is becoming more and more of a child, or rather the modern child is losing less of childhood in the process of becoming a man. Emphasis has been laid upon this prolongation of adolescence by Dr. G. Stanley Hall as one of the most notable features of modern human society. Professor N. M. Butler points out that "while the physiological period of adolescence is only 14 or 15 years, the educational period is nearly twice as long; indeed the period in which social heredity finds him still plastic has come to be about 30 years." In fixing the age for Congressman at 25, and for Senator at 30, the framers of the Constitution of the United States unconsciously safeguarded popular education for the future at least. The ages to come must interpret the saying of Schleiermacher: "Being a child must not hinder becoming a man; becoming a man must not hinder being a child."

ELLSWORTH GAGE LANCASTER (1861–1934)

THE CHARACTERISTICS OF ADOLESCENCE

THE period of adolescence is the focal point of all psychology.

However we may look upon the origin of the human intellect, whether from an evolutionary standpoint or otherwise, it is easy to conceive that mind as such awoke to self-consciousness at the adolescent period of the first man. Adam and Eve were evidently in the adolescent period when they awoke to self-consciousness.

The spirit of rebellion against authority and the whole account of the later scene in the garden is typical adolescent psychology. If we take man as an evolution, we must think of him as coming to self-consciousness in this period of life when the pendulum swings farthest and there is the greatest ferment known in the individual history. In other words adolescence is the time of the soul's awakening both in the race and in the individual. From this first awakening, mind has pushed up to full rational self-consciousness and then directed its attention backward over the path of its development to pre-adolescent stages, including not only the psychology of childhood but of animal life down to the lowest traces of intelligent activities.

Adult psychology begins in the adolescent period and child psychology with its hereditary influences ends here.

To understand the human mind in later life, adolescence must be studied to find what stages of development have been passed through and

SOURCE: E. G. Lancaster, The Psychology and Pedagogy of Adolescence. *Pedagogical Seminary*, 1897–1898, 5, 61–128. Selection from "Conclusions," Chapter 3, pp. 119–123. Footnotes deleted.

in what stages the development has been arrested. It is, then, the period on which the study of the psychology of the individual should focus.

The characteristics of the psychology of adolescence are, for the most part, distinct. The length of the period is indefinite. It varies with each individual.

The most prominent feature of adolescence is the emotional life. The emotions are not confined to the years 10 to 25, but they are much farther beneath the surface in later life, and can be awakened to expression only by different or stronger stimuli. The emotional nature seems to mature rapidly and nearly reach its maximum before the intellectual or rational side, if they may be separated, has developed. This gives preponderance to the emotions and characterizes the period.

The moods normally are strongest and most fluctuating during adolescence. Despondency, spontaneous joy, love, hate, selfishness, generosity, sloth and energy of both mind and body, all very intense in degree, are strictly adolescent phenomena. They are normally outgrown unless development is arrested.

The growth of the ethical nature and the deep, broad, intellectual interests root in the emotional life of adolescence. If the instinct emotions are properly guided, they will pass over into permanent intellectual interests.

The mind, including all psychic life, grows by sections. The interest may center in prize-fights or foot-ball one year, and the next in æsthetic culture. The musical side may absorb the energy for a time to pass and be forgotten. The growth of the mind may be compared to a circle which enlarges by extending one sector at a time out to a new circumference.

These absorbing and diverse interests may be compared to separate sectors which push out to reach their final limit. The circumference or final intellectual horizon of adult life is determined, therefore, by the intensity of these interests and the extent to which they are pushed. Many interests enthusiastically cultivated mean a wide intellectual horizon.

The discussion can hardly be laid aside without a suggestion as to the cause of these adolescent phenomena. The idea is often advanced that the development of the reproductory function on the physical side causes these mental phenomena. The present study suggests a different view.

It is true that the curves of most of these phenomena culminate within a year or two of the time of puberty. But some of the strongest adolescent emotions are reported by many individuals as occurring years before or years after puberty.

The strongest adolescent symptoms are found in the most highly developed organisms which are farthest removed from the physical or brute nature, and where reproductory power is often very weak.

Dr. Scott showed the relation between sex and art and took the position that art is an irradiation of sex. It might well be shown that there is a similar relation between sex and other things. There are many irradiations of sex. School and college life is one. Sex does not cause art any more than sex causes intellectual ability, but both draw their vitality from a common fountain, and when one draws more than its share the other suffers.

Adolescent phenomena sometimes appear with all their intensity in old age. This is not necessarily a recurrence or a retraversing of the neural paths or channels cut in adolescence, for one person, who has been carefully studied, has passed through an entirely new set of emotions in his senile adolescence which were unknown to him when a young man. In this particular case the sex element was very strong in youth, and the mental adolescence not marked by great fluctuations. After 70 years of age a very intense mental adolescence developed with vivid religious experiences unknown in earlier life.

The adolescent interests seem to depend on the size and quality of the brain in direct ratio, and are inversely proportional to the growth and vitality centering in the reproductive organs. That is, precocious and abnormal use of the reproductive function destroys mental adolescence, with its many sided interests, faster than anything else.

It is true that depression and a desire for solitude, and possibly other similar phenomena, may accompany such degenerate use of this function, but they are of a very different kind from the normal adolescent love of solitude and passing moods of depression. The final reason for my inability to believe that sex is the cause, is the fact that eunuchs have the same adolescent symptoms as others.

I have also found several cases of phimosis, which arrested all growth of the organs, but did not apparently affect in the least the mental adolescence. The effect of castration on animals arrests development of organs of combat and makes other changes. We cannot argue here from animals to man. Man learned long ago to rely on brain more than brawn. Castration or arrested development does not make changes in man which are comparable to the changes made in animals.

The physical change of features at this time suggests another reason for these adolescent phenomena. They indicate a change of hereditary influences. From the moment that the spermatozoon unites with the ovum there is a conflict of hereditary influences between the two, that the life contained in each may assert and express itself. Common observation shows that this conflict of these microscopic elements, even in the closed apartment, with all nervous connections to the rest of the body as yet undeveloped, is so violent as to cause a disturbance of the sympathetic and vaso-motor systems.

The fact that the type not only of features but also of family characteristics may change at adolescence, shows that these forces are still prominent and are struggling now in final conflict for the mastery and the opportunity of self-expression. This war of prepotencies, which causes or results in changed external features, is sufficient ground for the occasion of the adolescent mental phenomena. It is not the cause. It is also the occasion of the later development of the sex organs peculiar to the individual which will very likely be characteristic of the parent or family which he resembles in mental and physical characteristics. The cause must lie much farther back in the, as yet, unknown forces of life itself. When we know what life is, and where differentiations begin, we may speak of the cause of adolescent phenomena.

GRANVILLE STANLEY HALL (1844–1924)
THE PSYCHOLOGY OF ADOLESCENCE

HAPPILY for our craft, the child and youth appear at the truly psychological moment, freighted, as they are, body and soul, with reminiscences of what we were so fast losing. They are abandoned to joy, grief, passion, fear, and rage. They are bashful, show off, weep, laugh, desire, are curious, eager, regret, and swell with passion, not knowing that these last two are especially outlawed by our guild. There is color in their souls, brilliant, livid, loud. Their hearts are yet young, fresh, and in the golden age. Despite our lessening fecundity, our over-schooling, "city-fication," and spoiling, the affections we instil and the repressions we practise, they are still the light and hope of the world especially to us, who would know more of the soul of man and would penetrate to its deeper strata and study its origins.

Back of them, too, lies the great animal world, where often each species seems essentially but a feeling-instinct embodied, as the carnivora's cruelty, the rabbit's timidity, or the peacock's ostentation. A true science of character that goes beyond eye, ear, and motor mindedness, or activity

SOURCE: G. S. Hall. *Adolescence*, 2 vols. (New York: Appleton, 1904). Volume II. Selections from "Evolution and the Feelings and Instincts Characteristic at Normal Adolescence," Chapter 10, pp. 60–94. Abridged. Footnotes deleted.

and passivity, can not dispense with the deeper, older, and more fixed unary or binary or at most ternary compounds that were matured and compacted before man arose. In the new tentatives in ethology also, it is already apparent that true types of character can be determined only by studying the animal world; that man, e.g., inherits some of the aggressiveness of the carnivora and the timidity and deceit of creatures long preyed upon. Indeed, each animal group may represent some one quality in great excess, the high selective value of which made possible the development and survival of a species, genus, or group. It should not be forgotten that such psychological classification of psychic types may cross-section morphological divisions of species and genera. Each character type is thus a fulfilled possibility of development in some specific direction, and in man is based on unconscious, instinctive, prehuman, or animal traits, the elements of which are combined into aggregates of greater or less cohesion according to age or persistence in time, etc. This, of course, must be supplemented, first, by a quite independent study of the forms of degeneration; and, secondly, of the marked traits and dispositions in normal persons; and when the conclusions from all three classes of data concur, we may infer that we have a trait of more or less typical value. Individual psychology differs thus from comparative psychology chiefly in the fact that the former is concerned with slighter and more delicate variations, man's mode of adaptation being finer and more specific. These general considerations are here adverted to only to explain the general psychonomic law which assumes that we are influenced in our deeper, more temperamental dispositions by the life-habits and codes of conduct of we know not what unnumbered hosts of ancestors, which like a cloud of witnesses are present throughout our lives, that our souls are echo-chambers in which their whispers reverberate.

Assuming thus that the feeling-instincts of whatever name are the psychophores or bearers of mental heredity in us, some of which persist below the threshold of consciousness throughout our lives, while others are made over as instincts or are transformed to habits into directions of the will more or less persistent, we thus cross-section old methods and can approach this study with a mental horizon vastly widened and with an historic sense less atrophied. We have to deal with the archeology of mind, with zones or strata which precede consciousness as we know it, compared to which even it, and especially cultured intellect, is an upstart novelty, with everywhere a fuller and clearer expression of a part of the soul, but always partial, one-sided, and more accidental and precarious. Both the degree and the direction of development of intellect vary more with age, sex, environment, etc., and sharpen individuality, while the instinct-feelings in each person are broader, deeper, and more nearly comprehensive of the traits of the whole human race. It is in the latter alone that man is a microcosm, comprising anything like the large totality of human experience, so that for it, and not for conscious mind, it can be said that nothing human or prehuman is alien. These radicals of man's psychic life, while some of them are decadent, rudimentary, and superseded, are often important just in proportion to the depth of the phylogenetic strata into which they strike their roots. Hunger, love, pride, and many other instinctive feelings, to say nothing of pleasure and pain, can be traced far down through the scale of vertebrate and to invertebrate life.

It is plain, for these reasons, that they must be studied objectively and by careful observational methods, and that the genetic psychologist, while he must use introspection in the old way, or reenforced and perfected by experimental methods wherever they serve his purpose, will find it necessary, almost in exact proportion as his work becomes fundamental, to gather his data empirically from the comparative study of lower forms of life and of children and from the collation of the varied inner and outer experiences of many minds besides his own. Thus the psychologist of the future, if his science is to have a future, must turn to the past, by which alone it can be judged, and if he would be prophetic and helpful must move more freely with a far larger command of data up and down the phyletic scale. Thus, too, our ideals of what the most perfect knowledge of any fact or object really is, are coming to be more and more genetic. We really know things only when we trace their development from the farthest beginning through all their stages to maximal maturity and decay. Thus we shall never truly know ourselves till we know the mind of animals, and most especially those in our line of descent. We must recognize that some of them are our superiors in certain respects; that while we explain them by explication of those traits wherein we excel, they no whit less explain us by those of their traits which are superior to ours and of which our souls contain only relics; that if in general we are their realized entelechy, they are the key by which alone we can unlock many of the mysteries of our own origin and nature.

Thus again the same revolution in the studies that deal with soul impends that von Baer and Darwin represented for the body. Before their day, everything was classification, nomenclature, fixed species, just as with the pregenetic psychologists everything was faculties and processes, analyses and categories, as if the adult human mind, as we know it, were a fixed and settled thing. From the new standpoint, the human soul is one of many types of mind in the world. At best it may be a transition from a lower to a higher race to be evolved later. It is perhaps a temporary and accidental form which force or life has taken on in the world. If it is like a species, a stage of evolution, interrupted at a definite point, we can not truly know it until we have traced out all the roots and branches of the buried tree of its pedigree. We must study its changing phases historically. We can not know mind til we know minds. It is well not entirely to forget that in the great cosmic order revealed to the evolutionist, the mind, which modern analysts so carefully dissect, may be merely a developmental stage of that of a higher type as much above us as we are above the dwellers in Lemuria; that sometime even it may be studied as a link between the higher and the lower, and that it may itself some day become a missing one. . . .

Thus, in fine, the psyche is a quantum and direction of vital energy, the processes of which most need exploration and description, ordering and directing. By looking inward, we see for the most part only the topmost twigs of the buried tree of mind. The real ego is a spark struck off from the central source of all being, freighted with meanings that, could we interpret them, would give us the salient facts of its development history. Its essence is its processes of becoming. It is not a fixed, abiding thing, but grew out of antecedent soul states as different from its present forms as protoplasm is from the mature body. It tends to vary constantly and to depart indefinitely from what it is at any given moment. Every element has shaped and tempered it. Its long experience with light and darkness, day and night, has fashioned its rhythm indelibly. Heat and cold, the flickering of flame, smoke and ashes, especially since man learned the control of fire, have oriented it toward both thermal extremes. Cloud forms have almost created the imagination. Water and a long apprenticeship to aquatics and arboreal life have left as plain and indelible marks upon the soul as upon the body. Sky, stars, wind, storms, fetishism, flowers, animals, ancient battles, industries, occupations, and worship have polarized the soul to fear and affection, and created anger and pity. The superficial phenomena change, but all the deeper roots of the soul strike down and back to a past that long preceded history. The soul is thus a product of heredity. As such, it has been hammered, molded, shocked, and worked by the stern law of labor and suffering into its present crude form. It is covered with scars and wounds not yet healed. It is still in the rough, and patchworky, full of contradictions, although the most marvelous of all the products of nature. Where most educated and polished externally, it still has inner veins where barbaric and animal impulses are felt. Every individual soul is marked by limitations, defects, and arrests, often beside traits of marvelous beauty and virtue. None are complete, perfect, typical. Collective soul, however, is a sensorium of wondrous subtlety that reflects in its multipersonal facets most, perhaps all, that has been in the world. Our present quest is to detect some characteristic changes at that age of life when a certain group of powers emerges from the past; when heredity is bestowing its latest and therefore highest gifts; when the mind is most exquisitely sensitized to the aspects of nature and to social life, is repeating most rapidly the later neopsychic stages of phyletic experiences, and laying on this foundation the corner-stones of a new and unique adult personality.

These considerations must serve here to define the standpoint from which we now proceed to consider the more specific psychic changes which mark adolescence. We here face problems both more complex and more inaccessible than those connected with the somatic changes. The most important and basal of these are connected with the fact that powers and faculties, essentially non-existent before, are now born, and of all the older impulses and instincts some are reenforced and greatly developed, while others are subordinated, so that new relations are established and the ego finds a new center. In connection with the reproduction function, love is born with all its attendant passions—jealousy, rivalry, and all the manifold phenomena of human courtship. All the previous religious sentiments are regenerated and some now arise for the first time, motivating a wide plexus of new psychic relations between the individual and the race, and irradiating to the cosmos. Nature is felt and plays upon the soul with all its rich orchestra of influences. Art at this time may become an enthusiasm and is now first deeply and truly felt, even though it had been known and practised before. The ethical life is immensely broadened and deepened, because now a far deeper possibility and sense of sin and impurity arises. The floodgates of heredity are thrown open again somewhat as in infancy. As in the prenatal and infant stage man hears from his remoter forebears back perhaps to primitive organisms, now the later and higher ancestry takes up the burden of the song of life, and the voices of our extinct and perhaps forgotten, and our later and more human ancestry, are heard in the soul. Just as in the first birth the gifts of nature are of fundamental psycho-physic qualities, which are later elaborated and differentiated by development, so now her rich dotations are generic, and the accessory qualities that are unfolded out of them arise slowly from the feelings, instincts, impulses, dispositions, *Anlangen* and *Triebe*, which are the products of this later heritage.

In some respects, early adolescence is thus the infancy of man's higher nature, when he receives from the great all-mother his last capital of energy and evolutionary momentum. Thus the child is father of the man, far older and conditioning his nature. He is at the same time reduced back to a state of nature, so far as some of the highest faculties are concerned, again helpless, in need not only of guidance but of shelter and protection. His knowledge of self is less adequate and he must slowly work out his salvation. Character, temperament, emotions, and appetites are changed; the youth moves about in both an inner and an outer world unrealized. The parent and teacher must understand that mother nature has again taken her child upon her knee and must stand off a little to see and make room for her more perfect education. These years again, like infancy, should be sacred to heredity, and we should have a good warrant indeed before we venture to interfere with its processes.

Psychic adolescence is heralded by all-sided mobilization. The child from nine to twelve is well adjusted to his environment and proportionately developed; he represents probably an old and relatively perfected stage of race-maturity, still in some sense and degree feasible in warm climates, which, as we have previously urged, stands for a long-continued one, a terminal stage of human development at some post-simian point. At dawning adolescence this old unity and harmony with nature is broken up; the child is driven from his paradise and must enter upon a long viaticum of ascent, must conquer a higher kingdom of man for himself, break out a new sphere, and evolve a more modern story to his psychophysical nature. Because his environment is to be far more complex, the combinations are less stable, the ascent less easy and secure; there is more danger that the youth in his upward progress, under the influence of this "excelsior" motive, will backslide in one or several of the many ways possible. New dangers threaten on all sides. It is the most critical stage of life, because failure to mount almost always means retrogression, degeneracy, or fall. One may be in all respects better or worse, but can never be the same. The old level is left forever. Perhaps the myth of Adam and Eden describe this epoch. The consciousness of childhood is molted, and a new, larger, better consciousness must be developed, or increased exposure and vulnerability will bring deterioration. Before this, boys and girls have been interested largely in those of their own age and have had little interest in their future or in the life of adults. Their own life is too varied, intense, and absorbing. But the soul now realizes in a deeper sense the meaning of maturity and is protensive toward its higher plateau. Slowly the color and life fade from juvenile interests, which are deciduous like foliage or like milk teeth. Vocations beckon first faintly, and then more and more imperatively. Hero worship arises; youth aspires to excel, first perhaps by the order of nature in athletic contests, then in those of the mind. The young savage can not attain his new name or be initiated into adolescence until he has shown prowess or won some fame as a doer of deeds, as, e.g., by killing some large animal or in successful head-hunting. It is perhaps on the athletic field that youth has his first taste of gratified ambition and is fired thereby to constant discontent and *Sehnsucht* thereafter. He longs to struggle, make an effort, combat, loves a hard and strenuous and scorns an easy life. The great deeds and lives and prizes in the human world never shine so bright, seem so near, or beckon so alluringly. The youth wills all that he must or can; would be wise, strong, famous, talented, learned, rich, loved, and withal good and perfect. When the thought of death forces its presence upon his soul, though at first cast down, he reacts by immortal longings. The transcendental world opens before him; he dreams of an ideal future of the race or of a heaven where all his wishes shall be realized in the glory of the world to be; and in these "vague snatches of Uranian antiphony," instead of its finding reminiscences of the preexistent state of the soul, the more progressive Occidental world sees anticipations of a future immortality, as it has taken its conceptions of paradise from the past where antiquity placed them, and reconstructed them and set them up in the future.

This long pilgrimage of the soul from its old level to a higher maturity which adolescence recapitulates must have taken place in the race in certain of its important lines long before the historic period, because its very nature seems to involve the destruction of all its products and extinction of all records. Just as the well-matured adult, as is elsewhere shown, has utterly lost all traces and recollection of the perturbations of the storm and stress period, because they are so contradictory and mutually destructive and because feelings themselves can not be well remembered, so the race must have gone through a long heat and ferment, of which consciousness, which best develops in stationary periods, was lost, partly because growth was so rapid. Incidents are never better remembered by the individual, but they are never more transformed and changed, and just so the precious but often grotesque myths and legends of races, sacred to them but often meaningless to others, afford the only traces of ethnic adolescence which races retain. They are told about camp-fires, perhaps laboriously and allegorically interpreted or developed into literary form with the same gusto with which the man recounts in ever more mythic form the most vivid incidents his memory has rescued from the turmoil of these years of transformation and reconstruction, when nature's first call is heard to go out from the home to some promised land or career, to establish a new domicile for body and soul, and to be the progenitor of offspring of both, that to the inflamed youthful heart seem like the stars of heaven in number.

Youth loves intense states of mind and is passionately fond of excitement. Tranquil, mild enjoyments are not its forte. The heart and arteries are, as we have seen, rapidly increasing in size, and perhaps heightened blood pressure is necessary to cause the expansion normal at this stage. Nutritive activities are greatly increased; the temperature of the body is probably a trifle higher. After its period of most rapid growth, the heart walls are a little weak, and peripheral circulation is liable to slight stagnation, so that in the interests of proper irrigation of the tissues after the vascular growth has begun, tension seems necessary. Although we do not know precisely the relation between blood pressure and the strong instinct to tingle and glow, some correlation may safely be postulated. It is the age of erectile diathesis, and the erethism that is now so increased in the sexual parts is probably more or less so in nearly every organ and tissue. The whole psycho-physic organism is expanding, stretching out, and proper elasticity that relaxes and contracts and gives vaso-motor range is coordinated with the instinct for calenture or warming up, which is shown in phenomena of second breath in both physical and mental activity. In savage life this period is marked by epochs of orgasm and carousal, which is perhaps one expression of nature's effort to secure a proper and ready reflex range of elasticity in the circulatory apparatus. The "teens" are emotionally unstable and pathic. It is the age of natural inebriation without the need of intoxicants, which made Plato define youth as spiritual drunkenness. It is a natural impulse to experience hot and perfervid psychic states, and is characterized by emotionalism. This gives a sense of vitality and the hunger for more and fuller life. This desire to feel and to be very much alive, and the horror of inertness and apathy is one of the chief features which incline youth to intoxicants. Indeed, everything men strive for—fame, wealth, knowledge, power, love—are only specialized forms of the will to attain and to feel the maximum of vitality. Hence comes the proclivity to superlativeness, to high, lurid color and fast life, because youth must have excitement, and if this be not at hand in the form of moral and intellectual enthusiasms, it is more prone, on the principle of kinetic equivalents, to be sought for in sex or in drink. Athletic enthusiasm, the disposition of high school and college youth to yell and paint the town, to laugh, become boisterous and convivial, are better than sensuality and reduce temptation to it. Better that a few of the most promising youth should be maimed or even killed on the gridiron or in college rushes, or lose standing in their devotion to teams and to emotional culture, than that they should find excesses, some forms of which seem necessary now, in the lower life of sinful indulgence, which is so prone to stunt and arrest the precious last stages of growth in mind and body. More or less of this erethic diathesis is necessary and inevitable, and one of the chief problems of education is to prevent its lower forms and give it ever higher vents and fields. Interest in and devotion to all that is good, beautiful, and true is its loftiest expression, but it is often best cultivated on a lower plane, to be applied later on the higher.

We here see the instability and fluctuation now so characteristic. The emotions develop by contrast and reaction into the opposite. We will specify a few of its antithetic impulses now so marked.

1. There are hours, days, weeks, and perhaps months of over-energetic action. The young man trains with ardor; perhaps breaks a record; sleep may be reduced; he studies all night in a persistent cram; is swept away by some new fad; is exalted and hilarious and then reacts; is limp, languid, inert, indifferent, fatigued, apathetic, sleepy, lazy; feels the lack of motive power, and from overwork and excessive effort, when he goaded himself to do or die, he relapses to a dull state of relaxation and doubts whether anything is really worth while in the world. Thus youth now is really and easily overworked; is never so fresh or more rested as when at the top of its condition, but very easily wearied and exhausted with the languor due to overtraining. We have seen that early adolescent years are prone to be sickly, although the death rate is now lowest, and this is closely connected with the changes from overefficiency to low tension so frequent. Sometimes the stage of torpor comes first or predominates and causes friends to be anxious. Many great men loitered in their development, dawdled in their work and seemed to all about them entirely unpromising; but later woke up, went to work, made up for lost time, and outstripped their fellows. These changes are perhaps in slight degree modified by weather, like moods, and have no doubt a physiological basis. Sometimes it is as if anemia and hyperemia followed each other with extreme sloth and then almost convulsive activity of motor centers. There are periods when one can do easily twice the ordinary task without fatigue. Girls of fifteen or sixteen would often like to sleep or rest a week, and seem incapable of putting forth real effort, and then there are fevers of craving hard and even disagreeable work. Many returns show that in the spring there is very often great loathing to exert one's self, but this is occasionally broken by hours, days, or even weeks of supernormal activity, when stints are not only completed, but extra and self-imposed tasks are done with alacrity and satisfaction. Often there is a periodicity of activity in young men that suggests a monthly and sometimes a seasonal rhythm. The regular changes of day and night do not suffice, but this is complicated by some larger cycle of alternating recuperative and energetic periods of latent and patent, or inner and

outer work. This, like so much else, suggests an atavistic trace of savage life, more controlled by moon and tides and warm and cold seasons. Indeed, diurnal regularity of work, play, food, and sleep is a recent thing in the development-history of man, is hard to establish, and in the vagrant, criminal, vicious, and pauper class is often never reached. But spells of overactivity, alternating with those of sluggishness and inertness, still seem in these years like neural echoes of ancient hunts and feasts, fasts and famines, migration and stagnation. Now at least nature pushes on her work of growth by alternation, now centering her energies upon function, now upon increase in size of organs, and perhaps by this method of economy attains a higher level than would be reached by too much poise, balance, and steadiness. It is as if the momentum of growth energies had to overcome obstacles at every point, by removing now this, now that hindrance, where if its energies had been applied to all simultaneously they would have been less effective.

2. Closely connected with this are the oscillations between pleasure and pain—the two poles of life, its sovereign masters. The fluctuations of mood in children are rapid and incessant. Tears and laughter are in close juxtaposition. Their emotional responses to impressions are immediate. They live in the present and reflect all its changes, and their feelings are little affected by the past or the future. With the dawn of adolescence, the fluctuations are slower and often for a time more extreme, and recovery from elation and especially from depression is retarded. The past, and still more the future, is involved, and as the mental life widens, either tendency acquires more momentum. Youth can not be temperate, in the philosophical sense. Now it is prone to laughter, hearty and perhaps almost convulsive, and is abandoned to pleasure, the field of which ought gradually to widen with perhaps the pain field, although more. There is gaiety, irrepressible levity, an euphoria that overflows in every absurd manifestation of excess of animal spirits, that can not be repressed, that danger and affliction, appeals to responsibility and to the future, can not daunt nor temper. To have a good time is felt to be an inalienable right. The joys of life are never felt with so keen a relish; youth lives for pleasure, whether of an epicurean or an esthetic type. It must and ought to enjoy life without alloy. Every day seems to bring passionate love of just being alive, and the genius for extracting pleasure and gratification from everything is never so great.

But this, too, reacts into pain and disphoria, as surely as the thesis of the Hegelian logic passes over to its antithesis. Young people weep and sigh, they know not why; depressive are almost as characteristic as expansive states of consciousness. The sad Thanatopsis mood of gloom paints the world in black. Far-off anticipations of death come in a fore-boding way, as it is dimly felt, though not realized, that life is not all joy and that the individual must be subordinated and eventually die. Hence statistics show, as we have seen, a strange rise in the percentage of suicides. Now there is gloom and anon spontaneous exuberance. In 766 of Lancaster's returns, thirteen had thought seriously of suicide, al-though only three had successfully attempted it. Perhaps elation precedes and depression comes as a reaction in the majority of cases, although this is not yet clear. Some feel despondent on awakening, at school time, or at noon, suggesting nutritive changes. "The curve of despondency starts at eleven, rises steadily and rapidly till fifteen, culminates at seven-teen, then falls steadily till twenty three." Young people are often unaccountably pleased with every trifle. They can shout for joy from the very fact of being alive. The far-off destiny of senescence looms up, and in fatigue the atrabiliar psychic basis of pessimism clouds life for a time and brings into dominance a new set of associations like another personality. Youth fears inadequacy of its powers to cope with the world. How this is connected with the alternating extremes of sexual tension, we have seen, although this by no means explains all. Sometimes the tears are from no assignable cause, and often from factitious motives. Suspicion of being disliked by friends, of having faults of person or character that can not be overcome; the fancy of being a supposititious child of their parents, of having unwittingly caused calamity to others, of hopeless love; failure in some special effort; a sense of the necessity of a life of work and hardship—these bring moods that may be more or less extreme according to environment, heredity, temperament, and other causes, may succeed each other with greater or less frequency, and may threaten to issue in brooding, depression, and melancholy, or in a careless and blind instinct to live for the day; but these, too, are due to the fact that the range of pleasure and pain is increased, so that there are new motives to each, and perhaps a long period with occasional special dangers must elapse before a final adjustment.

This is the age of giggling, especially with girls, who are at this stage of life farthest from Vassey's view that man is not originally a laughing animal and that the gentleman and lady should never laugh, but only smile. If convulsive laughter is an epilepsy, it is one that begins in the highest regions and passes down the meristic levels. Goethe well says, that nothing is more significant of men's character than what they find laughable. The adolescent perhaps is most hilarious over caricature of nationalities, teachers, freshmen, the other sex, etc., who are mimicked, burlesqued, and satirized. Ridicule is now a powerful weapon of pro-priety. Again, the wit of the ephebos sometimes provokes a mental ticklishness about certain sacred and sometimes sexual topics, which may make jocularity and waggishness almost a plague. Another of the chief butts of adolescent fun is what is naive and unconscious; the blunders of the greeny, the unsophisticated way not only of the freshman, but of the countryman, the emigrant, and the *Bachfisch* girl now abound, while the simple idea of disaster or misfortune, which constitutes the humor of nine-tenths of the professional joke-makers, is rare. The horror of old or even once-told jests is never so intense, nor the appreciation for novelty so keen.

3. Self-feeling is increased, and we have all degrees of egoism and all forms of self-affirmation. The chief outcrop may be vanity and a sense of personal beauty and attractiveness, that is felt to be stunning to the other sex. It may be expressed in swagger ways; thrusting one's self into conspicuous places; talking, acting, dressing, to attract notice; or in complacency and even conceit for supposed superiority over others. Impudence, affront, insult, and sometimes even physical aggressiveness are forms of it. Growth of mind and body is so rapid that it is felt to the point of overestimation. Self-feeling is fed by all the compliment and sweet flattery of affection, which is the food often really tasted for the first time with true gusto, on which it shoots up with mushroom growth. The wisdom and advice of parents and teachers is overtopped, and in ruder natures may be met by blank contradiction. It is all a new consciousness of altitude and the desire to be, and to be taken for, men and women; to be respected, consulted, and taken into confidence. The new sense of self may be so exquisitely delicate that a hundred things in the environment, that would never rankle before, now sting and irritate. This is sometimes expressed in more or less conscious and formulated codes of honor, which among youth is often a strange and wondrous thing which must be defended by the wager of battle, with fists, or among German students with the sword, with all the punctilio of chivalry. Sometimes the formulæ by which honor and self-respect may be gained, maintained, impaired, and restored are detailed. Courage, honesty, parents, especially the mother, and perhaps a sweetheart, are involved, and the youth must perhaps represent honor for two. Ideals are so high and the tedious labor by which they are attained so constitutionally ignored that the goal seems very near and attainable if the purpose is high, so that the spirited, mettlesome ephebos or cadet summarily demands the world to take him on credit, as if the promise of his ambition were already fulfilled. The youth who has been amenable to advice and even suggestion, now becomes obstreperous, recalcitrant, filled with a spirit of opposition, and can not repress a sense of top-lofty superiority to the ways and persons of his environment. Age is often made to suffer

discourtesy, and it sometimes seems as though the faculties of reverence and respect, to say nothing of admiration, were suddenly gone.

But the ebb of this tide is no less pronounced, and may precede in time its flood. The same youth with all his brazen effrontery may feel a distrust of self and a sinking of heart, which all his bravado is needed to hide. He doubts his own powers, is perilously anxious about his future, his self-love is wounded and humiliated in innumerable ways keenly felt, perhaps at heart resented, but with a feeling of impotence to resist. The collapsing moods bring a sense of abasement and humiliation, which sometimes seems like a degree of complacency to all that comes, suggesting spiritlessness. Youth often fears itself lacking in some essential trait of manhood or womanhood, or wanting the qualities of success. He is often vanquished in innumerable rivalries and competitions that now make so much of life, and loses heart and face. The world seems all the more hopeless because of the great demands which the opposite mood has imposed. Sometimes a sense of shame from purely imaginary causes is so poignant as to plunge the soul for a time into the deepest and most doleful dumps; fancied slights suggest despair, and in place of wonted self-confidence there is a retiring bashfulness, which no coaxing or encouragement of friends can overcome or fathom, and which may express itself only in some secret diary or perhaps in prayer. This, too, of course, often shades into elation and depression from moral causes.

Youth, too, may become overfastidious and effeminate, and this may pervade toilet, manners, care for health, or even take the form of moral nicety, overscrupulousness, and casuistry. Time was when the freshman was really green, awkward, inept in speech, without repose, but now too often the sub-freshman is a polished gentleman, confident and at home everywhere, though happily often betraying in some respects the earmarks of the native roughness which goes along with strength, in the midst of the overrefinement, suggestive of weakness.

4. Another clearly related alternation is that between selfishness and altruism. Before puberty, children are fed, clothed, sheltered, instructed, and done for, so that all the currents in their environment, especially with parents who follow Froebel's injunction to live for their children, have flowed toward and converge in them. Now currents in the opposite direction arise and should normally gather strength until they predominate. Life is sacrifice, and in trite parlance, we really live for what we die for. Before, youth must be served; now, it must serve. Its wants, perhaps even its whims, have been supreme, but in the matin song of love the precepts of renunciation are heard. Just as the embryonic cell grows large till it can no longer be nourished from without and must then divide or die, so the individual must be subordinated to society

and posterity. Life is no longer ego-centric, but altro-centric. Politeness and courtesy, and respect for the feelings of others, are often hard at first, but are a school of minor morals graduating into that of the higher virtues. Sympathy, and especially love, wither the individual, until self-subordination may become a passion. Youth devotes himself, perhaps by a vow, to a lifetime of self-denial or painful servitude to some great cause, or a career in which some of the deepest of human instincts must be mortified and eradicated. He or she would go on missions; labor for the sick, ignorant, depraved, and defective classes; espouse great philanthropic causes, and very often practise in secret asceticisms in the common and harmless pleasures and comforts of life, in food, drink, sleep, it may be, to the point of impairment of health, as if now glimpsing from afar the universal law which makes all individual good merely ancillary to the welfare of the species. Self-sacrifice may be exorbitant and vows gifts; humiliations are enthusiastic; selfishness seems mean; the ideal becomes a "pure life ruled by love alone;" the unselfishness may sometimes come in streaks and is often secreted, young people giving food or sweetmeats, staying at home to give others pleasure, without telling. There is, on the one hand, increase of self-confidence, a sense that the individual "is important enough to be noticed anywhere;" but this is not incompatible with helping others as never before, and even performing disagreeable tasks for them, associating with the bad in order to make them better, and greater readiness to give up any individual good. Our returns here show outcrops of the grossest selfishness and greediness side by side with a generosity and magnanimity rarely found in adult life save in poetry and romance. Others' rights of possession, food, and clothing sometimes are rudely trampled under foot, while the most delicate attentions and services, involving both forethought and hardship, are carried out to others or perhaps to the same persons. It seems as if expressions of extremely puerile selfishness were now particularly prone to be compensated for by extremes of the opposite nature, and *vice versa;* that often those most tender and considerate, most prone to take pains, to prefer others' enjoyment to their own, and to renounce ease, abandon cherished plans, and conquer the strongest natural desires in doing this, were those most liable occasionally to fall lowest in gloating self-gratification at the expense of others.

Here, too, parents and teachers sometimes alternate between hope and despair for the young, before they slowly settle to fixed characteristics and conduct. Moreover, there is often arrest before the process of self-effacement is duly complete; so that we see in adults noble lives and acts veined with petty meannesses, which are the residual and unreduced organs of childhood.

5. Closely connected with the above are the alternations between good and bad conduct generally. Perhaps at no time of life can goodness be so exotically pure and true, virtue so spotless, and good works spring from such a depth of goodwill, which, since Kant, is often made the source of all real morality. Conscience, though not new-born, now can first begin to play a leading role. It awakens with a longing hunger and thirst for righteousness, prompts to highest aspiration and resolve. Benevolence and love to all persons and all being is fresh from its original source, and there are hearty good wishes for the general and special weal of others and ingenuity in anticipating and gratifying their desires, so that for brief periods youth and maidens sometimes seem too good for this earth.

But we need have no fear. From the same soil in which these budding virtues spring and bloom so delicately arise rank weeds; physical appetites are grossly indulged naively, even though they may sometimes seem almost bestial; propensities to lie break out, perhaps irresistibly, for a time. Anger slips its leash and wreaks havoc. Some petty and perhaps undreamed meanness surprises the onlooker. The common constraints of society are ruptured, or there are spasms of profanity; perhaps a sudden night of debauch, before knowledge had put up proper defenses; perhaps some lapse from virtue, which seems almost irretrievable, but which in fact should never be so readily pardoned and forgotten. The forces of sin and those of virtue never struggle so hotly for possession of the youthful soul. As statistics show, the age of most frequent conversions to true religion is precisely the years of the largest percentage of first commitments to houses of detention for crime. Now some new manifestations of vice surprise the soul in the midst of its ideal longings for absolute perfection, and wring it with grief and remorse. It seems a law of psychic development, that more or less evil must be done to unloose the higher powers of constraint and to practise them until they can keep down the baser instincts. The religious struggles of this stage bear abundant evidence to the violence of these storms and counter currents of which the human soul is now the arena. Temptations hitherto unknown to sins hitherto impossible bring redeeming agencies also new into action, and while the juvenile offender and the debauchee is arrested in his development and remains through life under the power of evil, growth is benign, and those who achieve normal maturity domesticate their baser instincts into the service of goodness.

6. The same is true of the great group of social instincts, some of which rest upon the preceding. Youth is often bashful, retiring, in love with solitude; perhaps wanders alone and communes with stars, sea, forest, animals; prefers nature to man; loves midnight walks; shuns the face

of man, and especially the other sex; becomes interested in its own inner states and careless of the objective while sunken in the subjective life. Some youth take to drink chiefly or solely to gain through it the courage to go into society. They know not how, or if they do so, find it hard to assert themselves sufficiently to do justice to their ideas of their own merits. This is most common among country youth, but it is also frequent enough in the city. Others spring into a new love of companionship; friendships are cemented; "mashes" and "crushes" occur; the gregarious passion vents itself in all kinds of convivial associations, in organizations of many kinds, sometimes in riotous bouts and carousals; some can never be alone and seem to have for a time no resources in themselves, but to be abjectly dependent for their happiness upon their mates. They lose independence, and not only run, but think and feel, with the gang and the class. Alone, they are uninteresting and uninterested, but with others, vivacious, lively, and entertaining. To the inner circle of their chosen associates they bare their inmost soul. There are no reserves or secrets, but a love of confessional outpourings in intimate hours together or sometimes in letters. The desire to please dominates some, and that to rule and lead, others; while the more passive and inert gradually lose the power of independent action, thought, or impulse, and come into the settled habits of dependent henchmen and followers. The psychology of crowds show us how all human qualities are kept in countenance and developed, when like is paired with like; how joys are doubled and pains divided; how responsibility is attenuated until the greatest outrages are perpetrated by masses, from which every individual would revolt. Alternations between these two extremes of excessive or defective sociability are less frequent in the same individual, and if they occur, are at longer intervals.

At times, young people feel that those who are liked fail to appreciate or even dislike them. They are repelled by society, feel sinful and lonely, and perhaps need a good cry, which quite relieves them. We find, too, admiration and contempt strangely mingled; now appreciation, which almost becomes abject hero worship or fanaticism for great and new ideas, gushing devotion to literary and art products, etc., but all alternating with satire, burlesque, and parody, which seem to indicate that the power of reverence is lost and all the charm and modesty, which Plato found so becoming in youth, for a season quite extinct.

There is always a wide range of change between more and less before a center of gravity is found and a definite social character established. Both, of course, are necessary, and there is much that is true in the Baconian adage, that character is perfected in solitude and talent in society. City life, the innumerable clubs, business aggregations, sodalities, political and religious fraternization, seem a characteristic of this growingly urban age, and have no doubt perturbed the oscillations of the compass, so that it settles more slowly toward the pole of man's destiny than in other historic periods. We have seen these phenomena unusually accented in the early lives of Savonarola, Newton, Shelley, Patrick Henry, Keats, Hawthorne, Gifford, Jeffries, Boyeson, Nansen, and in the scores of our returns from men and women unknown to fame.

7. Closely akin to this are the changes from exquisite sensitiveness to imperturbability and even apathy, hard-heartedness, and perhaps cruelty. Many youthful murderers, callous to the sufferings of their victims, have had the keenest sympathy with pets and even with children. Most criminals are unfeeling and unhumane. They can not pity, and the susceptibility to pathos is alien to them. The juvenile torturers often seem to have specialized psychic zones, where tenderness is excessive, as if to compensate for their defect. They weep over the pain, actual or imaginary, of their pets, while utterly hardened to the normal sentiments of kindness and help for suffering. The development of sympathy, as Sutherland has shown, has been slow and hard in the world, but it is basal for most of the factors of morality.

8. Curiosity and interest are generally the first outcrop of intellectual ability. Youth is normally greedy for knowledge, and that, not in one but in many directions. There is eagerness, zest, enthusiasm, which inspires corresponding activity to know that and only that which is of the highest worth. Wherever a new mine of great and fruitful discovery of truth is opened, a new field of activity appears, or new motives of self-sacrifice are made operative, there youth is in its element. It is the age of questioning, exploration, investigation, testing ideas, men, and the world. Expectation is at its best and the impulse to be ready for any new occasion is at its strongest. Now first it is really felt that knowledge is power, and the noetic fever sometimes becomes too hot for the convenience of others, for conventionality, the routine of life, or even for health.

But the opposite is no less germane to these years. Here we find the inert moods and types, which are apathetic, which can not be profoundly stirred, that regard passionate mental interest as bad form, and cultivate indifference, that can not and will not admire. No devoted teacher need attempt to arouse and fire the mind in this condition. Sometimes this is all an affectation, mental posing, provoked by fashion or environment, and unconsciously imitative. Sometimes, alas! it is the direct result of excess, which saps the springs of life and brings senescent inertia before its time. It may be a product of fatigue and reaction from excessive effort, as in the case of Stuart Mill. It is not pain or pessimism, although, if real, it is the raw material out of which the latter is made. To the wise adult this is always pathetic, for what is youth without enthusiasm? These states always need wise diagnosis, because if they are recuperative, they should be let alone, and if results of dissipation, they should be drastically treated. Institutions, especially the tone and traditions of colleges and high schools, differ widely in their prevailing atmosphere in this regard. Here, too, a considerable range is no doubt normal.

9. Another vacillation is between knowing and doing. Now the life of the study charms, and the ambition is to be learned, bookish, or there is a passion to read. Perhaps there is a love of poetic intoxication or of contemplation, such as Scott, Bryant, Fulton, Franklin, Newton, etc., experienced. This afferent, more passive, receptive mood is necessary, because in the civilized state youth always lives in the midst of a far higher culture than it could produce. But a reaction is almost always inevitable where this receptive passion is extreme, and soon either unconscious instinct or else purpose takes the youth out of doors, because he has fallen in love with nature, or, it may be, to cultivate muscle. His tastes and plans turn to active occupation. He would achieve rather than learn. He feels sometimes, more or less unconsciously, the vanity of mere erudition, and wishes to storm the world of reality and win his spurs, make his mark, and become an active and perhaps creative cause.

10. Less often we see one or more alternations between dominance by conservative and by radical instincts. The young man finds the world out of joint and would reform the church, school, perhaps social and family life; is sick at heart at the hollowness of established conventionality; is fired at the tyranny of wealth or trusts, and would himself reconstruct by doubting, casting out everything which does not seem to his own fledgling intelligence good, true, and beautiful. Some do and all ought to react from the party of progress to that of order, from burning the products of the past to worshiping them, to caring and working that no good already attained be lost; they should at some period feel the force of conventionalities, the truth of highly saturated creeds, the value of established institutions, despite their possible betterment. There is especial danger that temperament or environment will destroy this balance and precipitate the mind for life into one or another of these camps where extreme views are so easy and simple, and moderate ones so hard and complex. This is especially seen in the religious sphere, to which we shall turn later. The equipoise between atheism and bigotry is almost always disturbed; there is excess of skepticism or of credulity,

affirmation or denial, doubt or faith, and youth is especially prone to be distracted between the instincts that make the devotee and those that make the heretic.

11. We find many cases of signal interest in which there is a distinct reciprocity between sense and intellect, as if each had its nascent period. We have already seen how the senses are acuminated and sense interests modified and generally enhanced, so that occasionally youth is passionately devoted to seeing and hearing new things, is all eye, ear, taste, and would widen the surface of contact with the external world to the maximum, as if laying in stock for future mental elaboration; but there are also periods of inner absorption and meditation, when reality fades and its very existence is questioned, when the elements that make the content of the sensory shoot together into new unities. The inner eye that sees larger correspondences in time and space is opened; the bearings of familiar facts appear; wisdom is sought from books or friends, and is assimilated with amazing facility, so that a new consciousness is born within or above the old, and the attention is attracted to inner states which demand explanation. It is as if the projective system, which acts and reacts upon the external world, had now its innings, to be later followed by a period when the energy of psychic growth is largely turned to the associative fibers, both ends of which are in the brain.

12. Closely connected with this is the juxtaposition of wisdom and folly. Now there are high intuitions that anticipate maturity and even the best mental products of old age, an attitude of mind that seems to have anticipated the experiences of a lifetime, and to have found rest in the true goal of wisdom. Yet, interspersed with all this precocious philosophy, we find pitfalls of collapsing and childish folly. This may be ethical, in the form of irritability, greed, causeless and irrational freakishness and abandon to the lower impulses, or downright silliness. Those precocious in some are often arrested in other respects.

We have already seen that body growth is not symmetrical, but to some extent the parts, functions, and organs grow in succession, so that the exact normal proportions of the body are temporarily lost, to be regained later on a new plan. The mind now grows in like manner. It is as if the various qualities of soul were developed successively; as if the energy of growth now stretched out to new boundaries, now in this and now in that direction. This is biological economy, as well as recapitulatory, because in some way that we do not understand nature follows in the psychic field the familiar mechanical principle we must so often appeal to by which power is best developed over a large surface, to be later best applied at a point. The human plant circumnutates in a wider and wider circle, and the endeavor should be to prevent it from prematurely finding a support, to prolong the period of variation to which this stage of life is sacred, and to prevent natural selection from confirming too soon, the slight advantage which any quality may temporarily have in this struggle for existence among many faculties and tendencies within us. The educational ideal is now to develop capacities in as many directions as possible, to indulge caprice and velleity a little, to delay consistency for a time, and let the diverse prepotencies struggle with each other. Now everything psychic tends in its turn to be intense to the point of illusion or positive obsession, but nature's rhythm, if allowed to have its due course, prevents stagnation and hebetude, and the passion to change keeps all powers fluent and plastic, gives elasticity and develops power of sanification. Sometimes there seem almost to be dual or multiplex personalities. The venerable four temperaments of the phrenologists seem contending with each other for dominance, but the soul should make some place for all of them in its many mansions. It is veritably like a batrachian, or insect struggling to get out of its last year's skin or chitin, or like sloughing off the old consciousness of childhood for the new one of maturity. It is thus that the soul explores the maximum area possible of human experience. This is now the meaning of the freedom of the will, and captious though it often seems, it is thus that the foundations of wise choices that first hear from all parts and parties are preformed. The mind is now in what the biologists call its generalized form. It is as if man were polyphyletic in his origin and now the different ethnic stocks were successively harked back to. The possibility of variation in the soul is now at its height. Especially in races of mixed blood, our returns convince me, that more prepotencies clash or coincide, as the case may be, and we can often detect the voices of our forebears of very different races in the soul. Psychic life is thus for a term greatly perturbed. When the youth takes the helm of his own being, he navigates a choppy sea. Thus it would appear in nature's economy he must strive, fight, and storm his way up, if he would break into the kingdom of man. Here, too, many an impulse seeks expression, which seems strong for a time, but which will never be heard of later. Its function is to stimulate the next higher power that can only thus be provoked to development, in order to direct, repress, or supersede it. Never is it so true that nothing human is alien from each individual, as in this fever of ephebeitis, which has so many peculiar features in the American temperament.

The popular idea, that youth must have its fling, implies the need of greatly and sometimes suddenly widened liberty, which nevertheless needs careful supervision and wise direction, from afar and by indirect methods. The forces of growth now strain to their uttermost against old restrictions. It is the age of bathmism, or most rapid variation, which is sometimes almost saltatory. Nearly every latency must be developed, or else some higher power, that later tempers and coordinates it, lacks normal stimulus to develop. Instead of the phenomena of alternate generation, where certain potentialities lie dormant in one generation to appear in the next, we have corresponding psychic phenomena in one and the same individual by which faculties and impulses, which are denied legitimate expression during their nascent periods, break out well on in adult life—falsetto notes mingling with manly bass as strange puerilities. The chief end in view must now be to bring out all the polyphonous harmonies of human nature. The individual can never again expand his nature to so nearly compass the life of the species. The voices of extinct generations, sometimes still and small, sometimes strident and shrill, now reverberate, and psychic development is by leaps and bounds, of which psychological science has so far been able to know but very little.

Mental unity comes later. Consistency then has its place. The supreme Aristotelian virtue of temperance and the golden mean—which is courage well poised between timidity and foolhardiness, liberality midway between the extremes of avarice and prodigality, modesty which combines the good and rejects the evil by excess of bashfulness and impudence, self-respect which is neither vainglory nor self-abasement—slowly knits up the soul, coordinates its many elements, represses illusions, and issues in settled character. The logical as contrasted with the genetic ideal now arises and prompts to reason, consistency, and coordinations in ever higher associations as cosmos rises from chaos. We see over and over again that the metamorphic stages of early adolescence are forgotten, and how impossible it is for the mature mind to remember or even credit, when they are noted or told by others, the preceding phases of instinctive transformations. In one sense, youth loses very much in becoming adult. The ordered, regular life of maturity involves necessarily more or less degeneration for simple tendencies. Indeed, the best definition of genius is intensified and prolonged adolescence, to which excessive or premature systematization is fatal. Even in commonplace lives, higher qualities, and often the very highest, appear in the teens for a brief flitting moment, or at least they barely hint their existence and then fade, sometimes because the demands of adulthood are too early or too insistently enforced.

This law of a period of freedom that leans a little toward license before the human colt is haltered and broken to any of the harnesses of severe discipline, is favored by every aspect of the bionomic law. It is a fact of great significance not only unexplored but hitherto unnoted, that even as the psychic perturbations of this stage of multifarious impulsions are lost to recollection, because they are so inconsistent and blind, since they lack the intellectual factor of experience, just so the phyletic stages in the development of the race that correspond to puberty fall largely in the unhistoric period—the darkest of all dark ages, during which brute became man. Science explores the simian forms of life, but here our sense of ignorance is increasingly painful. The distribution of the gorilla is rapidly narrowing toward early extinction, and we know far less of its characteristics, or those of the gibbon, ourang, and chimpanzee, than we do of the lowest races of men. The interval between the highest anthropoid brain of 550 cubic centimeters, and that of the lowest man, 1,150 cubic centimeters, is almost as lost as a sunken Atlantis. If we take Canstadt man, perhaps the lowest in Europe, as the point of reemergence of man's phyletic history, we find the most radical transformations.

In the interval that separates the pithecoid from the troglodyte, many changes, perhaps more momentous than any in the historic period, took place. Arboreal life and a diet of fruits, nuts, and buds were exchanged for a life well adjusted to fluvial and littoral conditions. The shore—the most changing of all the life areas, the great feeding-ground of aquatic and terrestrial forms, where all land animals originally came from their primordial home in the sea, after long amphibian apprenticeship, and where the whale, seal, and other backsliders to aquatic life reverted after long experience on the land—had already been the highway of extended migration; and man, especially if monophyletic and if the qualities that gave him supremacy over the brutes were developed in a single narrow area, had multiplied rapidly; had learned the use of fire and cooking, thus freeing energy, hitherto needed for digestion, to higher uses; had entered the paleolithic stage of chipped stone for spear and arrow heads; had asserted his dominion over the mammoth, cave-bear, hyena, woolly rhinoceros, Irish elk; had invested himself with the freedom of the world; had become the most migratory of all species, thus favoring amphimixis and variation by exogamy, and knew no barrier because only man stops man. He had been forced from some primitive home or cunabula, perhaps by the slow submergence of Sclater's Lemuria, or driven from his pristine habitat on the high table-lands north of the Himalayas, and had already begun his career over the globe. During this period many of the scores of domestic animals had been tamed—perhaps mostly, as O. T. Mason thinks—by women who began pastoral life. Many of the two hundred and forty-nine species of plants of which de Candolle traces the history—all phanerogamous—were brought under culture also perhaps first by women, and thus settled agricultural life had been introduced. The hand had been developed much in structure, and far more in function, from a simple prehensile organ to a tool and weapon user and even maker. Dress had evolved, a momentous change had come about by focusing development upon intelligence as soon as its high survival and selective value made itself felt, leaving the body relatively unchanged while mind evolved enormously, if not disproportionately, like the giraffe's neck. Infancy had been prolonged, and, with it, parental care, love and home, and the possibilities of education unfolded. Speech and tradition had been acquired. From this point all is relatively easy of explanation, for as Lyell said, if all but one race of men in a single spot of the globe were exterminated, they would soon people the earth again though they were as low as the Eskimo or South Sea Islander. Perhaps primitive man had already grown to gigantic stature, as Principal Dawson conjectures, and did and dared at sea, in hunting, and in crossing barriers, that which modern man would not. Perhaps he was a pigmoid, as the horse has grown from the orohippus of fox size; perhaps he was Broca's estromelian, half monster and half man; or more akin to Lombroso's degenerate mattoid, or to Sergi's hominidæ. Perhaps McRitchie's conjecture that fairies were primitive dwarfs or mid-men is valuable; it is in line with the widespread superstition that arrow-heads are fairy darts. He may have been pliocene, diluvial, or even tertiary.

My own belief, as I have set forth elsewhere, is that man early became the wanderer and the exterminator *par excellence*. Less than any other animal, can man tolerate rivals in the struggle for existence. The instinct which impelled him to exterminate the North sea-cow in 1767, and, in the nineteenth century, the great awk in 1840, the African quagga in 1870, and scores of other animals and birds that in recent times have gone forever even beyond the reach of the collector, that is now rapidly reducing to the vanishing point the American bison, the Indian lion and rhinoceros, the walrus, the zebra-giraffe, halibut, oyster, lobster, etc., and that prepares and sells the skins of two million birds a year, which are dying out that man may have food, safety, or sport, is the same instinct which in prehistoric times destroyed chiefly or with aid of other causes the gigantic extinct mammals, and has forever scarred man's soul with fear, anger, and wanton cruelty. The same enmity against the lower races, which in our day has exterminated forever the Boethuks, the Tasmanians, and is reducing so many lower human ethnic stocks to make way for favored races, is but a relic of the rage which exterminated the missing links and made man for ages the passionate destroyer of his own pedigree, so that no trace of it is left.

A great number of the phyletic corollates of some of the most marked stages by which prepubescent boyhood passes to maturity exist only in the later phases of this transition from anthropoid to savage life, although many are found earlier and others later yet. To much in this dark interval early adolescence is the only key, but even here the record is so distorted, falsified, so often inverted, so mingled with what belongs to later phases, that we know as yet but little how to use this key. To-day youth is passed in an environment of culture, nearly every element of which is far superior to anything that it could produce. The powers of imitation and appropriation are so developed and perhaps hypertrophied that it is impossible to distinguish what comes from indigenous and what from acquired sources. The past and future contend with each other for mastery. In his elegiac moods, youth seems to long for a lost idea in a way that suggests transmigration of a Platonic Wordsworthian type, as plants dream of the sun, and on the other hand, his esthetic sensibilities are presentiments of a superior stage of the race that will develop out of the present human type which it is the function of art to prophesy and anticipate. The processes last to be attained are least assured by heredity and most dependent upon individual effort, in aid of which nature gives only propulsion, often less defined the later it can be acquired, like the Kantian pure autonomous "oughtness," which the individual must laboriously shape by a wise use of heteronymous and consciously regulated motives. While adolescence is the great revealer of the past of the race, its earlier stages must be ever surer and safer and the later possibilities ever greater and more prolonged, for it, and not maturity as now defined, is the only point of departure for the superanthropoid that man is to become. This can be only by an ever higher adolescence lifting him to a plane related to his present maturity as that is to the well-adjusted stage of boyhood where our puberty now begins its regenerating metamorphoses.

Comment

GENETIC psychology was not without its critics. Among those who loomed large on the horizon, none found both the discipline and the recapitulation theory more repugnant than did Edward L. Thorndike. Injecting a new rigor into the developmental sciences, Thorndike disdained anthropomorphic inferences about the human qualities of lower animals, scorned Neo-Lamarckianism and the presumed effects of acquired characters, and most emphatically spurned teleological principles. The historical record has been kind to Thorndike. After he joined the faculty at Teachers College, Columbia University, in 1899, he worked indefatigably for four decades, shaping the destiny of the developmental sciences. His theoretical views and research methods in general have withstood the severity of numberless investigations, and even today his durable influence on experimental, developmental, and educational psychology continues unabated.

Thorndike, who was thirty years younger than G. Stanley Hall, was just beginning his professional career, with all the attendant uncertainties, when genetic psychology brushed as close to eminence as it ever would. In 1904 Hall's *Adolescence* overwhelmed nearly every developmental specialist of the day. Now, more than a half century later, the book is still frequently eulogized as the first great compendium on adolescent growth and the first systematic treatise on human development. The preceding selection from *Adolescence* all too poignantly divulges, however, that many of those who laud the contents of the text have probably never read it thoroughly. Thorndike did read the two volumes from cover to cover, and in a review that appeared only a few months after the book had been published he disclosed the temerity with which he willingly took on the genetic psychology movement.

The general make-up and style of President Hall's book are such, it must be confessed, as to trouble even an enthusiastic reader. The richness of the summaries of fact and opinion does not atone for the failure to state clearly the probable answer to the main problem. At times irrelevant details blur the issue. Torrents of rhetorical enthusiasm over youth, love, genetic psychology, and other matters will irritate the scientific student and probably will befuddle the "general reader." One has to gyrate about from whales to vital statistics, to the lives of saints, to Jacksonian epilepsy, to the Hopi dancers until one prays for a range of knowledge equal to President Hall's to empower him to see the unity and organization of the book or any chapter in it.[6]

History records Thorndike as having been in the Neo-Darwinian camp. Evolutionary theory by his time had settled man squarely in the animal kingdom. Weismann had been vindicated in part by the rediscovery of Mendel's papers, and the biological sciences were finally gaining a scientific, nonteleological footing. Mendelism had dispelled Neo-Lamarckian optimism for swift evolutionary progress. The nineteenth-century interweaving of teleology and recapitulation theory had proven infeasible. Thorndike, poised on the threshold of the new era, moved unhesitatingly to the fore. In Volume I of his classic 1913 edition of *Educational Psychology*, he pronounced what amounts to the last rites for recapitulation theory and genetic psychology.

[6] E. L. Thorndike, The Newest Psychology, *Educational Review*, 1904, **28**, 217–227, p. 224.

EDWARD LEE THORNDIKE (1874–1949)

OBJECTIONS TO THE
THEORY OF RECAPITULATION

THE Recapitulation Theory in its clearest form is that the order of appearance of original tendencies in the individual is more or less exactly that in which they have appeared in the race—that is, in the entire ancestry of the individual—and that the intervals from the fertilization of the ovum to the dates of appearance of the individual's original tendencies bear more or less exactly the same proportions one to another that the intervals from the beginning of life in the animal kingdom to the dates of appearance of the same tendencies in the race bear one to another. The order and dates of disappearance in the individual parallel in a similar manner the corresponding facts in man's ancestry. The reason assigned for this parallelism between an individual and his entire ancestry in the order and dates of appearance and disappearance of original tendencies by the recapitulation theory is the supposed bionomic law. This is a law of the germ's development whereby any change made in it is made with an additional mechanism that sets the date of the change's effect on the individual developing from that germ later than the dates of the effects of changes made hitherto in the germ. Suppose, for example, that for a thousand centuries from the origin of life, man's ancestors floated aimlessly, then for a thousand swam by cilia, then for a thousand wriggled like snakes, then for a thousand walked on four feet, then for a thousand both walked, climbed and swung as do the monkeys. Let us suppose further that each new tendency was accompanied by the loss of the old one. Then, by this extreme form of the recapitulation theory, the human individual should, beginning at the start of his individual life, possess these tendencies in that same order, retain each for an equal time, and lose them one after another (except of course the last, whose loss would depend upon whether the individual's ancestry had lost it).

SOURCE: E. L. Thorndike. *Educational Psychology: The Original Nature of Man* (New York: Teachers College, Columbia University, 1920). Originally published 1913. Selections from "The Order and Dates of Appearance and Disappearance of Original Tendencies," Chapter 16, pp. 245–258. Abridged. Reprinted by permission of the publisher.

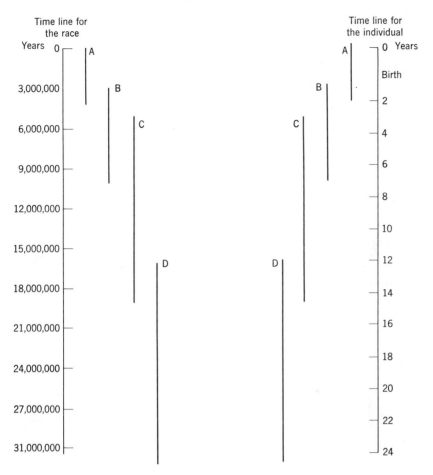

Figure 1

A more general illustration in graphic form will help to fix this extreme form of the Recapitulation Theory in memory. Suppose tendencies A, B, C, D, etc., to have appeared in man's ancestry at the times shown by the upper ends of the lines at the left hand of Figure 1 and to have been lost at the times shown by the lower ends of these lines. Then tendencies A, B, C, D, etc., will appear in man's life and, apart from outside influence, will disappear therefrom, as shown by the lines at the right of Figure 1.

This clear extreme form of the recapitulation theory is probably held by no student of human nature; for, obviously, the time during which the early ancestral tendencies are possessed by the individual is, if not

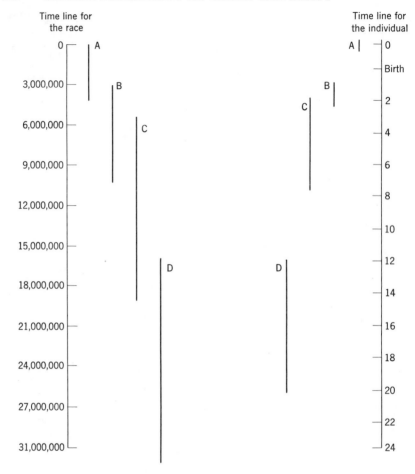

Figure 2

zero, at least a far smaller fraction of the time during which the late ancestral tendencies are possessed by him than is the case with the times in the case of the race. So the parallelism of individual and race is universally amended by supposing the early racial tendencies to be in the individual abbreviated in some rough proportion to their earliness.

Instead of Figure 1, then, we would have something like Figure 2, wherein A's stay in the individual is one-tenth as long a fraction of the period from conception to the adult condition, as A's stay in the individual is of the period from the protozoa to modern man; B's stay is two-tenths; C's is four-tenths and D's is seven-tenths. . . .

THE EVIDENCE

Advocates of the recapitulation theory rely upon the analogy between the development of the mind and that of the body, and the assumption that in the latter the order of change from the fertilized ovum to the adult structure is the order of change in the race from the protozoa to *homo sapiens*. "Since ontogeny repeats phylogeny in the growth of the body, it probably does in the growth of behavior," is the one repeated argument.

The facts are, however, that the only valid analogy would be between the development of the mind and that of the central nervous system, that the latter does not develop in man in anything at all closely like the way in which it has developed in the total ancestry of man, and that in the body as a whole the duplication of phylogeny by ontogeny is by no means a general law of growth. These three points will best be discussed in the reverse order.

The recapitulatory, or bio-genetic, or bionomic, law that "ontogeny repeats phylogeny" is true in only a very vague and partial way. Only in rough outlines and in the case of a fraction of bodily organs does nature make an individual from the fertilized ovum by the same series of changes by which it made his species from the primitive protozoa. No competent biologist would, for instance, dare to infer, from the series of stages through which the lungs, arms and legs, and cerebral hemispheres pass in individual development, what the exact origin of lungs, arms and fore-brain were in the race. The likenesses of a man at successive periods to the adult forms of a fish, reptile and early mammal are faint and questionable. No one would mistake the human embryo at any stage for any adult fish or reptile or mammal. No one can tell from ontogeny what the phylogeny of man has been in the great changes from invertebrate to vertebrate, from early generalized mammal to primate, from early primate to man. The clearest cases of recapitulation are those where the way taken to produce the structure is a likely way apart from any tendency to recapitulate for recapitulation's sake. Thus, for a four-chambered heart to be made by making one chamber, dividing it, and then dividing each of the halves; for a backbone to be deposited in a mould of cartilage; for a multicellular animal to grow by cell division, or for the total structure of an animal to be first laid down in a series of segments, might be efficient ways irrespective of ancestry. We must not forget that the animal has to grow *somehow*.

The facts of ontogeny and of phylogeny in the case of the central nervous system are notably discouraging to the expectation that the dates of original tendencies in intellect and character from birth to manhood can be prophesied from the history of the race. Man's brain in general follows in its growth a course enormously unlike that by which it developed in the race. His backbone and heart may at one stage be much like that of a reptile, but his brain is not. His head may show traces of gill slits, but his brain never develops the lateral-line system of the fishes. The fusion of tail vertebrae may be followed in his coccyx, but the fusion of segments in the brain is almost or quite untraceable. Moreover, by the time a baby is born, his brain has long, long outgrown any forms comparable to those of fish, amphibian, reptile or early mammal. So also in the number of its neurones. The growth of the neurones' connections has not been traced, but this seems least of all likely to repeat racial history. Oddly enough the chief variation of the brain's growth from that of the body as a whole is a most unlikely variation to come on the recapitulatory hypothesis: his brain is specially *big* for his body, the new-born being in this respect the super-man!

Now for any valid expectation that a child should have at a certain age original tendencies to thought or action such as are characteristic of a fish or monkey or primitive man, one should have reason to expect the parts of his brain concerned to be at that age like the corresponding parts of the brain of the primitive man or the monkey or the fish. Such reasons are lacking.

The argument from analogy with bodily development thus fails to justify the hypothesis that the order and dates of human original tendencies will correspond with their order of acquisition and length of maintenance in man's total ancestry. The question should be settled, not by overstraining an analogy, but by actually comparing the individual and the racial course of development.

Neither series is well enough known to allow more than occasional and inadequate comparisons; but what little is known is rather decidedly against any close parallelism of the two. For example, reaching for objects, holding them, putting them in the mouth, sitting up, standing erect, walking, climbing, hunting, migration, fighting and the sex instincts, whose dates of appearance in individual development are fairly well known, come in nothing like the order and at nothing like the dates of racial development.

Even the cases suggested as examples of the parallelism by advocates of the theory often are strong evidence against it. For example, Stanley Hall states as possible parallels, in the individual, of the fish stage in the race, the following:

"A babe a few days old . . . made peculiar paddling or swimming movements."

"In children and adults . . . we find swaying from side to side or forward or backward, not infrequent. This suggests the slow oscillatory movements used by fish."

"Children . . . after the first shock and fright take the greatest delight in water."

"Others older or less active can sit by the hour seeing and hearing the movement of water in sea or stream." (1904, Vol. 2, pp. 192–195, *passim.*)

The fish stage is thus paralleled all the way from four days to forty years, even if we doubt the existence in fishes of anything like the elderly contemplation of water by one sitting on the bank.

The life of the early primates according to Hall (1904, Vol. 2, p. 214 ff.) is recapitulated by the prehensile power of the new-born, the fear of thunder and lightning, the fear of serpents, the fear of high winds, the somnolence of infants when rocked, the fear of open places, the "untaught horror of water" and the fact that man does not instinctively swim, the fear of falling, the clinging of infants to the parent, the love of climbing in boys, and the fact that "man has an instinctive pleasure to get up high and look down and afar," imitativeness, the facts that children instinctively and without teaching ascribe "emotion, sense, intelligence, morality, to trees" and that "dense forests soothe, hush, and awe the soul and feel 'like church.' "

Roughly the individual would seem to pass through the primate stage somewhat earlier than the fish stage, especially since we can confidently acquit our monkey ancestors of any tendency to ascribe "intelligence and morality to trees" or to feel "like church." But within a single page Hall has the childish interest in trees recapitulating, not the life of the primates, but that of the primitive man! The same author makes the early teens recapitulate "the darkest of all ages during which brute became man," the times of astrology and ancient myths of stars, and the times of "pastoral and agricultural life" as well as the times of the fishes and apes. The new-born baby not only "makes paddling and swimming movements" *qua* fish, but also has a "horror of water" *qua* monkey. Such defenses of the recapitulation theory are obviously more dangerous to it than the most violent attacks.

Certain obvious exceptions—such as the very late appearance in the individual of the instincts of sex which arose very early in the race, or the very early appearance in the individual of babbling, laughing, weeping, grasping and putting in the mouth—have forced the adherents of the recapitulation theory to admit that, in the individual, the racial order is much distorted, and that some of its elements are omitted altogether, or passed through so rapidly as to be hardly discernible. When it is admitted that such distortions and omissions are very frequent, little more is left of the theory than a useless general scheme for explaining facts whose existence has to be proved by direct observation entirely apart from the theory, or a body of dubious suggestions for investigation. A rule for the exceptions becomes more instructive than the rule itself.

On the whole, the recapitulation theory in the case of mental traits seems to be an attractive speculation with no more truth behind it than the fact that when a repetition of phylogeny, abbreviated and modified, is a useful way of producing an individual, he may be produced in that way. In intellectual capacities the child of two years has passed all the stages previous to man. It is difficult to find even one instinct in ten that occupies in his ontogeny the same relative position in time that it occupied in his phylogeny. No fact of value about either the ontogeny or phylogeny of behavior has, to my knowledge, been discovered as a result of this theory. Consequently one cannot help thinking that the influence which it has exerted upon students of human nature is due, not to rational claims, but to its rhetorical attractiveness.

Name Index

Pages of selections are shown in boldface type.